GEOGRAPHERS AND THE TROPICS:

LIVERPOOL ESSAYS

Edited by
Robert W. Steel and
R. Mansell Prothero of the
University of Liverpool

Geographers and the Tropics: Liverpool Essays

Longmans

LONGMANS, GREEN AND CO LTD
48 Grosvenor Street, London, W.1
Associated companies, branches and representatives throughout the world

© *The University of Liverpool 1964*
First published 1964

Printed in Great Britain by
The Camelot Press Ltd., London and Southampton

CONTENTS

Preface   vii

Geographers and the Tropics   I
R.W. STEEL *John Rankin Professor of Geography, University of Liverpool*

Evidence of lake-level changes from the northern
shoreline of Lake Victoria, Uganda   31
P.H. TEMPLE *Lecturer in Geography, Makerere University College,
Kampala, Uganda*

Landforms in the Northern Territory of Australia   57
E.M. DRISCOLL *Lecturer in Geography, University of Liverpool*

Annual, seasonal and monthly rainfall over Moçam-
bique   81
S. GREGORY *Senior Lecturer in Geography, University of Liverpool*

Rainfall and the water resources of East Africa   111
JOAN M. KENWORTHY *Lecturer in Geography, University of Liverpool*

The land of Zanj: exegetical notes on Chinese know-
ledge of East Africa prior to A.D. 1500   139
PAUL WHEATLEY *Professor of Geography and History, Centre of South-
East Asia Studies, University of California, Berkeley*

Continuity and change in African population mobility   189
R.M. PROTHERO *Lecturer in Geography, University of Liverpool*

Changing patterns of African employment in Southern
Rhodesia   215
I.F. MASSER *Associate Planner, Graeme Shankland Associates*

Aspects of Ushi settlement history: Fort Rosebery   235
District, Northern Rhodesia
G. KAY *Leverhulme Fellow in Commonwealth Studies, University of Hull*

Land use in the Maracas–St Joseph Basin, Trinidad   261
ALICE DYSON *Senior Lecturer in Geography, C.F.Mott Training College, Prescot*

Chinese settlement in the Kulai Sub-District of Johore, Malaysia   277
F. LEES *Central Office of Information, London*

Aspects of Regional Planning in India   297
L.S. BHAT *Regional Survey Unit, Indian Statistical Institute, New Delhi*

Retrospect on a project in applied regional geography, Mysore State, India   323
A.T.A. LEARMONTH *Professor of Geography, School of General Studies, Australian National University, Canberra*

Liverpool and the Tropics   349
R. LAWTON *Senior Lecturer in Geography, University of Liverpool*

PREFACE

THE essays in this volume have been brought together and published to coincide with a symposium on the tropics which the Department of Geography in the University of Liverpool is organizing immediately before the assembly of the xxth International Geographical Congress in London in July 1964. They are introduced in the first essay which provides the title for the volume. Here we wish to thank all who have made the work possible. We have enjoyed the fullest co-operation of the contributors each of whom has accepted most gracefully the inevitable editorial requests. The maps, except for those in Professor Wheatley's essay, have been drawn by Mr A. G. Hodgkiss, Senior Draughtsman in the Department of Geography, University of Liverpool, and they bear witness to his skill and interest. Mrs F. B. Thomson and Miss Ann Stephenson have typed large parts of the manuscript.

We gratefully acknowledge the permission given by the Asia Publishing House and the Indian Statistical Institute, and the East African Meteorological Department and the East African Agriculture and Forestry Research Organization, to reproduce and adapt maps in the essays of Professor Learmonth and Miss Kenworthy respectively.

Mr E. W. Parker of Messrs. Longmans, Green & Co. was particularly interested and helpful in the earliest stages of preparing this volume and his successor, Mr J. R. C. Yglesias, and his colleagues, have continued in the same way. We are most grateful to them for all they have done to make publication possible in the very limited time that has been available.

ROBERT W. STEEL
R. MANSELL PROTHERO

Liverpool
April 1964

Geographers and the Tropics

GEOGRAPHERS have always been interested in the tropics from Ptolemy and Strabo in classical times to Alexander von Humboldt and the geographers of the twentieth century. In stressing the peculiarities of the environments found in the tropics, some have implied that there is a particular branch of geography, 'tropical geography'. Thus P. Gourou, in *Les pays tropicaux: principes d'une géographie humaine et économique* (1947, English translation, 1953, p. 1) states quite categorically: 'hot, wet lands have their own special physical and human geography'. W. B. Morgan has argued that there may be a case in Africa for an 'African viewpoint' that might 'provide a revitalizing contribution to a subject which has hitherto concentrated mainly on the areas occupied by European peoples' (1954, p. 18); he thinks, for example, that in view of the emphasis placed by Africans on kinship rather than on land in the definition of a community, the proper approach to regional studies in a country like Nigeria should be based essentially on 'the study of . . . tribal communities in their environmental relationships' (p. 11).

In contrast B. W. Hodder, whose overseas experience, like Gourou's, began in the Asian tropics and later extended to Africa, has questioned whether there is any such thing as a specifically 'tropical' problem in geography (1958, p. 2). He doubts whether it is possible to formulate 'generalizations about the humid tropics which will be valid both for a country, like Malaya, within the tropical rain forest region, and for a country, like most of Nigeria, within the "savannah" tropics' (1957, p. 7), and advocates the development of comparative studies in geography. By the cultivation of the comparative attitude in thinking and in writing, he believes that the geographer's research will be set in perspective and may thus help to develop geographical knowledge about the tropics. Only in these ways, Hodder suggests, can conclusions be reached about 'the alleged peculiar nature of the geography of the tropics' (p. 7).

The present writer shares the view with the other geographers contributing to this volume that there is no special branch of the subject to be recognized as 'tropical geography' and that 'the geography of the tropics' implies no more – and no less – than the study by geographers of tropical areas, adopting, in general, similar approaches and methods to those used for the study of any other part of the world.

GEOGRAPHERS AND TROPICAL AFRICA

Geographers have given increasing attention during recent years to the study of a wide variety of problems in the tropics, and current developments in geography in tropical areas, in both teaching and research, reflect very closely the overall progress and the dominant trends in the subject generally at the present time. But to keep a survey of the work of geographers in the tropics within reasonable bounds some limitation is necessary, and this essay concentrates more particularly upon inter-tropical Africa, the area where the writer's own fieldwork has been done and with which he is most closely in touch, although the volume which it introduces includes studies from other parts of the tropics. It focuses attention especially upon the British or former British areas within Africa and upon the work and publications of English-speaking geographers, while fully recognizing the major contributions of French-speaking, Portuguese-speaking and other geographers.

Africa is probably the most fascinating and dynamic area, and the scene of some of the most dramatic political changes, in the tropical world today. Along with remarkable economic and social developments and the political transformation of recent years, there has been outstanding progress in the scientific study of the continent, especially since the end of the Second World War. In this advancement of knowledge geographers have contributed significantly through the new opportunities provided by the establishment in recent years of universities, colleges and research institutions in many parts of tropical Africa. Thus while in 1938 there was but scant reference to geography as such in either Lord Hailey's *An African Survey* or in E. B. Worthington's companion volume *Science in Africa*, there were important, though still incomplete, references to the work of geographers in the post-war revisions of these volumes (Hailey, 1957; Worthington, 1958). The best single piece of evidence of the contribution of geography to African studies today is the major study of *Tropical Africa*, financed by the Twentieth Century Fund of New York and directed and written by a geographer, G. H. T. Kimble (1960).

Despite Britain's economic and political involvement in inter-tropical Africa between the wars, the interest shown by British and other English-speaking geographers was only slight (Steel, 1952, pp. 93-7). A Research Committee of Section E (Geography) of the British Association for the Advancement of Science, set up in 1926, encouraged administrative officers, missionaries and others in Africa to record geographical information and, sometimes, to publish it. In his presidential address to Section E in 1933, A. G. Ogilvie analysed the replies to a comprehensive questionnaire sent out by the Committee received from all the Districts of Northern Rhodesia (Ogilvie, 1934). Individual geographers travelled and worked in Africa, including S. J. K. Baker (1937), H. C. Darby (1932), D. M. Doveton (1937), H. L. Shantz (1923, 1940-3), L. D. Stamp (1938), R. W. Steel (1939) and D. Whittlesey (1937, 1938); and C. Gillman, an official of the Tanganyika Government, who had studied geography in Berlin, produced an important map of population (1936), besides numerous official reports on transport, water-supply and other topics. In general, however, the opportunities for research were very limited.

War service extended the experience of European and American geographers, providing them with opportunities for travel and observation that might otherwise never have come their way. The analysis of the climatic conditions of the inter-tropical zone by P. R. Crowe (1949-51), for example, was a product of work done

3

in the Meteorological Office during the war. Several of the Geographical Handbooks of the Naval Intelligence Division were concerned with tropical areas, three of them in Africa (French West Africa, French Equatorial Africa and the Belgian Congo); these drew heavily on the work of geographers, though rarely upon their fieldwork, for which in any event there was little opportunity during the war years. Though now out of date in many respects they remain standard books of reference, and through working on their compilation some geographers were stimulated to specialize in the geography of the tropics after the war.

POST-WAR DEVELOPMENTS

After 1945 developments in geography in the then British colonial territories were greatly encouraged by the extension of higher education and of research activities of various types which had been planned during the war, reasonable financial provision for such purposes being made available for the first time through the Colonial Development and Welfare Act of 1940. In all the university colleges developed in British tropical Africa in the immediate post-war years, apart from that at Salisbury, Southern Rhodesia, geography departments were established at the beginning, and these now flourish in Ghana, Kenya, Nigeria, Sierra Leone, the Sudan and Uganda. Closely linked with these colleges, most of which now have full university status, there are research institutes with which geographers have been associated. Most geographical research has so far been done by the staff of the teaching departments of geography who have written, for example, standard textbooks on Nigeria (Buchanan and Pugh, 1955), Ghana (Varley and White, 1958; Boateng, 1959) and the Sudan (Barbour, 1961). In the French-speaking parts of West Africa geographers have worked largely under the auspices of the Institut Français d'Afrique Noire (I.F.A.N.) (e.g. Richard-Molard, 1949). In former Belgian Africa geographers, notably P. Gourou and his associates, have shared in the work of the Institut pour la Recherche Scientifique d'Afrique Centrale (I.R.S.A.C.).

4

Simultaneously with these developments in tropical Africa, there was an outburst of interest in the continent among geographers resident in Europe and North America, and close cooperation has been developed between geography departments within and outside Africa. Through secondment of staff, the award of travel scholarships and research studentships, and the provision of facilities for research workers at all levels, there has developed a valuable two-way traffic in both staff and students of mutual benefit to all, and research has been stimulated over a wide field. There have also been important increases in the financial and other provisions for research on tropical Africa available in countries like Britain, not only in geography but also in sociology, economics, demography and history, among other subjects. The Colonial Social Science Research Council included a geographer in its membership during most of its existence and sponsored, either directly or through the Colonial Economic Research Committee, investigations that included a socio-economic study of the Colony villages of Sierra Leone (Richardson and Collins, 1954), a survey of the subsistence crop geography of Uganda (McMaster, 1962) and, elsewhere in the tropics, studies of land use and population in Tobago (Niddrie, 1961) and Fiji (Ward, 1963). Geographers have also been seconded to some of the research institutes, or have published work under their auspices. R. M. Prothero's first field studies of migrant labour, for example, were undertaken as a Fellow of the West African Institute of Social and Economic Research (1956, 1957*b*, 1959); V. C. R. Ford's *The trade of Lake Victoria: a geographical study* (1955), was published by the East African Institute of Social Research; and G. Kay's geographical and historical studies in Northern Rhodesia (e.g. 1960, 1962) were carried out while he was Research Officer (Human Geographer) in the Rhodes-Livingstone Institute.

RESEARCH PUBLICATION

Just as the opportunities for research in the tropics by geographers have increased greatly during recent years, so there has been a marked extension of the outlets for the publication of their work. Most of the established geographical periodicals in the English-speaking world and in many European countries carry a fair proportion of papers on tropical Africa. There are, moreover, several journals specifically devoted to the publication of geographical work on tropical Africa, including the *Nigerian Geographical Journal* (Ibadan), the *Bulletin of the Ghana Geographical Association* (Accra), the *East African Geographical Review* (Kampala) and *Les Cahiers d'Outre-Mer* (Bordeaux). Papers by geographers also appear in the *Bulletin d'I.F.A.N.* (Dakar), *Zaïre* (Brussels), the *Journal of the Rhodes-Livingstone Institute* (Lusaka), *Africa* (the Journal of the International African Institute) (London), and the *Journal of Overseas Administration* (formerly *Journal of African Administration*) (London). The *Journal of Tropical Geography* (Singapore and Kuala Lumpur) began its existence in 1953 as the *Malayan Journal of Tropical Geography*: its change of title (in 1958) was deliberately designed to indicate a broadening of its field, and occasional issues have been largely concerned with non-Asian parts of the tropics, but the main emphasis, and the residence of a majority of its contributors, continue to be South-east Asia. *Pacific Viewpoint* (Wellington, New Zealand) is similarly primarily concerned with the Pacific and Asia but is now publishing papers on comparable areas in other parts of the world.

Geographers have published a considerable number of books and monographs on the tropics since the war. Some of these are in series such as the publications of the World Land Use Survey (e.g. Niddrie, 1961; McMaster, 1962); the Rhodes-Livingstone Institute (e.g. Kay, 1960; Scudder, 1962); the East African Institute of Economic and Social Research (e.g. Ford, 1955); and the University of Chicago Department of Geography Research Papers (e.g. Munger, 1951; Van Dongen, 1954; Larimore, 1959). Of outstanding importance is Kimble's survey of *Tropical Africa*, in two volumes (1960): of the six consultants, two were geographers (B. J. Garnier and J. H. G. Lebon), and of the forty papers specially commissioned for the project, seven were prepared by geographers, most of them working at the time in tropical Africa.

L. D. Stamp's *Africa: a study in tropical development* (1953) has proved a convenient summary of the whole continent, and *Africa and the Islands* (1964) is a comprehensive and up-to-date account by four geographers, R. J. Harrison Church, J. I. Clarke, P. J. H. Clarke and H. J. R. Henderson. There is a very real need for geographical works on all the major divisions of Africa, comparable with Harrison Church's *West Africa: a study of the environment and of man's use of it* (1957) or J. H. Wellington's *Southern Africa: a geographical study* (1955) which includes Southern Rhodesia, Northern Rhodesia and Nyasaland, though it considers them in nothing like the detail provided for South Africa itself. Even more desirable would be further works on individual countries of the calibre of those on Nigeria, Ghana and the Sudan to which reference has already been made.

Other useful contributions by geographers lie in their collaboration with one another or with students of other related disciplines. An example of the exchange of information between geographers is provided by the symposium on natural resources, food and population in inter-tropical Africa held at Makerere College, Uganda, in 1955 (Stamp, 1956). *Essays on African population*, edited by K. M. Barbour and R. M. Prothero (1961), illustrates the varied contributions of geographers, sociologists and demographers to a fuller understanding of some of the population problems of inter-tropical Africa.

THE FIELDS OF GEOGRAPHICAL RESEARCH

The fields of research concerned with the geography of tropical Africa, of which the publication of papers, monographs and books is the tangible sign, are already so many, and are ever increasing, that to survey them is no easy task. It may most usefully be done by considering the different branches of geography, even though some research falls into more than one category and much of the best work has been in close association with students of other disciplines.

Important work is in progress in all the main branches of

7

physical geography, although of the geographers holding academic posts in universities and colleges in tropical Africa, certainly in former British areas, more are concerned with the study of socio-economic conditions than with problems of the physical environment. This concentration of energy upon the study of economic and social conditions is readily understandable in view of the political and other pressures which are common in emerging states that are concerned with the speedy development of their physical and human resources. It is significant that the number of Africans who are primarily physical geographers is still very small, and that many of the contributions made by physical geographers have been in the fields of applied geomorphology and applied climatology where their studies contribute directly to some of the problems that are of practical interest – the incidence of soil erosion, for example, the relationship between rainfall and crop production, and the effect of water supply upon population distribution and patterns of settlement.

Geomorphology

Notable work is, however, being done in pure geomorphology, climatology and biogeography, with the appointment of well-trained young geographers to various departments in Africa and stimulated by work done in southern Africa by L. C. King (e.g. 1947, 1949, 1951), F. Dixey (e.g. 1938, 1942, 1944), J. H. Wellington (e.g. 1955) and others. Some of these studies, begun in South Africa, were extended to the Rhodesias and, later, to areas farther north; the influence of King's ideas upon geomorphologists working in tropical Africa has been especially marked. In Nigeria, the investigations of J. C. Pugh (e.g. 1954, 1956), begun while he was an officer of the Nigerian Survey Department and before his appointment to a university post, are being followed up in greater detail and with more precise measurement. Important contributions have been made by A. T. Grove whose work in West Africa has been based on regular visits extending over more than a dozen years (e.g. 1951*a*, 1951*b*, 1952, 1957, 1961) and by R. A. G. Savigear whose special interest has been in slope development. In

Ghana geomorphological work has been done by R. W. Clayton (1956), J. M. Hunter (1959, 1961*b*) and the geographers employed in the Soil and Land Use Branch of the Ministry of Agriculture, where the methods of soil survey under tropical conditions devised by C. F. Charter (1949) are based essentially upon geomorphological techniques.

In East Africa there has been less comprehensive work, apart from the classical studies of the Great Rift Valley, largely made by geologists, though the Ruwenzori Massif has received attention both from R. F. Peel, a member of the Leeds University Expedition of 1952 led by the geologist, W. Q. Kennedy, and from the Makerere geographers and others whose glaciological and other investigations on the mountain were associated with the International Geophysical Year (Whittow, 1959). Attention has been given to the study of erosion surfaces and other geomorphological problems by geographers and by members of the Geological Surveys of the East African countries (e.g. J. W. Pallister, 1956, 1963). L. Berry has studied the development of landforms under arid and semi-arid conditions in the Sudan (1961, Berry and Ruxton, 1961*a*, 1961*b*) in association with the University of Khartoum's Arid Zone Research Committee.

Climatology

Climatic and vegetation conditions in the African tropics have been analysed by members of the Humid Tropics Commission of the International Geographical Union in an attempt to demarcate the extent of the humid tropics (Fosberg *et al.*, 1961). As in geomorphology, the influence of South African workers has been considerable, especially in the more southerly parts of tropical Africa: the preparation of a climatological atlas for the whole continent is being directed from Johannesburg by S. P. Jackson on behalf of the Commission for Technical Co-operation in Africa south of the Sahara (C.C.T.A.). Such an international effort, which has not been without its difficulties and delays, has become possible through the increased availability of climatic data, itself the result of the establishment of more adequate Government

B

9

meteorological services during and since the war, largely because of developments in air transport.

More and better data have encouraged more detailed studies of climatic conditions, as in S. Gregory's essay on Moçambique in this volume, and for West Africa generally (Church, 1957), Nigeria (Miller, 1952), and parts of Ghana (Hubbard, 1954, 1956). The records of the climatological station of the Department of Geography at Ibadan have been widely distributed for more than ten years and have been the basis of much of B. J. Garnier's work on Nigerian climatic conditions, including his studies of evapotranspiration (1956). C. W. Thornthwaite's ideas in this field (1948, 1951) have been applied to the Rhodesias and Nyasaland (Howe, 1953) and used for the preparation of maps for the whole continent by D. B. Carter (1954), while G. T. Trewartha has given detailed consideration to some of the climatic peculiarities of Africa in *The Earth's problem climates* (1961). Geographers in official meteorological services have contributed to the understanding of tropical meteorology and of the problems of forecasting (e.g. Thompson, 1957).

Rainfall and other data have been analysed in relation to agricultural potentialities. Work done at the East African Agricultural and Forestry Organization in Kenya, notably by J. Glover and J. P. Henderson, was used very effectively by the East African Royal Commission in its Report (1955) which included maps showing probability of rainfall on which were based its conclusions on likely developments in crop cultivation and stock raising. Further work along these lines has been undertaken, some of it by geographers (Kenworthy and Glover, 1958). Associated with these studies of climatic conditions and their bearing upon agriculture have been investigations of problems of hydrology and water-supply. F. Debenham's report to the Colonial Office (1948) underlined the importance in Africa of the study of water-supply problems such as Gillman had undertaken in Tanganyika (1944). Latterly there have been several studies by geographers of hydrological changes (e.g. Ledger in Nigeria, 1961) and of the relationship between patterns of settlement and the availability of water, especially in arid and semi-arid areas like the Sudan (e.g. Lebon, 1961; Graham, 1963).

Biogeography

Following on the pioneer work of H. L. Shantz and C. F. Marbut on the vegetation and soils of tropical Africa (1923) many studies have been undertaken by Government departments such as agriculture, forestry and soil survey, and by collaboration between scientists as in the ecological survey of Northern Rhodesia (Trapnell *et al.*, 1937, 1943, 1948). Gillman (1949) produced the first vegetation-types map of Tanganyika. The comprehensive vegetation map for the whole continent, prepared by R. W. J. Keay and others (1959) for C.C.T.A., effectively summarizes much of the detailed work done for many individual countries and has proved an invaluable map for geographers and others. A soil map of Africa south of the Sahara at a scale of 1 : 25,000,000 has been published by the Inter-African Pedological Service of C.C.T.A. *The natural resources of East Africa* (Russell, 1962) contains many useful maps, including maps of natural vegetation and major soil types.

Geographers who have contributed to biogeographical studies include M. M. Cole whose investigations of savanna vegetation in the tropics have embraced parts of Africa, notably the Rhodesias (1963); officers of the Soil and Land Use Branch of the Ministry of Agriculture in Ghana (e.g. Ahn, 1961); and R. P. Moss whose work on soils and slopes in south-western Nigeria (1963) also considers the implications for the planning of agricultural development in tropical Africa. Such investigations of the physical environment have a clear bearing on many of the economic and social problems that are the concern of African governments at the present time.

Social geography

Geographers, along with other social scientists, have been concerned with the socio-economic problems of tropical Africa, paying particular attention to the distribution and density of population and to the forms and patterns of settlement. The post-war censuses, notably the relatively detailed counts in the Gold Coast (1948), East Africa (1948), Nigeria (1952-3) and the Sudan (1955) have provided some of the necessary data. In several countries university geographers have collaborated closely with the census authorities, as in the Sudan (e.g. Barbour, 1958; Davies, H. J. R. and G., 1958) and in Ghana where J. M. Hunter was seconded for special duties during the census of 1960 (Hunter, 1961*a*). T. E. Hilton's *Ghana population atlas* (1960), though not an official publication, draws heavily on official information, as well as on extensive fieldwork, and R. M. Prothero's population maps of the Northern Region of Nigeria have been published by the Federal Survey Department, Lagos, and by the Directorate of Overseas Surveys (Prothero, 1958, 1960). Geographers have been actively involved in several population mapping projects, which have been discussed in detail, together with other related matters, in an essay by Prothero on population maps and mapping in Africa south of the Sahara (Barbour and Prothero, 1961, pp. 63-81). This clearly is a field for profitable collaboration with other students of population. It is also one in which governments are likely to show an increasing interest and where results have already been used in the planning of development projects.

The study of settlement, especially in rural areas which are characteristic of so much of tropical Africa, received some attention during the inter-war years from those who collaborated with the British Association Committee, in Northern Rhodesia and elsewhere, especially from administrative and other officers whose initial training had been in geography (e.g. Leakey and Rounce, 1933; Miller, 1938). More recently it has been systematically approached by geographers like Collins in Sierra Leone (Richardson and Collins, 1954), Boateng in south-eastern Ghana (1955) and Kay in Northern Rhodesia (1962). Urban geography, though it is concerned with less than 10 per cent of the total population, has developed considerably in tropical Africa, as in many other parts of the world. The work in this field by geographers and others has been summarized by Steel (Barbour and Prothero,

1961, pp. 249-78). Of the small townships of many parts of Africa with administrative and/or commercial functions there are few detailed studies by geographers: that of Fort Rosebery, Northern Rhodesia by Kay (1960) is an exception. Considerable attention has been given to the unique Yoruba towns in Nigeria (e.g. Mitchel, 1961; Mabogunje, 1962) and there are useful studies of larger towns such as Freetown (Jarrett, 1956) and Khartoum (Hamdan, 1960), and of the ports of both the Atlantic and Indian Ocean coasts of Africa south of the Equator (Hance and Van Dongen, 1956-8). But there are still no comprehensive surveys by geographers, working alone or in collaboration with others, of many tropical African towns, including some of the largest and most rapidly growing, such as Nairobi and Salisbury.

Economic geography

Since the future progress of all tropical areas in Africa and elsewhere must depend largely on their economic development, it is unfortunate that no geographer has so far produced a study of the economic geography of the tropics that can be placed alongside the essays of S. H. Frankel (1953) or G. Myrdal's *Economic theory and under-developed regions* (1957) or *The economics of under-developed countries* by P. T. Bauer and B. S. Yamey (1959). Reference should, however, be made to Jin Bee Ooi's monograph (1959) on rural development in tropical areas, with special reference to Malaya (1958), to W. A. Hance's case studies in *African economic development* (1958), and to A. B. Mountjoy's *Industrialization and under-developed countries* (1963). There are a few useful surveys of what have been called 'inventories of land and people' (Steel, 1960), including regional studies such as those of Nigeria (Buchanan and Pugh, 1955), the Sudan (Barbour, 1961) and the Kenya Highlands (W. T. W. Morgan, 1963), together with many unpublished postgraduate theses or official reports written by geographers in government service. In time there may be a series of such accounts, published by the World Land Use Survey: to date, however, only one (McMaster, 1962) has been concerned with a part of tropical Africa. A geographer, J. B. Wills, edited *Agriculture and land use in Ghana* (1962) and B. N. Floyd has published a large work, with an atlas, on *Changing patterns of African land use in Southern Rhodesia* (1961). There are numerous papers on aspects of land use and economic development, usually of fairly small areas in many different countries: for example the Accra plains (White, 1954) and southern forest area (Hunter, 1961*c*, 1963) in Ghana; Katsina (Grove, 1957) and Soba (Prothero, 1957*a*) in Nigeria; the Wadi Azum in the Sudan (Barbour, 1954); Bukoba in Tanganyika (McMaster, 1960); Karamoja in Uganda (Deshler, 1960); the Shire valley in Nyasaland (W. B. Morgan, 1953); and Matabeleland, Southern Rhodesia (Prescott, 1961*a*).

Changes effected in the landscape by the European advent in Africa have been discussed for southern Nigeria by W. B. Morgan (1959). Such changes will become even more striking as industrialization increases, as is probable in the continent with the greatest potential supplies of hydro-electricity in the world. A. E. Larimore's study (1959) of patterns of settlement in Busoga, Uganda, pays particular attention to Jinja, the growing industrial town on the Nile by the Owen Falls Dam (cf. Hoyle, 1963). Some of the consequences of the construction of the Kariba Dam on the Zambezi have been discussed by W. H. Reeve (1960) and M. M. Cole (1962), and among the first of the Rhodes-Livingstone Institute's Kariba series of studies is an account by a geographer (Scudder, 1962) of the Valley Tonga people whose resettlement has become necessary by the flooding of their homeland.

New means of communication may also affect the landscape considerably even in areas like East Africa where, as Van Dongen has shown (1954), the transport network is poorly developed by comparison with many parts of Europe or North America. A. M. O'Connor (1963*a*), however, has recently suggested that in parts of Uganda road transport remains all-important and that so far the construction of new railways has had a negligible influence upon the trade of the areas through which they pass. His conclusions have obvious relevance to other areas where extensive rail developments are under consideration as, for example, in eastern Africa where there has been a revival of interest in the possibility of a rail link between Tanganyika and Northern Rhodesia.

Political geography

Compared with the concern shown by geographers like C. A. Fisher and others (e.g. East and Spate, 1961, pp. 193-264; Steel and Fisher, 1956, pp. 271-344; Fisher, 1962, 1963) in the political developments of South-east Asia, insignificant attention has been given to the political geography of tropical Africa. Apart from K. M. Buchanan's study (1953) of political duality in northern Nigeria, there has been little follow-up to the earlier work of D. Whittlesey (1937, 1938, 1944). This is unfortunate at a time of great political change and experiment in areas like East Africa, the Zambezi basin and Nigeria, where there should have been the same careful analysis by geographers that there has been by historians, economists and political scientists. The remarkable and rapid transformation of the political map of Africa in recent years, particularly since 1955, makes especially relevant the study of the basis of the emergence of individual states and the assessment of their economic and political viability: an example is a recent paper on Gabon (Hilling, 1963). A comprehensive analysis of some aspects of the new political geography of Africa has been undertaken by G. Hamdan (1963), while the boundaries of inter-tropical Africa have been studied by Barbour (Barbour and Prothero, 1961, pp. 303-23) in an attempt to stimulate further research into both the geographical and the historical aspects of boundary-making. A detailed study has been made for Nigeria by J. R. V. Prescott (1959, 1961*b*), and similar work is needed in many other parts of the continent at a time when changes of political control are focusing attention on both the strength and weakness of some of the inter-territorial and internal boundaries drawn in the past, often when little was known of the geographical conditions of the areas and peoples through which they passed.

Applied geography

The concepts and methods of geographers are being increasingly applied today to the study of the problems of the tropical world, and reference has been made to investigations that are helping to solve problems posed by the variability of climatic conditions, the inadequacy of water supplies and the nature of the soils. The analysis by geographers of demographic data and the mapping of population distribution and density, or of land use, are other examples of applied geography. Here reference is restricted to examples of the appointment or secondment of professional geographers for special duties or investigations for which they were particularly suited. Thus in the Ashanti Social Survey, which worked in the Gold Coast in 1945-6 to establish 'a broad, general picture of the social and political structure of Ashanti . . . and to investigate . . . those aspects in which ecological and economic factors play the biggest part' (Fortes, Steel and Ady, 1947, p. 151), a geographer was associated with a social anthropologist and an economist. Much of Grove's geomorphological research in Nigeria (e.g. 1951*a*, 1951*b*, 1952) has been undertaken at the request of Government departments, notably the Geological Survey and the Ministry of Agriculture. 'A geographer with the World Health Organization' was Prothero's apt description (1962) of his work as a consultant for the W.H.O. programme for malaria eradication in tropical Africa in 1960 and in Morocco in 1962. Church has acted as an adviser to the United Nations Economic Commission for Africa in a survey of irrigation projects in many different parts of Africa. These are but selected examples, all of them taken from British universities. In addition there are frequent on-the-spot consultations between university teachers in Africa, including geographers, and Government officials. There are, too, considerable numbers of graduates in geography who, in Her Majesty's Overseas Service and in commercial organizations, put to good use their training in surveying, the interpretation of air photographs, the analysis of climatic data and the methods of land use and other geographical survey (e.g. Priestley and Greening, 1956).

GEOGRAPHERS AND THE NON-AFRICAN TROPICS

This essay, though deliberately concentrating on the interest of geographers in tropical Africa, would be incomplete without some reference, however brief, to the work of geographers elsewhere in the tropics. In many respects research in all fields, including geography, is better established and more advanced in Latin America and the tropical parts of Asia than it is in Africa. In many South American countries there are universities of long standing, often with well-established departments of geography, and in the Asian tropics there were universities and research institutions long before any centres of higher education were founded in tropical Africa. There are well-known departments of geography in India, Pakistan and Ceylon, and periodicals like the *Indian Geographical Journal* (whose special jubilee volume appeared in 1952) have been published for many years. Hong Kong University was established in 1912, and Raffles College, Singapore, was well on the road to full independent status as a university by the outbreak of war in 1939.

It is not surprising, therefore, that the lead in the study of the geography of the tropics has often been taken by geographers and geographical centres in southern or south-eastern Asia. Reference has already been made to the *Journal of Tropical Geography*, in which so much of the geographical research on the tropics has been published in recent years. The regional conference organized by the International Geographical Union in 1962 at Kuala Lumpur drew 160 delegates from twenty-five countries to study the problems of South-east Asia.

The Asian tropics have always been of vital concern to the United States of America, and to some American geographers (e.g. Pelzer, 1941, 1945, 1951), because of their links, direct or indirect, with the Pacific Ocean. They also seem relatively near to Australia – psychologically if not geographically – and the interests of Australian geographers in tropical Asia, Australasia and the Pacific, already well-established, will probably develop further with the appointment during recent years to chairs in

Australia of several British geographers whose special interests have been in India and Pakistan. O. H. K. Spate, who has had an interest in the Indian sub-continent for many years, and whose *India and Pakistan* (1954) is the standard geographical work, has already influenced the research programmes of several Australian geographers working in the Australian National University and the Commonwealth Scientific and Industrial Research Organization (C.S.I.R.O.). Examples of their work include Spate's own study in Fiji (1959) and a variety of research projects in New Guinea (e.g. Brookfield, 1960-2; Brown and Brookfield, 1959, 1962). Among New Zealand geographers similar lively interest in the Pacific tropics is evidenced by R. G. Ward's work on land use and settlement in Fiji (1963), and the publication by the Department of Geography, Victoria University of Wellington, of *Pacific Viewpoint*.

Recently there has been a marked quickening of interest in Latin America among geographers in North America and in Europe. The Caribbean, for long neglected by geographers, has attracted several geographers, though there is still no department of geography in the University of the West Indies and only limited geographical work has been done under the auspices of the Institute for Social Research at Kingston, Jamaica. The American Geographical Society has long had an important interest in the adequate mapping of Hispanic America, but there has been little work done by geographers from outside Latin America, particularly on the tropical parts of the continent. There are valuable general surveys of the whole of Latin America by P. E. James (first published in 1942) and G. J. Butland (1960), and the xviiith International Geographical Congress held at Rio de Janeiro in 1956 stimulated further research in South American geography among American, British and other geographers. In Britain, with increased opportunities for travel and research, there have been significant developments in several departments of geography, and a committee of the University Grants Committee is at present collecting information on Latin American research generally in British universities, prior to submitting recommendations for its further development. The basis of the committee's appointment is very similar to that of the Hayter Committee which was concerned with Oriental, Slavonic, East European and African research and whose report (H.M.S.O., 1961) recommended the establishment of the area-study research centres which now exist in several British universities.

BRITISH GEOGRAPHERS AND THE TROPICS IN 1964

The appointment of two committees by the British Government in recent years is evidence of its belated recognition of the importance of studies of areas which include large parts of the tropics, and of the special staffing, financial and other problems involved in the organization and carrying out of worthwhile research projects concerned with them. The whole situation for geography, as for other subjects, is likely to be transformed by the establishment of the centres proposed by the Hayter Committee, with adequate financial provision, and by the encouragement of work already in progress in other universities in Britain. These include the University of London with its 'special relationship' scheme that has for many years encouraged the development of new university institutions in different parts of the world, the University of Durham (now the Universities of Durham and Newcastle upon Tyne) with old-established links with the University College of Sierra Leone, the three universities (Cambridge, Oxford and London) where the training of officers for Her Majesty's Overseas Service has been concentrated, and the University of Liverpool with long-standing contacts with many parts of the tropics, especially through the Liverpool School of Tropical Medicine. Interests in the tropics have been further stimulated in these and other universities in the Commonwealth by the appointment in recent years of staff who have taught in universities and colleges in the tropics; and recently some universities (e.g. Khartoum and Reading) have entered into agreements designed to facilitate the recruitment of teachers and research workers for short-term service overseas whereby appointments are made jointly by the two institutions concerned, one in the tropics and one in Britain.

The remarkable increase in the research of British geographers working on problems in various tropical areas may be illustrated by a comparison of the situation little more than ten years ago with that of today. In the early fifties the present writer with C. A. Fisher brought together a collection of papers by British geographers on the tropics, later published as *Geographical essays on British tropical lands* (1956). Though the volume of ten essays by eight geographers was (p.v) 'avowedly varied and selected . . . a series of sample studies by some British geographers interested in tropical problems', it constituted a fair proportion of the research based upon fieldwork that was available at the time in a form suitable for publication. In 1964, by contrast, it is possible to produce the volume which this essay introduces where all fourteen contributors are geographers who have been associated – as undergraduates, postgraduate research workers, research fellows or members of the teaching staff – with a single department of geography in a British university.

The Department of Geography in the University of Liverpool is one of the oldest in the British Isles. P. M. Roxby, who held classes in geography from 1905, at first within the Department of Economics, became the first John Rankin Professor of Geography in 1917, when the Honours School of Geography in the Faculty of Arts – the first in any British university – was also instituted. Roxby's special research was centred upon the Far East, but his interests also embraced the tropical parts of Asia where subsequently several of his Asian and other students became university teachers. He was chairman of the British Association's Research Committee on the human geography of tropical Africa (see p. 3), and one of his staff, S. J. K. Baker, carried out population research in East Africa under the Committee's auspices in 1933. On his return Baker introduced courses on Africa which have continued ever since apart from a break of a few years after 1946 when he left the Department for Makerere College, Uganda, where he later became Professor of Geography.

Roxby retired in 1944 – and died in China three years later –

and Asian studies followed different lines with the appointment to the staff in 1949 of A. T. A. Learmonth whose special interests, arising directly from war service in India, were in the geography of southern Asia and in medical geography: his work in the latter field was greatly helped by contact with the Liverpool School of Tropical Medicine. The Department's interests in the tropics generally were further developed with the appointment of R. W. Steel to the John Rankin Chair of Geography in 1957 and of other persons to the staff with tropical experience.

This collection of essays is the fruit of the work and interest of the Department in the development of geography and in the study of problems in the tropics. Apart from the author of the essay on Liverpool's links with the tropics, each contributor has carried out fieldwork in the tropics at various times during the last twenty-five years, mostly in recent years. Six of the fourteen authors are present members of the staff of the Department, and another was a lecturer from 1949 to 1962; one was recently Leverhulme Research Fellow; and the remainder are graduates of the Department all of whom hold, or have held, academic appointments in Britain or in the tropics, except for F. Lees. He is representative of the considerable number of graduates who have taken up appointments overseas, in administration, commerce or other fields, and his account of Chinese settlement in a district in Malaya is based on one of his own official reports, which draws considerably on his initial training as a geographer.

To some readers, especially those who are not geographers, the field covered by this volume may seem broad and perhaps disparate: they might wish for a concentration of attention on a smaller number of themes which could then be more fully developed. The essays do, however, fairly indicate the nature and extent of the Department's interests, and indeed those of geographers in general, in tropical areas: they suggest, too, the diversity of the contribution that geographers are making towards a fuller understanding of the landscapes, the peoples and the problems of the tropics today.

REFERENCES

AHN, P. (1961) *The soils of the lower Tano Basin, south-western Ghana*. Ghana Ministry of Agriculture, Scientific Services Division, Soil and Land Use Survey Branch, memoir no. 2.

BAKER, S.J.K. (1937) 'The distribution of native population over East Africa', *Africa*, *10*, 37-54.

BARBOUR, K.M. (1954) 'The Wadi Azum', *Geogr. J.*, *120*, 174-82.

— (1958) In KROTKI, K.J., *21 facts about the Sudanese, First population census of Sudan, 1955-1956*.

— (1961) *The Republic of the Sudan: a regional geography*.

BARBOUR, K.M. and PROTHERO, R.M. (eds.) (1961) *Essays on African population*.

BERRY, L. (1961) 'Some large scale alluvial islands on the White Nile'. *Rev. de geomorphologie*, *12*, 105-108.

BERRY, L. and RUXTON, B.P. (1961*a*) 'Notes on faceted slopes, rock fans and domes on granite in the east-central Sudan'. *Amer. Journ. Sci.*, *259*, 194-206.

— (1961*b*) 'Weathering profiles and geomorphic position on granite in two tropical regions'. *Rev. de géomorphologie*, *12*, 16-31.

BOATENG, E.A. (1955) 'Recent changes in settlement in south-east Gold Coast', *Trans. Inst. Brit. Geogr.*, *21*, 157-69.

— (1959) *A geography of Ghana*.

BROOKFIELD, H.C. (1960) 'Population distribution and labour migration in New Guinea: a preliminary survey', *Australian Geographer*, *7*, 233-42.

— (1961) 'The highland peoples of New Guinea: a study of distribution and localization', *Geogr. J.*, *127*, 436-48.

— (1962) 'Local study and comparative method: an example from Central New Guinea', *Ann. Ass. Amer. Geographers*, *52*, 242-54.

BROWN, PAULA and BROOKFIELD, H.C. (1959) 'Chimbu land and society', *Oceania*, *30*, 1-75.

— (1962) *Struggle for land: agriculture and group territories among the Chimbu of the New Guinea Highlands*.

BUCHANAN, K.M. (1953) 'The Northern Region of Nigeria: the geographical background of its political duality', *Geogr. Rev.*, *43*, 451-73.

BUCHANAN, K.M. and PUGH, J.C. (1955) *Land and people in Nigeria: the human geography of Nigeria and its environmental background*.

BUTLAND, G.J. (1960) *Latin America: a regional geography*.

CARTER, D.B. (1954) 'Climates of Africa and India according to Thornthwaite's 1948 classification', John Hopkins University, Laboratory of Climatology, Publications in Climatology, *8*.

CHARTER, C.F. (1949) 'Methods of soil survey in use in the Gold Coast', *Bull. Agri. du Congo Belge*, *40*, 109-20.

CHURCH, R.J. HARRISON (1957) *West Africa: a study of the environment and of man's use of it*, 21-62.

— (1961) 'Problems and development of the Dry Zone of West Africa', *Geogr. J.*, *127*, 187-204.

CLAYTON, R.W. (1956) 'Linear depressions (*Bergfussniederungen*) in savanna landscapes', *Geogr. Studies*, *3*, 102-26.

COLE, M.M. (1962) 'The Rhodesian economy in transition and the role of Kariba', *Geography*, *47*, 15-40.

— (1963) 'Vegetation and geomorphology in Northern Rhodesia: an aspect of the distribution of the savanna of Central Africa', *Geogr. J.*, *129*, 290-310.

COTTON, C.A. (1961) 'The theory of savanna planation', *Geography*, *46*, 89-101.

CROWE, P.R. (1949) 'The trade wind circulation of the world', *Trans. Inst. Brit. Geogr.*, *15*, 37-56.

— (1950) 'The seasonal variation in the strength of the trades', *Trans. Inst. Brit. Geogr.*, *16*, 23-47.

— (1951) 'Wind and weather in the equatorial zone', *Trans. Inst. Brit. Geogr.*, *17*, 21-76.

DARBY, H.C. (1932) 'Pioneer problems in Rhodesia and Nyasaland', in JOERG, W.L.G. (ed.) *Pioneer settlement: co-operative studies.* Amer. Geog. Soc. special publication, no. 14, 192-220.

DAVIES, H.J.R. and G. (1958) in *The population of the Sudan*, Khartoum and (1958) *21 facts about the Sudanese*, Khartoum.

DEBENHAM, F. (1948) 'Report on the water resources of the Bechuanaland, Protectorate, Northern Rhodesia, the Nyasaland Protectorate, Tanganyika Territory, Kenya and the Uganda Protectorate'. *Colon. Res. Publ.*, *2*.

DESHLER, W.W. (1960) 'Livestock trypanosomiasis and human settlement in northeastern Uganda', *Geogr. Rev.*, *50*, 541-54.

DIXEY, F. (1938) 'Some observations on the physiographic development of central and southern Africa', *Trans. Geol. Soc. S. Afr.*, *41*, 114-70.

— (1942) 'Erosion surfaces in central and southern Africa'. *Trans. Geol. Soc. S. Afr.*, *45*, 151-81.

— (1944) 'The geomorphology of Northern Rhodesia', *Trans. Geol. Soc. S. Afr.*, *48*, 9-46.

DOVETON, DOROTHY M. (1937) 'The human geography of Swaziland', *Inst. Brit. Geogr.*, 8.

East Africa Royal Commission 1953-1955 Report (1955) Cmd. 9475, H.M.S.O.

EAST, W.G. and SPATE, O.H.K. (1961) *The changing map of Asia.*

FISHER, C.A. (1962) 'Southeast Asia: the Balkans of the Orient? A study in continuity and change', *Geography*, *47*, 347-67.

FISHER, C.A (1963) 'The Malaysian Federation, Indonesia and the Philippines: a study in political geography', *Geogr. J.*, *129*, 311-28.

FORD, V.C.R. (1955) *The trade of Lake Victoria: a geographical study.* East African Institute of Social Research, East African Studies, no. 3.

FORTES, M., STEEL, R.W. and ADY, P. (1947) 'Ashanti survey, 1945-46: an experiment in social research', *Geogr. J., 110,* 149-77.

FOSBERG, F.R., GARNIER, B.J. and KUCHLER, A.W. (1961) 'Delimitation of the humid tropics', *Geogr. Rev., 41,* 333-47.

FRANKEL, S.H. (1953) *The economic impact of under-developed societies: essays on international investment and social change.*

GARNIER, B.J. (1956) 'A method of computing potential evapotranspiration in West Africa', *Bull. de l'I.F.A.N.* 18, series A, 665-76.

GILLMAN, C. (1936) 'A population map of Tanganyika Territory', *Geogr. Rev., 26,* 353-75.

— (1944) 'Water consultant's report No. 6—1940. A reconnaissance survey of the hydrology of Tanganyika Territory in its geographical settings. Government Printer. Dar es Salaam.

— (1949) 'A vegetation-types map of Tanganyika Territory', *Geogr. Rev., 39,* 7-37.

GRAHAM, A.M.S. (1963) 'Water supply and population in the Gedaref District of the Sudan'. Unpublished Ph. D. thesis, University of London.

GROVE, A.T. (1951*a*) 'Soil erosion and population problems in south-eastern Nigeria', *Geogr. J., 117,* 291-306.

— (1951*b*) 'Land use and soil conservation in parts of Onitsha and Owerri Provinces', *Bulletin of the Geological Survey of Nigeria, 21.*

— (1952) 'Land use and soil conservation in the Jos plateau', *Bulletin of the Geological Survey of Nigeria, 22.*

— (1957) *Land and population in Katsina Province,* Kaduna.

— (1961) 'Population densities and agriculture in Northern Nigeria' in BARBOUR, K.M., and PROTHERO, R.M. (eds.), *Essays on African population,* 115-36.

HAILEY, LORD (1957) *An African survey, revised 1956: a study of problems arising in Africa south of the Sahara.*

HAMDAN, G. (1960) 'Growth and functional structure of Khartoum', *Geogr. Rev., 50,* 21-40.

— (1963) 'The political map of the new Africa', *Geogr. Rev., 53,* 418-39.

HANCE, W.A., and VAN DONGEN, I.S. (1956) 'The port of Lobito and the Benguela Railway', *Geogr. Rev., 46,* 460-87.

— (1957) 'Beira, Mozambique; gateway to Central Africa', *Ann. Ass. Amer. Geographers, 47,* 306-35.

— (1958*a*) 'Matadi, focus of Belgian African transport', *Ann. Ass. Amer. Geographers, 48,* 41-72.

HANCE, W.A., and VAN DONGEN, I.S. (1958*b*) 'Dar es Salaam, the port and its tributary area', *Ann. Ass. Amer. Geographers, 48,* 419-35.

HILLING, D. (1963) 'The changing economy of Gabon: developments in a new African Republic', *Geography, 48,* 155-65.

HILTON, T.E. (1960) *Ghana population atlas: the distribution of population in the Gold Coast and Togoland under United Kingdom Trusteeship.*

HODDER, B.W. (1957) 'A note on delimiting the humid tropics: the case of Nigeria in West Africa', Univ. Coll., Ibadan, Dept. of Geog. Research Papers, no. 10.

— (1958) 'The comparative method and tropical studies', Univ. Coll., Ibadan, Dept of Geog. Research Papers, no. 11.

HOWE, G.M. (1953) 'Climates of the Rhodesias and Nyasaland according to the Thornthwaite classification', *Geogr. Rev., 43,* 525-39.

HOYLE, B.S. (1963) 'The economic expansion of Jinja, Uganda', *Geogr. Rev., 53,* 377-88.

HUBBARD, J.H. (1954) 'A note on the rainfall of Accra, Gold Coast', *Geogr. Studies, 1,* 69-75.

— (1956) 'Daily weather at Achimota, near Accra, Gold Coast', *Geogr. Studies, 3,* 56-63.

HUNTER, J.M. (1959) 'Aspects of the erosional history of the Upper Birim Basin', *Journ. W. Afr. Sci. Assn., 5,* 108-25.

— (1961*a*) 'An exercise in applied geography: geographical planning in urban areas for the 1960 census of Ghana', *Geography, 46,* 1-8.

— (1961*b*) 'Morphology of a bauxite summit in Ghana', *Geogr. J., 127,* 469-76.

— (1961*c*) 'Akotuakrom: a case study of a devastated cocoa village in Ghana', *Trans. Inst. Brit. Geogr., 29,* 161-86.

— (1963) 'Cocoa migration and patterns of land ownership in the Densu valley, near Suhum, Ghana', *Trans. Inst. Brit. Geogr., 33,* 61-87.

JAMES, P.E. (1942) (and later editions) *Latin America.*

JARRETT, H.R. (1956) 'Some aspects of the urban geography of Freetown, Sierra Leone', *Geogr. Rev., 46,* 334-54.

KAY, G. (1960) *A social and economic study of Fort Rosebery:* Part I, The Township, Part 2, The Peri-urban area. Rhodes-Livingstone Institute Communications, no. 21.

— (1962) 'Agricultural change in the Luitkila Basin Development Area, Mypika District, Northern Rhodesia', *Rhodes-Livingstone Institute Journal, 31,* 21-50.

KEAY, R.W.J. *et al.* (1959) Vegetation map of Africa south of the Sahara, C.C.T.A.

KENWORTHY, J.M. and GLOVER, J. (1958) 'The reliability of the main rains in Kenya', *E. Afr. Agri. Journ., 23,* 267-72.

KIMBLE, G.H.T. (1960) *Tropical Africa:* Vol. I, Land and livelihood; Vol. II, Society and policy.

KING, L.C. (1947) 'Landscape study in southern Africa', *Trans. Geol. Soc. S. Afr.*, *50*, 23-52.

— (1949) 'On the origin of African land surfaces', *Quart. Journ. Geol Soc.*, *104*, 439-59.

— (1951) 'The geomorphology of the eastern and southern districts of Southern Rhodesia', *Trans. Geol. Soc. S. Afr.*, *54*, 33-64.

LARIMORE, A.E. (1959) *The alien town: patterns of settlement in Busoga, Uganda. An essay in cultural geography.* Univ. Chicago, Dept. of Geog., Research Paper no. 25.

LEAKEY, E.A. and ROUNCE, N.V. (1933) 'The human geography of the Kasula district, Tanganyika. The land of the Abaha', *Geography*, *18*, 293-305.

LEBON, J.H.G. (1956) 'Rural water supplies and the development of the economy in the Central Sudan', *Geografiska Annaler*, *38*.

LEDGER, D.C. (1961) 'Recent hydrological change in the Rima Basin, northern Nigeria', *Geogr. J.*, *127*, 477-87.

MABOGUNJE, A. (1962a) 'The growth of residential districts in Ibadan', *Geogr. Rev.*, *52*, 56-77.

— (1962b) *Yoruba towns.* Ibadan.

McMASTER, D.N. (1960) 'Changes of regional balance in the Bukoba District of Tanganyika', *Geogr. Rev.*, *50*, 73-88.

— (1962) *A subsistence crop geography of Uganda.* World Land Use Survey, occasional papers, no. 2.

MILLER, R. (1938) 'Katsina, a region of Hausaland', *Scot. Geog. Mag.*, *54*, 203-19.

— (1952) 'The climate of Nigeria', *Geography*, *37*, 198-213.

MITCHEL, N.C. (1961) 'Yoruba towns' in BARBOUR, K.M. and PROTHERO, R.M. (eds.), *Essays on African population*, 279-301.

MORGAN, W.B. (1953) 'The lower Shire valley of Nyasaland: a changing system of African agriculture', *Geogr. Journ.*, *119*, 459-69.

— (1954) 'The approach to regional studies in Nigeria', Univ. Coll., Ibadan, Dept. of Geog. Research Papers, no. 6.

— (1959) 'The influence of European contacts on the landscape of southern Nigeria', *Geogr.*, *125*, 48-64.

MORGAN, W.T.W. (1963) 'The "white highlands" of Kenya', *Geogr.*, *129*, 140-55.

MOSS, R.P. (1963) 'Soils, slopes and land use in a part of south-western Nigeria: some implications for the planning of agricultural development in intertropical Africa', *Trans. Inst. Brit. Geog.*, *32*, 143-68.

MUNGER, E.S. (1951) *Relational patterns of Kampala, Uganda.* Univ. Chicago Dept. of Geog. Research Paper, no. 21.

NIDDRIE, D.L. (1961) *Land use and population in Tobago: an environmental study.* World Land Use Survey, regional monograph no. 3.

O'CONNOR, A.M. (1963a) 'Rail Transport in the economic geography of Uganda'. Unpublished Ph.D. thesis, University of Cambridge.

O'CONNOR, A.M. (1963*b*) 'Regional inequalities in economic development in Uganda', *E. Afr. Geogr. Rev.*, *1*, 33-44.

OGILVIE, A.G. (1934) 'Co-operative research in geography: with an African example', *Scot. Geogr. Mag.*, *50*, 353-78.

OOI JIN-BEE (1959) 'Rural development in tropical areas, with special reference to Malaya', *J. Trop. Geogr.*, *12*, 1-222.

PALLISTER, J.W. (1956) 'The physiography of South-Central Uganda', in STAMP, L.D. (ed.), *Natural resources, food and population in inter-tropical Africa*, 16-19.

— (1963) 'Notes on the geomorphology of the Northern Region, Somali Republic, *Geogr.*, *129*, 184-7.

PELZER, K.J. (1941) *Economic survey of the Pacific area*, Vol. I, Population and land utilization.

— (1945) *Pioneer settlement in the Asiatic tropics: studies in land utilization and agricultural colonization in south-eastern Asia*, Amer. Geog. Soc., special publication, no. 29.

— (1951) 'Geography and the tropics' in G. TAYLOR (ed.), *Geography in the twentieth century*, 311-44.

PRESCOTT, J.R.V. (1959) 'Nigeria's regional boundary problems', *Geogr. Rev.*, *49*, 485-505.

— (1961*a*) 'Overpopulation and overstocking in the native areas of Matabeleland', *Geogr. J.*, *127*, 212-25.

— (1961*b*) 'The evolution of Nigeria's political boundaries'. Unpublished Ph.D. thesis, University of London.

PRIESTLEY, M.J.S.W. and GREENING, P. (1956) *Ngoni land utilisation survey, 1954-1955*. Government Printer, Lusaka.

PROTHERO, R.M. (1956) 'Population patterns and migration in Sokoto Province, Northern Nigeria', in STAMP, L.D. (ed.), *Natural resources, food and population in inter-tropical Africa*, 49-54.

— (1957*a*) 'Land use at Soba, Zaria Province, Northern Nigeria', *Econ. Geogr.*, *33*, 72-86.

— (1957*b*) 'Migratory labour from north-western Nigeria', *Africa*, *27*, 251-61.

— (1958) Northern Nigeria, 1/2,000,000 map of density of population (1952 census), Federal Survey Department, Lagos.

— (1959) *Migrant labour from Sokoto Province, Northern Nigeria*. Kaduna.

— (1960) Northern Region, Nigeria, 1/1,000,000 map of distribution of population (1952 census). Directorate of Overseas Surveys (Misc.) 237.

— (1961) 'Population mapping in Africa south of the Sahara' in BARBOUR, K.M. and PROTHERO, R.M. (eds.), *Essays on African population*, 63-81.

— (1962) 'A geographer with the World Health Organization', *Geogr. J.*, *128*, 479-93.

PUGH, J.C. (1954) 'High-level surfaces in the Eastern Highlands of Nigeria', *S. Afr. Geogr. J.*, *36*, 31-42.

PUGH, J.C. (1956) 'Fringing pediments and marginal depressions in the inselberg landscapes of Nigeria', *Trans. Inst. Brit. Geogr.*, *22*, 15-31.

REEVE, W.H. (1960) 'Progress and geographical significance of the Kariba Dam', *Geogr. J.*, *126*, 140-6.

RICHARD-MOLARD, J. (1949) *Afrique Occidentale Française.*

RICHARDSON, E.M. and COLLINS, G.R. (1954) *Economic and social survey of the Rural Areas of the Colony of Sierra Leone.* A report to the Colonial Social Science Research Council.

RUSSELL, E.W. (ed.) (1962) *The natural resources of East Africa.* Nairobi.

SCUDDER, T. (1962) *The ecology of the Gwembe Tonga.*

SHANTZ, H.L. (1940-3) 'Agricultural regions of Africa', *Econ. Geogr.*, *16*, 1-47, 122-61, 341-89; *17*, 217-49, 353-79; *18*, 229-46, 343-62; *19*, 77-109, 217-69.

SHANTZ, H.L. and MARBUT, C.F. (1923) 'The vegetation and soils of Africa', American Geogr. Soc. Research Series, no. 13.

SPATE, O.H.K. (1959) *The Fijian people: economic problems and prospects.* Council paper no. 13 of the Legislative Council of Fiji.

STAMP, L.D. (1938) 'Land utilisation and soil erosion in Nigeria', *Geogr. Rev.*, *28*, 32-45.

— (ed.) (1956) *Natural resources, food and population in inter-tropical Africa.* Report of a symposium held at Makerere College, Sept. 1955. Geog. Publicns.

STEEL, R.W. (1939) 'The human geography of Sierra Leone'. Unpublished B.Sc. thesis, University of Oxford.

— (1952) 'The progress of geography in British tropical Africa', *Proceedings, Eighth General Assembly and Seventeenth International Congress Washington D.C., 1952*, 1955, 93-7.

— (1960) 'An inventory of land and people', *Journ. of Afr. Administration*, *12*, 211-23.

— (1961) 'The towns of tropical Africa' in BARBOUR, K.M. and PROTHERO, R.M. (eds.), *Essays on African population*, 249-78.

STEEL, R.W. and FISHER, C.A. (eds.) (1956) *Geographical essays on British tropical lands.*

THOMPSON, B.W. (1957) 'Some reflections on equatorial and tropical forecasting', East Afr. Meteorol. Dept. Technical Memorandum, no. 7.

THORNTHWAITE, C.W. (1948) 'An approach towards a rational classification of climate', *Geogr. Rev.*, *38*, 55-94.

— (1951) 'The water balance in tropical climates', *Bull. Amer. Meteorol. Soc.*, *32*, 166-73.

TRAPNELL, C.G. (1943) *The soils, vegetation and agriculture of north-eastern Rhodesia.* Second edn., 1953.

TRAPNELL, C.G. and CLOTHIER, J.N. (1937) *The soils, vegetation and agricultural system of north-western Rhodesia.* Report of the Ecological Survey.

TRAPNELL, C. G., MARTIN, J. D. and ALLAN, W. (1948) Vegetation-soil map of Northern Rhodesia, with memoir by C. G. Trapnell.

VAN DONGEN, I. S. (1954) *The British East African transport complex*. Univ. Chicago Dept. of Geog. Research Paper no. 38.

VARLEY, W. J. and WHITE, H. P. (1958) *The geography of Ghana*.

WARD, R. G. (1963) 'Land use and population in Fiji'. Unpublished: a geographical study report to Colonial Social Service Research Council.

WHITE, H. P. (1954) 'Environment and land utilization on the Accra Plains', *Journ. W. Afr. Sci. Soc.*, *1*, 46-62.

WHITTLESEY, D. S. (1937) 'British and French colonial technique in West Africa.' *Foreign Affairs*, *15*, 363-73.

— (1938) 'Reshaping the map of West Africa', in COLBY, C. C. (ed.), *Geographic aspects of international relations*.

— (1944) *The earth and the state: a study in political geography*, esp. pp. 304-94.

WHITTOW, J. B. (1959) 'The glaciers of Mount Baker, Ruwenzori', *Geogr. J.*, *125*, 370-9. Cf. also the *Reports* of the Makerere College Ruwenzori Reconnaissance.

WORTHINGTON, E. B. (1958) *Science in the development of Africa*.

Evidence of lake-level changes from
the northern shoreline of
Lake Victoria, Uganda

THE northern shoreline of Lake Victoria between Entebbe and Mjanje is characterized by a very irregular outline. Along most of its length, shallow bays, partially infilled at their heads by extensive papyrus swamps, separate long, irregular headlands reaching far out into the lake. Offshore there is a multitude of islands, great and small, and rocky islets separated one from another and from the mainland by deep channels (Figures 1 and 2). Only along the coast of South Kyagwe east of Nyoba Point does the shoreline become more regular in outline following the strike of a series of steeply dipping quartzites, but where these have been breached, as at Grant Bay, the lake has flooded the granitic depression behind to form an irregular bay.

This indented outline is the result of the partial submergence of a sub-maturely dissected landscape bearing evidence of several partial cycles of erosion. These have been described in some detail by J. W. Pallister (1960), as has the topography of the lake fringe in Buganda (Pallister, 1957). Both in Buganda and to the east of the Nile in Busoga the relief is fairly subdued, particularly on the outcrops of granites and schists, with rounded hill-tops, even hill-slopes and broad, open, often papyrus-floored valleys; but in some parts, and particularly in South Kyagwe, where resistant quartzite ridges are common, the hill tops rise to greater heights and are flat-topped and capped with a thick layer of indurated laterite or duricrust. The characteristic hill summits are remnants of the Buganda surface and range in height between 4,250 and 4,400 feet. The slopes below suggest downcutting in a series of stages to a well-marked valley floor level which is itself beginning to be attacked by the most recent phase of rejuvenation. The drainage pattern at present comprises a series of broad papyrus-choked swamps, structurally well adjusted, through which water-flow is sluggish and which generally drain northward or away from the lake to the Mayanja, Sezibwa and other affluents

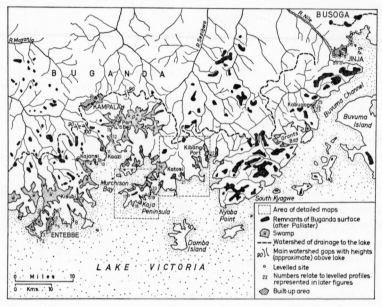

Figure 1. The northern shoreline of Lake Victoria between Entebbe and Jinja

of Lake Kyoga. These streams rise in an ill-defined and sinuous watershed, in places lying within a mile of the present shore of the lake and in places cut by a series of well-marked low through-valleys or gaps. This pattern can be readily seen on Figures 1 and 2. The streams draining to the lake are short and generally sluggish with frequent signs of recent reversal, but in coastal Kyagwe there is a series of short, free-flowing streams cutting rapidly to the lake through deep valleys filled with forest.

Submergence, already invoked as the cause of the irregular shoreline, and the disruption and drowning of old valleys, resulted from upwarping connected with the development of the Western Rift. This upwarping occurred transverse to the old westward drainage lines and resulted in the drowning of vast areas to the east, Lake Victoria being the largest. The history of these changes is complex and is described elsewhere (Wayland, 1929; Solomon, 1939) but it will be seen that relative downwarping explains the nature of the drainage to the north of the lake, the closeness of

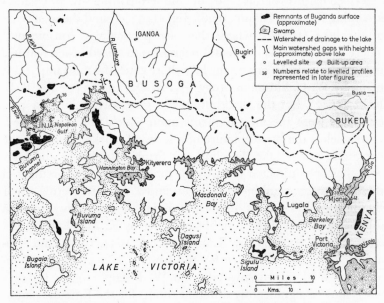

Figure 2. The northern shoreline of Lake Victoria between Jinja and Mjanje

the watershed to the shore, and also the contrast in form between the drowned northern shoreline and the emergent western shoreline of Lake Victoria.

None the less, despite the predominantly submerged aspect of the northern shoreline of the lake, it can be shown that the latest changes to occur have brought about emergence of the shoreline. Intermittent falls in lake level are evidenced by a well-marked series of raised beaches which are prominent in many areas. It is with the description and possible interpretation of these features that this paper is primarily concerned.

PREVIOUS WORK

Evidence of former higher levels of the lake in the form of wave-cut notches and raised beach deposits was first described from the Entebbe peninsula by E. J. Wayland (1920). He subsequently described features of this type from numerous other sites in Uganda including Buvuma Island (1926), Jinja (1934*a*), and the west coast of the lake (1934*b*), where they are particularly conspicuous. There are numerous incidental references to raised beach features in later geological work on the lake shore zone, the most important being by W. C. Simmons (1923), K. A. Davies (1933) and P. E. Kent (1942), but the descriptions are generally lacking in precision, as were the measurements upon which they were based. Nevertheless the broad picture of a series of marked stages in the regression of the lake shoreline was firmly established and later work has been directed towards the more precise measurement of these features combined with attempts at interpreting their significance. The most important items of later work were a fuller description of the Entebbe evidence by K. Marshall (1954), work on the Katonga by R. L. Johnson (1954, 1955), and a re-assessment of the evidence for the western lake shore based on accurate field measurement by W. W. Bishop (1956). Bishop's work showed significantly different results for the Entebbe peninsula from those obtained by Marshall. Bishop stated his aims in re-examining these sites as follows: 'It seemed desirable, before commencing mapping of the coastline west of Entebbe and between the rivers Kagera and Katonga, to develop and test a field method which, if proved reliable, could be applied with confidence to the whole region.' Work by the present writer described here, using similar detailed methods, confirms for the northern shoreline of the lake many of the findings of Bishop to the west. A summary of the more important work, with suggested correlations, is given below.

TABLE I   A summary of the more important work on the raised beaches of the Uganda shoreline of Lake Victoria

Simmons, Sese Is. (*1923*)	*Wayland, Buvuma* (*1926*)	*Davies, Busoga* (*1933*)	*Wayland, Jinja* (*1934*)	*Wayland, Kagera* (*1934*)	*Marshall, Entebbe* (*1954*)	*Johnson, Katonga* (*1955*)	*Bishop, Entebbe and West* (*1956–8*)
	200				250	190–200	200–220
		150		170	175	80–170	
100	125			125		115	110–115
	85	80			80	80	
75			60	70			65
	40–50	50	45		50		40–45
25–30		25	26	20–30	25	30	
10		15	10–15	15	10	17	12

Heights are given in feet above the level of Lake Victoria

Although a fair amount of numerical agreement is displayed if the figures are correlated as shown, the actual correlation remains in doubt, and it was felt that more detailed work was needed before valid conclusions were possible for the northern shoreline. Considerable overall disagreement appears in relation both to the number and the height of the various stages.

PROBLEMS AND METHODS

The discrepancies between the results obtained by previous workers and set out in Table I probably result from several factors. In the first place it is improbable that any one area preserves evidence of every stage, and the lake must have stood at least some time at every height between its highest point and its present level. Different workers may have regarded different points as significant in relation to the heighting of any one stage. Results described by the present author relate to the inferred position of the concave break of slope at the base of the cliff before it became obscured by talus. Most significant of all in explaining the discrepancies are probably errors of recording. Of the previous workers only Bishop actually levelled the features he described and drew accurate ground profiles. Another probable contributory factor in explaining the discrepancies between the results of earlier workers is short-term fluctuation in lake level, this having been used as a datum for measurement. With these discrepancies in mind, it appeared profitable to conduct a fairly extensive survey to try to evaluate previous work and also to tie it together.

Field work was commenced in the Entebbe area to tie in with earlier work and progressed by stages eastward, to Mjanje. Wherever levelling was possible, accurate profiles were surveyed using the lake level (adjusted for local fluctuations) as a datum. The results were plotted directly on aerial photographs at a scale of 1 :40,000. Only for some of the townships areas (notably Entebbe and Jinja) were maps of larger scale than 1 :50,000 available. Even the 1 :50,000 sheets are not available for the eastern part of the area which thus remains without adequate map coverage. This eastern area is not only heavily forested and difficult of access, but was also, until very recently, a closed area because of sleeping sickness; information on raised beaches is therefore less there. Detail about the beach deposits was obtained by augering and by the examination of scattered sections.

RESULTS

Although the survey aimed at reasonable completeness, it was found most profitable to concentrate on certain more important areas, described in turn below, and to cover the intervening shoreline by rapid reconnaissances, generally by levelling open sites but, in less accessible areas, by stereo-plotting.

Entebbe

Bishop (1956) first defined three major raised beach stages here which he termed the Hippo Bay stage (approximately 10-12 feet above present lake level), the Discovery stage (40-45 feet a.l.l.) and the Kigungu level (60 feet a.l.l.). He did not plot the position of these ancient shorelines, although he fixed their heights

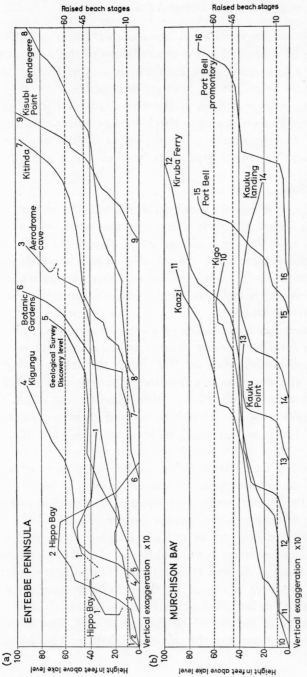

Figure 3. Levelled profiles of raised beaches on (a) the Entebbe peninsula (Some profiles from Murchison Bay are included (7, 8 and 9). Profiles 1-6 are re-drawn from Bishop (1956) and show his type-sites (1, 4 and 5)); (b) the western side of Murchison Bay, south of Kampala. The numbers alongside the levelled profiles correspond to the locations numbered on Figure 1.

by levelling and described briefly some of their features. With the production of a detailed topographical sheet of this area, at the scale of 1:2,500, much more information on the detailed morphology of the peninsula has been made available.

Little new work was done at Entebbe although a few supplementary profiles were drawn to check on the earlier work. Figure 3(a) shows a representative series of levelled profiles for Entebbe and includes those of the type areas (profiles 1, 2, 4 and 5).

Murchison Bay

Between Entebbe and the head of Murchison Bay at Port Bell, there is a number of clearly defined promontories, which show clear signs of cliffing at different levels. Associated with these stages in many areas there are extensive raised beach deposits. Many of these features were levelled and a representative selection of the results is shown in Figure 3(b). The same sequence is found here as at Entebbe.

The highest beach can be traced north-east across Entebbe Bay to Kitinda (profile 7) where there is an impressive line of cliffs backing well-marked flats 60 feet above the lake. At Kisubi (profile 9) the steep slopes below the Seminary are notched at this height as are many of the other spurs farther north, e.g. Kaazi (profile 11). To the east of Kajansi there are extensive deposits of beach sands related to this stage which are in places up to 25 feet thick and which show some interesting sections.

Well-marked flats related to the 45-foot stage were found on almost all the promontories. Extensive deposits of beach sands related to the 45-foot beach were found at Bendegerere and east and south of Kajansi; this 45-foot feature is particularly well displayed at Port Bell (profile 15). The fringing terrace of the 10-foot stage can be almost continuously traced behind the present shoreline all round the bay. It is particularly prominent where the shore has not been obscured by the development of papyrus, though where this has taken place there is a smooth rise from the lakeward edge of the swamp to the 10-foot cliff. The extensive development of papyrus on this shore as a whole has been favoured by the recent shallowing of the lake shore indicated by the presence of the youngest raised beach.

Koja peninsula

To the east of Murchison Bay lies the Koja peninsula. Topographically it is similar to the areas already described, generally low-lying and deeply penetrated by arms of the lake, but in parts its quartzite backbone rises to higher levels and carries remnants of the Buganda surface. Figures 4 and 5 show the morphology and the distribution of raised beach features in this area.

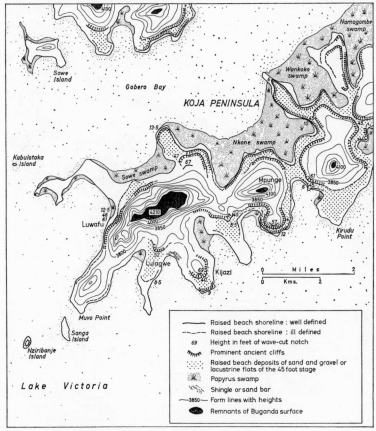

Figure 4. Raised beach features on the Koja peninsula

A very closely comparable pattern of features is revealed to that already described for the areas to the west; the levelled profiles shown in Figure 6(*a*) support this. Almost all the sites examined on the peninsula showed some evidence of the highest stage, at 60 feet above the lake, but only at Lulagwe (profile 18) were there obvious beach deposits related to it in the form of considerable spreads of rounded quartzite pebbles at the concave break of slope marking the old shoreline. Elsewhere the stage was marked

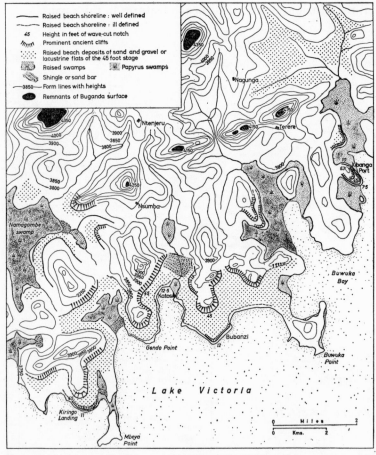

Figure 5. Raised beach features around Kibanga Port

by a more or less extensive platform with a sharp rise behind. Below this level, the more extensive 45-foot stage is generally well developed. This is particularly so to east and west of Katosi landing (Figure 5) where there are very large areas of open, flat, grey-white, grassy sands and gravels behind which rise steep and impressive ancient cliffs. Unconsolidated beach deposits are rare farther west except around Mpunge (profile 19) for the very narrowness of the spurs militates against preservation of deposits. Spreads of low level laterite underlie the flats to the west. The 10-foot stage is found as a narrow coastal strip of flat land. It is a fairly prominent feature at Kibanga Port where it is backed by impressive cliffs cut in laterite (profile 22) but in other places it is not extensive. Sand bars developing at this stage dammed the entrances of a series of inlets in the east and when the lake level fell from the 10-foot stage to its present level, these inlets were left above mean lake level as raised swamps (Figure 5). Bishop has described similar features elsewhere (1959).

South Kyagwe

The South Kyagwe coast is relatively straight in outline except where the steeply dipping quartzite ridges, which form it, break down and give way to granites which underlie the bays and inlets. The presence of resistant outcrops along the shoreline has meant that evidence of raised beaches is poor and fragmentary; wave-cut notches would be poorly developed in relation to relatively short stages, and there would not be much material available to develop extensive built-terraces. Added to this there is the uniform outline of the coast providing few sites for the preservation of good beach sequences. Therefore not only were these features probably originally less significant than in other areas but they were also much more liable to be removed by subsequent erosion. The only good sequences of deposits are found in the embayments where streams break through to the lake.

In the few areas where evidence of raised beaches is preserved, the same sequence as found farther west is traceable. Flats associated with concave slope breaks at the appropriate heights were levelled in several places and just south of Kabugoge above Kindi Market, pockets of sand (presumably lacustrine) were found on flats at 60 feet on indurated laterite. On either side of this level, deep humose sands (in excess of 3 feet and flat bedded) were found as fringing terraces 15 feet or so below (45 feet a.l.l.). At Kabugoge and at several sites along the shore of the Buvuma channel in this area, bedded sands of the 10-foot stage are exposed in the walls of shallow sand pits. A fine section of the material forming this youngest beach is exposed at Byumbe (profile 25), one and a half miles north-east of Kabugoge, and shows:

9. 3·0 ft. Pale red-brown humose sand with some pebble horizons
8. 0·2 ft. Sub-angular quartz gravel and laterite gravel
7. 0·2 ft. White quartz sand
6. 0.1 ft. Rounded laterite gravel with some quartz; black stained
5. 0·1 ft. White quartz sand
4. 0·3 ft. Sub-angular quartz pebbles and rounded laterite gravel
3. 0·6 ft. Fine white quartz sand
2. 0.01 ft. Fine red quartz sand
1. 3·5 ft. Fine white quartz sand darkening downwards

A series of levelled profiles from this area forms part of Figure 6(*a*).

Jinja
The present outlet of Lake Victoria is by way of the Victoria Nile through the Owen Falls dam at Jinja but it was previously con-trolled by the height of the prominent rock bar which gave rise to the now submerged Ripon Falls, about half a mile upstream of the dam. Detailed topographical maps cover the areas within the township and these were used to supplement field surveying.

Detailed levelling again revealed the same general pattern of three main stages in the fall of the lake level (Figure 6(*b*)).

However, no beach deposits were found in this area at around 60 feet a.l.l., although flats and concave breaks of slope were prominent at that height (profile 34). Again most of the profiles show clear evidence of the 45-foot stage (profiles 26, 27, 28, 29, 31, 32, 33). Beach material of this stage is exposed extensively in 'borrow-pits', at the moment being worked for road material, at Bungungu on the western side of Napoleon Gulf just across from Jinja. Bone (unidentifiable) and a few implements (Levalloisian) were found in these deposits.

One of the interesting features of the Jinja area is the variation in the nature of the lowest raised beach stage. Not only did it show, within a fairly limited area, considerable height variation (from 5 to 12 feet) but also marked changes of aspect. At Walu-kuba Point, the platform is cut in solid rock with steep backing cliffs 10 to 15 feet high (profile 34), at Kirinya it is marked by an extensive flat of deep red lateritic earth (profiles 29 and 30), whereas below the Ripon Falls Hotel (profile 27) a low, narrow sandy flat fronts impressive laterite cliffs. The slopes behind these raised features are again very variable, though this is not brought out by the profiles drawn in Figure 6(*b*).

Lakeshore areas east of Jinja

To the east of Jinja, in coastal Busoga and Bukedi, the general relief is more subdued than to the west, although higher areas border Napoleon Gulf immediately to the east and it is only much farther east, on the Kenya coast in Nyanza, that areas of moderately high relief fringe the shoreline again.

The shoreline outline is very irregular (Figure 2) and in places it is characterized by extensive and developing areas of papyrus, particularly where the position is exceptionally sheltered as to the south of Hannington Bay. Because of problems of access, much of the mapping in this area was done from aerial photographs, this being tied in to a series of levelled profiles.

The relatively few levelled profiles obtained from this area show the same three major stages as have already been described (Figure 6(*c*)). Particularly interesting is profile 41 at Sio Port,

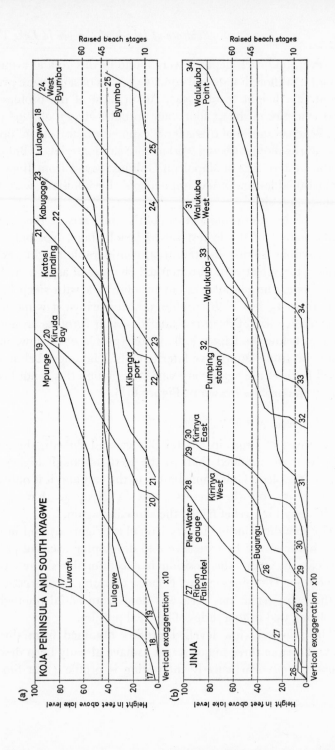

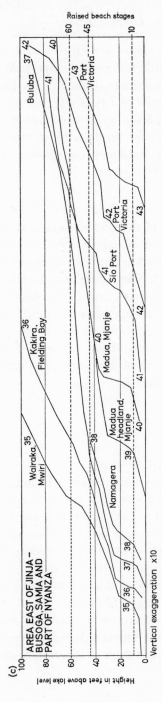

Figure 6. Levelled profiles of raised beaches, (*a*) on the Koja peninsula and south Kyagwe; (*b*) around Jinja; (*c*) east of Jinja, in Busoga, Samia and West Kenya The numbers correspond to the sites numbered on Figure 2

Nyanza. Here all three stages are clearly evident on the one profile and associated with the 45-foot stage pale brown sandy clay 1-2 feet thick overlies indurated laterite. The clay is obviously not derived from the laterite and is interpreted as a lake deposit. No deposits associated with the upper two stages were found elsewhere in this area, except for the lateritic terraces which are so well marked a feature of the slopes immediately adjacent to the lake along its whole northern shore.

Summary diagram

As only a small number of the sites examined and levelled have been described above, and as only a representative selection of the profiles can be presented, a summary diagram of the levelling results is given in Figure 7. Sites where these levelled profiles were measured are shown in Figures 1 and 2. The diagram sets out the profiles from west to east in approximate order. It will be noticed that no raised beach stages above 60 feet have been recognized in this area. At heights much above this level the lake basin no longer holds water because of low watershed gaps both in the south and in the north (Pallister, 1957).

DISCUSSION

(i) *Variations in the heights of the stages*

In Figure 7, as in the diagrams showing the actual profiles, the various stages recognized above have been marked in by a heavy dotted line. It will be seen that there is a considerable height variation for individual sections around this mean figure. This height variation probably results from a combination of factors. First, there will be original differences resulting from whether the feature was cut at the head of a bay or at the point of a promontory. Secondly, the height plotted on Figure 7 is a concave slope break, which is sometimes a wave-cut feature without deposits and sometimes the top of a largely uneroded terrace of lacustrine deposition, either a delta or a beach. Some considerable height variation is to be expected as a result of this. Thirdly, short-period lake level fluctuations must be considered. Even during the sixty years or so during which accurate instrumental records have been kept the variation of mean monthly levels in Lake Victoria has been in excess of 6 feet. With fluctuations of this extent within so comparatively short a period, it would seem likely that there should be considerable height variations in the

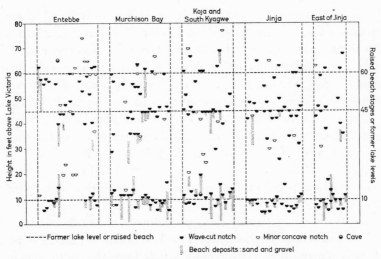

Figure 7. Height-spacing diagram of raised-beach remnants along the northern shoreline of Lake Victoria, Uganda

features produced by the lake, for there is little to suggest that the present fluctuating pattern is exceptional. Indeed, it is more likely that an even greater range of lake levels would be evidenced by a longer sequence of recording. Superimposed upon these very considerable fluctuations are shorter period oscillations; these have, however, little morphological significance.

In Figure 7 the results of the beach levelling from Entebbe to Mjanje are plotted from left to right across the diagram. Thus the Entebbe profiles figure on the left of the diagram and the beach profiles from West Kenya on the extreme right. It appears from this diagram that there is no progressive change in the height of the features. Such height changes as are evident result from the influences already described and are to some extent random. The approximate mean figure of a stage can be defined by a horizontal line on the diagram, as is shown. The features are therefore un-warped in a west-east direction. The possibility of north-south-warping of the basin will be dealt with later.

(ii) *Variation of the raised features in plan*

In general it may be said that the most impressively developed erosional features are located on headlands where the attack of breaking waves at the period of their formation was concentrated and where subsequently they have suffered comparatively little erosion, e.g. many of the promontories at Entebbe. The depositional sequences are best preserved and formed at bay heads where unconsolidated material could accumulate both by deltaic and lacustrine deposition, e.g. Kajansi near the head of Murchison Bay and north of Bugungu across Napoleon Gulf from Jinja.

Another influence upon the distribution of well-marked lacustrine features is orientation in relation to both dominant winds and length of fetch. As Johnson (1955) was first to remark, wave-cut features are generally most pronounced on south-east facing slopes and relatively poorly developed on north-east facing slopes. This is the result of predominant winds from the south blowing over the lake. Because of the intricate outline of the shore, however, the predominant influence upon wave erosion would appear to be the length of fetch available. The location and development of papyrus swamps along this shoreline seem to be essentially related to those areas which accidents of coastal topo-graphy have sheltered from the attack of large waves; thus sediments can accumulate undisturbed and aquatic vegetation develop undamaged.

(iii) *The nature of the lacustrine features*

In some areas the nature of the beaches is simple. A concave break of slope of fairly uniform height separates a steep fossil cliff behind from a somewhat downgraded depositional feature to lakeward of it. However, there is considerable variation in the form of these features even within a limited area.

As might be expected the older upper beaches have been less clearly preserved than the younger features; with the upper beaches the cut-notch is harder to identify and there is progressively less in the way of deposits associated with the upper stages compared with the lower ones. This is evident on many of the levelled profiles and also from Figure 7. These contrasts result largely from different amounts of subsequent erosional modification, although the extensive platforms and deposits of the 45-foot stage suggest that it may mark a somewhat longer still-stand.

The major problem with most of these beach levels is their relationship to the indurated laterite which underlies many of them. It is often assumed tacitly that all the laterites close to the lake shore have been formed in the same way; more detailed study of this problem suggests that this is not so. Wayland (1920) was the first to notice this, observing that in many areas laterite sheets extend smoothly over slopes of considerable angles (up to 10°) and pass under the lake surface as a continuous sheet. These laterite sheets must be old features and they have simply been notched by the various lake levels.

By contrast, some of the laterites would appear to be roughly contemporary with the beach accumulations (Du Bois and Jeffery, 1955). Not only did the morphological history of the area ideally favour the development of indurated horizons related to each stage of the lake level, but there was also an abundant supply of iron-rich material derived from the erosion of older laterites existing at a variety of heights on the slopes and summits of the hills around the lake shore, which was concentrated by downwashing at or about lake level within the permeable beach deposits. This secondary material therefore provided the necessary indurating agent and it accumulated where the drainage was poor; in other words, at the water-table geared to the then existing level of the lake surface. As the level of the lake fell, bringing about a negative change in local base level, erosion would begin on the former lake flats, the more easily mobilized elements would be leached out and the surface would become modified; but also, as the result of the fall of the water-table, the beach material would experience oxidation which would accompany the drying out of the former water-logged zones. This oxidation would cause the precipitation of the poorly soluble reduced compounds and induration of this precipitated and immobilized material would follow rapidly. This process has been described by R. Maignien (1956) for tropical West Africa and explains not only the association of laterite with each terrace level but also the nature of the cliff sections themselves, for 'increased drainage near the breaks in relief explains the . . . thickness of the cornices of fossil cuirasses (indurated laterite) dominating water collecting depressions'. Continued erosion would progressively lay bare the laterite pavement. Evidence of the beginning of this process was seen near Buluba east of Jinja where sands of the 10-foot stage had been extensively quarried. The sands were banked as a well-defined terrace against an extensive flat cut across deep iron-rich soils. Close to the present lake level, the sands were iron-stained and were too hard, at the surface, to be broken without the use of a hammer. This observation supports both concentration at lake level and the fact of induration upon exposure. To summarize, the relationships between the raised features and the lake-fringe laterites involve the discussion to a two-fold process:

(*a*) the enrichment of the beach material of various sorts, though often quartz sand, by iron-rich solutions and secondary lateritic material; and

(*b*) a negative change in base-level (due to fall in lake level) leading to the exposure of the enriched horizons to oxidation, precipitation and finally induration.

The nature of the laterite itself supports supports these ideas. Very frequently these laterites show, in detail, considerable amounts of quartz sand set in an indurated matrix, and this sand is interpreted as a beach deposit.

On top of these lateritized horizons there sometimes still

remains unlateritized beach material. A detailed study of this material and the beach deposits, where they have remained unlateritized, shows that there are, as might be expected, strong soil differences associated with the different stages (Radwanski, 1960). There is considerable local variation but generally associated with the youngest stage is loose, structureless yellow to grey sand, often podsolized and sometimes humus stained. The depth of this material is variable. Associated with the somewhat higher and older stages is soil consisting of a humose topsoil merging into brown sandy loam, often overlying a zone of quartz pebbles and a clayey substratum. Again the depth of the profile is variable and it frequently overlies indurated laterite.

(iv) *Dating of the raised features*

It is evident that the formation of the beaches must post-date the formation of the lake. The earth movements which brought the lake into being would appear to date from early middle Pleistocene; furthermore, the lake would fill up gradually rather than all at once. It would therefore appear that the lacustrine deposits so far described are upper Pleistocene in age. It is possible, however, to be more precise than this.

Within the deposits themselves there is an almost complete absence of characteristic fossils and even of pollen. This would appear to be due to rapid oxidation. Archaeological evidence is slight as the naturally heavily forested environment must have presented great problems to primitive man, even along the lake edge. However, west of the lake, upwarped lacustrine terraces immediately pre-dating the 60-foot raised beach can be approximately dated on archaeological grounds as between 25,000 and 30,000 years old (post-middle Sangoan) (Bishop and Posnansky, 1960). This gives a maximum lower date for the oldest features described above. Within, and contemporary with, deposits of the youngest raised beach at Entebbe rolled charcoal was found by Bishop which has been dated by radio-carbon methods, giving the youngest raised beach a date of 3,240 years before present (Flint and Deevey, 1960).

The beaches themselves are often very clearly preserved, having suffered little by way of erosion. This again is suggestive of their relative youth, as is the absence of maturely developed soil profiles on most of the deposits.

INTERPRETATION

The major point arising from the discussion is that, throughout the area described (almost the whole of the northern shoreline of the lake), a distance of almost 120 miles, three major raised-beach stages can be traced, with very considerable continuity, and that these features stand at a constant level above the present lake surface. This is a conclusion of some significance, for in an area as tectonically unstable as East Africa in the recent geological past it proves that in this area there has been no warping since before the cutting of the 60-foot beach. Bishop (1958), in summarizing his work on the western shoreline of the lake, reaches the same conclusions. This therefore excludes the possibility of north-south warping accounting for the pattern found on the northern shoreline. Therefore warping cannot be invoked to explain the presence of these features and other reasons must be sought.

There are three possible explanations: (i) the reduction of inflow into the lake as the result of capture of part of the lake drainage; (ii) intermittent lowering of the lake outlet at Jinja, as the result of headward erosion by knick-points along the course of the Nile; and (iii) climatic changes.

Little detailed work has so far been done on the evolution of drainage in Uganda, yet because of the tectonic and morphological history of the areas draining to the lake from the west, capture must be considered. The aggressive streams draining west to the rift, with strong base-level advantages, are in process of pushing the present swamp watersheds eastward and may well, within the comparatively short time-span covered by the evolution of these beach levels, have diverted water from the sluggish affluents of the lake. Although the possibility of capture cannot be ignored as a possible influence on lake level, it is unlikely that the results could be of a sufficient magnitude, even after a considerable period, to account for the impressive reduction in water volume evidenced by the raised beaches described above.

A second possible explanation is that the level of the lake outflow at Jinja has been intermittently reduced (Bishop, 1958). Downstream of the site of Ripon Falls, the old course of the Nile was marked by an impressive series of rapids for many miles, and these features represent a series of knick-points migrating upstream. Detailed mapping was carried out along the first few miles of the Nile to see if the morphology of the valley provided any clues as to the suggested correlation of knick-point recession and lake-level fall. The results were inconclusive; the deep incision of the river in this sector has resulted in the banks being both steep (generally 35-40°) and straight. If there were once evidence of intermittent downcutting in the form of terraces, it is there no longer. Only much lower down do terrace remnants fringe the river.

The third possible explanation of lake-level variations is to invoke climatic change (Flint, 1959). Even the relatively slight changes in climatic conditions over the last seventy years have, as has been shown above, caused lake-level fluctuations of a very considerable amplitude. Climate determines the precise lake level to a very considerable extent by governing the supply from rivers flowing in, by rainfall directly and by controlling the amount of evaporation. C. E. P. Brooks (1925) has discussed these relationships in so far as they bear on the water balance of Lake Victoria at the present time. He showed that the rise or fall of the lake over the period he studied was almost exactly proportional to the excess or deficit of rainfall compared to the average. It is conceivable in this context that long-term alteration of lake level might be achieved if a series of 'wet' years, by present standards, were not followed by a series of 'dry' years but by a fluctuating balance of wet and dry years similar to the present. The high lake-levels then established in the wet years might not subside but might be maintained. Conversely a sequence of dry years could lead to a lowering of level which might well achieve a degree of permanency if it did not happen to be followed by a series of wet years. Thus climate might affect progressive change in lake level without becoming 'wetter' or 'drier' but rather by a concentrated phase followed by more normal conditions.

However, within the period of the formation of these raised beaches (see above), there is fairly good evidence of several wetter periods within the area of the Eastern Rift (Flint, 1959), and it would be surprising if major climatic changes in that area did not have important repercussions on the lake plateau to the west. Even small-scale changes in precipitation could have important effects over a period.

It would therefore appear that the intermittent falls in lake level, evidence of which has been described above, cannot with certainty be attributed to any single cause. The various possible explanations put forward are not mutually exclusive, and more detailed work is required before any more definite conclusion can be reached; this work is now in progress.

ACKNOWLEDGEMENTS

I am grateful to the Director of the Uganda Geological Survey for permission to consult the unpublished reports quoted, to the Lands and Surveys Department for the loan of aerial photographs and to Professor S. J. K. Baker, Dr W. W. Bishop and Dr S. Gregory for reading the manuscript and making helpful suggestions.

REFERENCES

BISHOP, W.W. (1956) 'Former lake levels of the Entebbe peninsula', Unpublished report, *Geol. Surv. Uganda*, 1-5.
— (1958) 'A review of the Pleistocene stratigraphy of the Uganda Protectorate', Joint meeting, *East-central, west-central and southern regional committees for Geol. Leopoldville*, 91-105.
— (1959) 'Raised swamps of Lake Victoria', *Rec. geol. Surv. Uganda*, 1955-6, 1-10.

BISHOP, W.W., and POSNANSKY, M. (1960) 'Pleistocene environments and early man in Uganda', *Uganda J.*, *24*, 44-61.

BROOKS, C.E.P. (1925) 'The fluctuations of Lake Victoria', *J. E. Africa Uganda nat. Hist. Soc.*, *22*, 47-55.

DAVIES, K.A. (1933) 'Bukoli county (Busoga) and Samia county (Budama)', *Bull. Geol. Surv. Uganda, 1932*, 36-40.

DUBOIS, C.G.B. and JEFFERY, P.G. (1955) 'The composition and origin of the laterites of the Entebbe peninsula, Uganda Protectorate', *Overseas Geol. Min. Resour.*, *5*, 387-408.

FLINT, R.F. (1959) 'Pleistocene climates in eastern and southern Africa', *Bull. Geol. Soc. Am.*, *70*, 343-74.

— (1960) 'On the basis of Pleistocene correlation in East Africa', *Geol. Mag.*, *96*, 265-84.

FLINT, R.F., and DEEVEY, E.S. (ed. 1960) Y688; Hippo bay cave, Entebbe, Uganda', *Radio-carbon*, *2*, 56.

JOHNSON, R.L. (1954) Report on NA. 36. U. III. SW. (Mitala Maria sheet), part of NA. 36. U. III. NW. (Mityana sheet), and part of SA. 36. C.I.NW. (Goru peninsula). Unpublished report. *Geol. Surv. Uganda*, 1-11.

— (1955) 'Lake levels and the river Katonga'. Unpublished report, *Geol. Surv. Uganda*, 1-3.

KENT, P.E. (1942) 'The country round the Kavirondo gulf of Victoria Nyanza', *Geogr. J.*, *100*, 22-31.

MAIGNIEN, R. (1956) 'Soil cuirasses in tropical West Africa', *Afr. Soils*, *4*, 4-41.

MARSHALL, K. (1954) 'The pre-history of the Entebbe peninsula', *Uganda J.*, *18*, 44-57.

PALLISTER, J.W. (1957) 'The physiography of Mengo district, Buganda', *Uganda J.*, *21*, 16-29.

— (1960) 'Erosion cycles and associated surfaces of Mengo district, Buganda', *Overseas Geol. Min. Resour.*, *8*, 26-36.

RADWANSKI, S.A. (1960) 'The soils and land use of Buganda', *Mem. Res. Div. Dept. Agric. Uganda, Ser. 1*, *4*, 81-5.

SIMMONS, W.C. (1923) 'A rapid geological survey of the western Sese islands, Lake Victoria'. Unpublished report. *Geol. Surv. Uganda*, 1-16.

SOLOMON, J.D. (1939) 'The Pleistocene succession in Uganda', in O'BRIEN, T.P. *The prehistory of the Uganda Protectorate.*

WATER DEVELOPMENT DEPARTMENT, UGANDA (1962) Hydrology section in *Atlas of Uganda*. (Includes diagram of monthly mean gauge readings in metres of Lake Victoria levels at Jinja from 1899.)

WAYLAND, E.J. (1920) Some facts and theories relating to the geology of Uganda', *Geol. Surv. Uganda, Pamphlet 1*, 46.

— (1926) 'Notes on a rapid geological survey of Buvuma island'. Unpublished report. *Geol. Surv. Uganda*, 1-5.

WAYLAND E. J. (1929) 'Rift valleys and Lake Victoria', *CR. XV Int. Geol. Congr.* South Africa, 323-53.

— (1934*a*) 'Note on Pleistocene erosion levels in the vicinity of Jinja'. Unpublished report. *Geol. Surv. Uganda*, 1-3.

— (1934*b*) 'Pleistocene geology and prehistory', *Bull. Geol. Surv. Uganda, 1933,* 71-7.

Landforms in the
Northern Territory of Australia

THE landforms of the tropical zone present many problems to the geomorphologist. The relationship between the present climatic environment and the development of the landforms is of particular interest. This cannot be examined without reference to the long and complex Mesozoic and Kainozoic evolution of the main continental areas. The landforms of the Northern Territory of Australia have developed under conditions which include deep weathering during the Kainozoic, successive deformation of the surface by warping, and changes in the climatic environment. In addition the peculiar factors of low gradients and small available relief have had their impact upon the resulting land surface. The processes in operation at present are related to climatic conditions which range from humid tropical in the north to arid margin in the south and are refashioning a landscape of considerable age. The earlier parts of this essay examine the evolutionary history and then certain areas are considered in greater detail.

PHYSIOGRAPHY[1] (Figure 1)

Three main physiographic divisions may be distinguished for the purposes of this discussion.

1. The Northern Rivers and Arnhem Land.
2. The Intermediate Basin and Plain Zone.
3. The Range and Basin area of Central Australia.

[1] David (1950), vol. 2, provides a general physiography of the Northern Territory while the memoirs of the Commonwealth Scientific and Industrial Research Organization (C.S.I.R.O.) mentioned later give local detailed divisions.

E

The first two divisions are characterized by low gradients, low available relief and broad transition zones between the main physiographic regions. They may be distinguished on drainage criteria. In the north the drainage is exoreic and integrated into a series of basins such as those of the Victoria, Daly and Roper rivers. During the dry season only the lower parts of the main streams contain flowing water. The river basins are separated by extensive plateaux which rise to approximately 1,500 feet in Arnhem Land. Southward the watershed areas frequently lie on featureless plains with little perceptible gradient change.

The Basin and Plain Zone is dominated by even horizons broken only by low mesas at basin margins. These constitute the 'ranges' marked on Figure 1, although the northern margin of the Barkly Tableland has relatively steeper gradients. Drainage is directed towards a series of interior basins with small central salt lake areas. The Georgina River depression in the south-east marks the change in drainage direction towards the Great Artesian Basin.

Central Australia is dominated by a series of west-east ranges such as the MacDonnells and Musgraves which rise to nearly 5,000 feet above a general intermontane basin level of 2,000–2,500 feet. Lake Amadeus, a salt lake, occupies a major depression between the two ranges. The major ranges consist of a series of linear ridges separated by strike vales. In the southern Mac-Donnells the main drainage lines cut across the ridges in a series of spectacular gorges trending towards the Lake Eyre basin in the south-east. Throughout this region, and in the Basin and Plain region, rivers rarely contain water and generally only in the form of flash floods. Basin areas generally have broad depositional surfaces with central salina zones. West and south-east of Central Australia a transition occurs to sand ridge desert.

Geomorphogeny

Much of the Northern Territory is underlain by Archaean and Proterozoic rocks often highly metamorphosed and with large igneous intrusions. In Central Australia a late Palaeozoic orogeny produced a series of east-west structures although, as is evident

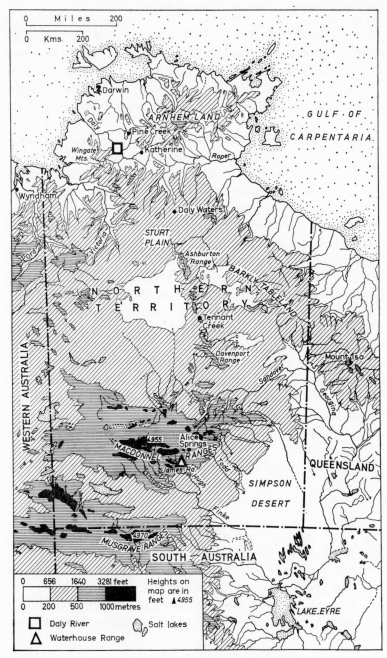

Figure 1. Northern Territory, Australia: relief and drainage

from the undisturbed Cambrian sediments of the Georgina Basin, most of the Territory has been tectonically stable for a very long period (Walpole, 1962). Crustal stresses have generally been resolved by periods of warping affecting large areas and this provides the background to the post-Palaeozoic evolution of the surface.

The Lower Mesozoic was dominantly a continental phase (David, 1956) with deposition occurring in marginal basins outside the limits of the Territory, e.g. Canning and Carpentaria basins. Periods of warping are indicated by stratigraphical breaks at late Triassic/early Jurassic and at late Jurassic, of which the latter was most profound. It was followed, probably after a period of erosion, by an extensive marine transgression during the Lower Cretaceous. This transgression covered much of the Northern Territory extending as far south as 17° South, and north as far as Barrow Creek. These limits (shown on the tectonic map of Australia) may be extended with future mapping but northern and southern sectors were separated by a land area extending southwest from the Tennant Creek area. To the north of this divide the Cretaceous sea advanced over an area of low relief, possibly of peneplane character (Malone, 1961, Randal, 1962). South of Barrow Creek the marine transgression advanced into an area of considerable local relief, at least 1,000 feet in some areas (Quinlan, 1962), infilling a series of intermontane basins in the ranges of Central Australia. The mid-Cretaceous regression and warping phase, possibly associated in date with the Maryborough movements in Queensland, revealed a surface with three main contrasting zones:

(i) in the north an area overlain by thin marine deposits;

(ii) the Tennant Creek divide, an area subjected to continuous erosion and weathering throughout the Mesozoic and possibly much of the Palaeozoic;

(iii) Central Australia, linear ridges with Mesozoic landforms and drainage patterns rising above basins of Cretaceous infilling.

This surface, with its physiographic divisions, provided the initial surface for the Kainozoic cycles of erosion. The nature of the initial surface in the different areas can be significant in the development of the present surface. In the north exhumation of the sub-Cretaceous surface is always a possibility as C. R. Twidale (1956) noted in a similar area in Queensland; the Tennant Creek divide with very deep weathering zones of 400-550 feet (Ivanac, 1954) imposed on Palaeozoic and older rocks presents a different case; while in Central Australia the lineaments of the Mesozoic landscape probably still dominate the relief. The Mesozoic warping patterns are difficult to distinguish from Kainozoic phases, which may have been along the same axes, but the Tennant Creek divide was subjected to uplift (Walpole, 1962) as was the Central Australian area. These axes were also active at various periods during the Kainozoic. The altitude of the main duricrust surface – the Australian surface of L. C. King (1962) – rises from 600 feet in the south, on the margins of the Lake Eyre Basin, to a maximum of 2,200-2,350 feet in the northern MacDonnells, with a down-gradient to the north towards the Barkly Tableland (Quinlan, 1962). Where large areas of the duricrust surface are preserved, as in the Barkly Tableland (Noakes and Traves, 1954), it is possible to trace a downwarp extending south-east – north-west across the Tableland with increased gradients towards the south-east in the Georgina Basin. The northern coastlands seem to have suffered down-warping towards the coast, with Arnhem Land remaining as a dome.

There is, however, considerable difficulty in dating the movements which produced these patterns, although two phases, Miocene and Pleistocene (Kosciusko), are usually invoked. The main problem is the age of the duricrust surface which forms such a prominent feature of the landscape. Duricrusts of varying age have been reported, e.g. post-Pliocene near Darwin (Mabbutt, 1961), while frequently the plateau surface or mesa remnants are eroded duricrust features with lower parts of the weathering profile providing the cap-rock, e.g. the silica cap remnants in south-western Queensland (Hill and Denmead, 1960). Considerable variation is possible and, considering the size and present climatic range of the area, probable. As Mabbutt (1961) points out, at one extreme a single erosion surface can embody the weathering of several phases while at the other erosion proceeding within one climatic phase can result in duricrusts at various levels. Unfortunately the Kainozoic deposits of the Territory are scattered and insufficiently known to be of great use although some lake deposits clearly post-date the main duricrust layer. In many areas, therefore, although it is possible to recognize a major phase of duricrust formation, to fix a date for this is difficult and correlation over wide areas is uncertain.

Stages in the dissection of the duricrust layer can be traced in many areas (King, 1962) while in the Central Australian area it is clear that some of these were accompanied by considerable changes in climate (Mabbutt, 1962). The post-duricrust stages are generally restricted to the basin areas although in the north they can extend to wide planation surfaces which may bear later duricrust layers. There also appears to have been an increase in the climatic differences between various parts of the Northern Territory mainly reflected in the increasing aridity of the south. This culminated in the disruption of the drainage and the development of sandridge desert, e.g. Simpson Desert.

The areas selected for further investigation are part of the central basin of the Daly River, and the central part of the Waterhouse Range. The slopes considered below are related to successive stages in the dissection of the main duricrust layer of their area and are, with the reservations noted above, roughly comparable in the period of time which has elapsed since their initiation. This can be significant in an area where relict features are present in the landforms. Both areas have underlying sedimentary formations, providing a contrast with the igneous areas elsewhere in the Northern Territory, and have duricrust layers later in date than the main weathering profile. In other respects strong contrasts are evident particularly in base-level control, with the Daly being related to coastal base-levels and the River Hugh (Waterhouse) to interior basins. However, the strongest contrast emerges in their present climatic environment. This is illustrated in the table below.

	Average annual rainfall	% of rainfall in period October–March	Maximum monthly average temperature	Minimum monthly average temperature
Daly River area	40 in. (approx.)			
Katherine[1]	35·45 in.	96	100° F October/ November	56° F June/ July
Waterhouse Range	8 in. (approx.)			
Alice Springs[1]	9·93 in.	76	95° F December	39° F July

[1] These are the nearest recording stations. Figures are from Perry (1960).

These figures reveal the main climatic characteristics of summer rainfall maxima and the rainfall difference between the two areas. The isolation of those climatic factors relevant to the operation of process is, however, difficult in the absence of micro-climatic studies, and also, probably, laboratory studies of weathering. There are some data available, mainly designed for agricultural use (Slayter, 1960 and 1962), and from this an arbitrary selection can be made to amplify the figures given above, and to obtain a slightly closer approximation to climate than is revealed by the annual temperature and rainfall.

Rainfall intensity and run-off are of prime importance in a study of process and even when annual average figures are quoted the contrast between the two areas is marked. Rainfall intensity, crudely measured as rainfall per rain-day, gives values for Katherine of 0·6 inches rain per rain-day (annual average) increasing to monthly average totals of 0·75 inches per rain-day for some wet season months. Alice Springs has figures of 0·21-0·40 inches per rain-day. This can be extended by considering the average annual number of rain-days with rainfall exceeding certain amounts at Katherine:

22·26 days per year with rainfall of over 0·5 inches
11·48 days per year with rainfall of over 1·0 inches
3·5 days per year with rainfall of over 2·0 inches

This obviously has a relation to the run-off values and in the case of Alice Springs it has been estimated that a 2·0 inches wet period (days of consecutive rain) is needed to produce significant run-off sufficient to recharge soil moisture, etc., while 1·0 inches produces slight run-off:

> 5·47 wet periods per year with rainfall over 0·5 inches
> 3·27 wet periods per year with rainfall over 1·0 inches
> 1·43 wet periods per year with rainfall over 2·0 inches

It is difficult to apply these critical run-off values, derived from field experience, to the Daly area in view of the different surface conditions, particularly in vegetation cover. However, Katherine has higher total rainfall, higher rainfall intensity and a higher reliability of rainfall (coefficient of variability 20 per cent). G. A. Stewart (1956), after considerable field experience in the area, commented that 'sheet erosion is very active'. Weathering is also influenced by availability of moisture under high temperature conditions: the Daly River area has heavy dews for the first half of the dry season (Randal 1962) and these are evident also later in the dry season.

Central Australia in contrast has low rainfall totals and low availability of moisture. Dews are infrequent except immediately after rain periods and rainfall is uncertain, e.g. the 1928 rainfall, 2·28 inches. The incidence of droughts is high (360 months of rainfall deficiency in sixty-nine years of record, Foley, 1957) and dust storms are frequent. Winter temperatures are low enough to allow a frost period but the impact of this must be inhibited by lack of moisture. The greatest single difference between the two areas is their present climatic environment and the field evidence can be considered with these points in mind.

THE DALY RIVER BASIN

The western part of the Daly River Basin, in the Claravale area, is bounded by the dissected escarpment of the Wingate Plateau and the river itself. The basin consists of low mesas separated by wide tributary valley slopes. The Daly River forms the eastern boundary and, during the dry season, provides the only permanent water. The range of height between plateau surface and the Daly base-level is approximately 600 feet and overall gradients are low – the river in this section falling at less than one foot per mile. The main elements in the geological succession can be seen on the edge of the Wingate Plateau. Here Mullaman beds (Cretaceous) unconformably overlie Cambrian sediments (Randal, 1962). The Cambrian rocks range from quartzites to limestones but like the Mullaman beds have been deeply weathered and altered during the Tertiary period. This has proceeded to the point where the original structures have been almost completely altered. The surface of the Plateau is formed by a massive ironstone layer with the thick mottled and pallid zones of a deep weathering profile below. The Cambrian rocks have also been altered in depth, commonly by secondary silicification, while the mottled and pallid zones have been similarly altered. In the lower parts of the basin solid exposures are rare and alluvium of various types is widespread on the lower slopes. Occasionally outcrops of Cretaceous and Cambrian rise above the alluvium and it would seem that the base of the Cretaceous is lower in the centre of the basin than on the Wingate Plateau, either due to warping or to factors of initial deposition.

Into the surface of highly altered Cretaceous sediments the present landforms have been cut. Various stages of evolution are present with at least three main stages of base-levelling represented by two dominant mesa levels within the basin in addition to the general basin floor which is now being dissected (Wright, 1961). These have been cut to various depths into the main weathering profile and are themselves associated with weathering profiles of various types. This series of duricrust layers merits further attention and can best be considered in relation to Figure 2, which shows a sketch profile of the main escarpment due west of Claravale.[1] The 'laterite' cap consists of massive pisolitic ironstones 15-20 feet thick, with mottled and pallid zones extending to possibly 100

---

[1] All profiles were compiled from Abney level measurements of slope facets combined with pacing of distances.

feet below this. It was not possible to measure the depths accurately at any point visited on the escarpment because of scree development on the slope. Both the mottled and pallid zones appear as steeper sections in the profile owing to induration of certain layers apparently associated with silicification. This was a general feature of this section of the escarpment over a distance of

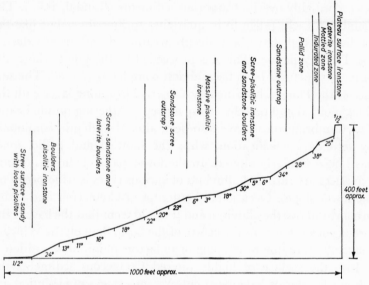

Figure 2. Sketch profile of Wingate escarpment, Daly River area

at least ten miles and is possibly associated with lowering of the water-table subsequent to the main period of weathering.

Below these layers another near vertical face in ironstone is present. This on general height characteristics would seem to be associated with the first erosion stage younger than the main plateau surface and it differs in certain respects from the 'laterite' cap at the plateau level. It is composed of massive pisolitic ironstone in blocks without the regularity of pisolite pattern obvious in the higher layer. Moreover in other sections of the escarpment this facet is often absent and there is no sign of a general ironstone layer in the rock succession. It seems to indicate that this is probably cemented scree material. Similar features are in the process of formation in the modern screes at the base of the main escarpment. Away from the plateau edge many of the mesa forms representing the younger stages have ironstone caps of similar form, one of which is represented in Figure 3. In this profile the ironstone cap is of variable composition. Fragments of pisolitic ironstone are common and so are fragments of ferruginized sandstone, these being cemented by an ironstone matrix containing scattered pisolites. The summit, situated less than a mile from the main escarpment, showed no obvious signs of mottled and pallid zonation beneath the ironstone, and solid rock, ripple-marked sandstone, is exposed within a short distance of the ironstone cap. Other ironstone caps which were examined varied in their composition, some having few large fragments, over 2-inch long axes, while others consisted almost entirely of pisolites embedded in a limonitic matrix, occasionally with signs of rough stratification.

There seems to be a strong case for regarding these ironstone layers as quite distinct from the 'laterite' cap with its deep weathering profile, both in form and origin. They are ironstone breccias, although from their site occurrence they can be referred to as valley ironstones. They appear to be formed by surface cementation of debris at points where soil water is released. This occurs at present at the base of slopes and, during periods of planation, could spread widely over the areas of gentle gradient. Surface ironstone is found at a number of points in the Katherine–Darwin area (Stewart, 1956). Along the Daly River near Oolloo large areas of river gravels have been cemented in this way. Anomalous cases exist here where creek sections expose a well-developed pallid zone of weathering capped with ironstones of the valley ironstone type. This has probably been produced by truncation of a weathering profile and then subsequent ironstone development, since no true mottled zone is present. In such cases confusion with full 'laterite' successions (as seen in the upper part of Figure 2) is easy and can possibly be resolved in the field only by careful examination of the content of the ironstone layer.

The main source of the fragments incorporated in the valley ironstones is obviously the steeper slopes which border the lower-lying areas. These slopes, capped either by thick laterite sections on the main Wingate escarpment or by valley ironstones, can be divided into a series of facets.

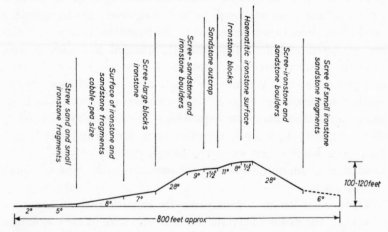

Figure 3. Sketch profile of a mesa, east of Wingate escarpment, Daly River area

(i) *Ironstone layer*

This is a steep or near vertical facet 15-25 feet high on the main escarpment, but lower and scree-obscured in other cases. This has been attacked by two main agencies. First, weathering attack on the ironstone by crumbling of the limonitic matrix produces loose pisolites, and this also operates at the base of the ironstone layer where the upper part of the mottled zone is worn back to a recess until an overhang results. Secondly, breakaway action occurs by collapse of the ironstone over the overhang section. The ironstone frequently has well-developed open cracks at distances of up to 20 feet from the edge of the escarpment.

(ii) *Active scree slopes*

These are restricted to the main escarpment and to points on the lower mesas where streams closely approach the slope. In some areas the movement was rapid, involving landslipping on a large scale. Gully heads were also evident in some areas. Insufficient examples were available to generalize although the proximity of active stream beds to the escarpment appeared to be significant. Normally the active scree slopes are represented by a thin layer of scree over a rock slope. In places it was clear that the rock slope was contributing to the scree material and was being lowered. It is quite probable that in addition to gravitational movement this scree is affected by the wet season downpours sweeping the rockface and mobilizing large blocks already near their angle of rest.

(iii) *Stabilized scree slopes*

These form the main facet on most slopes and on the lower mesas completely replace the active scree slopes. Slope angles varied from 15°-25° and scree fragment size from large blocks (more than two feet) through to smaller fragments (three-inch long axis). Many scree fragments were weathered, e.g. pisolites loosened, and hollows within the scree were being infilled with finer material. These slopes frequently support savanna woodland of eucalypt varieties.

(iv) *'Wash' slopes*

The base of the stabilized scree slopes is generally bordered by a zone in which the rugged scree is replaced by smooth slopes. These vary in character of surface away from this junction, becoming lower in angle and finer in the grade of surface debris. Slope angles vary from 10°-7°, at the transition to the lower slopes, to 5°-1° and merge with the maze of stream channels which drain the area. Aerial photographs indicate that these form zones around the mesa residuals and also marginal to the main escarpment. Their surface coloration in aerial photographs indicates some general patterning of waterflow but this is often imperceptible on the ground.

(v) *Stream channels*

These have a dendritic pattern and, in the upper sections, merge into the wash-slopes described above. Stream channels are wide, often sandy, but with areas of coarser debris possibly marking the limits of certain rapid flows of water. During the dry season these are dry, with the exception of certain waterholes, but are clearly adapted to the large water volumes of the wet season. Many of the channels examined were in the process of cutting down in their lower section to the Daly River creating minor canyon forms with very steep sides. Above this rejuvenation section gradients of the streams were too low to measure accurately by Abney level (i.e. under $\frac{1}{2}°$).

The general impression gained from this area, and from others of similar climatic conditions in Northern Australia, was that slope retreat is still active. The retreat of the free face is possibly mainly in localities where available relief is high or stream channels approach closely to the escarpments. This can be seen on aerial photographs where incipient gullies appear in the scree slopes above stream channels. Elsewhere, however, many scree slopes have been stabilized and the main reduction of the surface is proceeding by the action of weathering of the scree and removal of fragments by slope wash. This is evident from the general smoothness of the slopes, the sorting of debris, and the general absence of definite channels in the area between the steeper slopes and the stream channels.

The majority of the landforms are related to dissection of the upper parts of the weathering profile, with duricrust layers providing the most striking features. In certain areas towards the centre of the Daly Basin it is possible that the lower parts of the weathering profile are exposed and have been exhumed. This generally appears in the form of piles of rounded boulders or as low domes up to 20 feet in height. The cases examined were all formed of a fine-grained siliceous material of quartzitic nature. These are probably highly altered Cretaceous sediments of the type referred to as silicified pallid zone in the geology sheet memoir (Randal, 1962). The cases examined were, in fact, near exposures of the pallid zone. There are several anomalous features associated with these landforms. The boulders, although rounded on the outside of the mass, are frequently irregular and cut by jagged partings towards the centre. This may be a feature of initial deposition or of silici-fication, but in several cases it was hard to avoid the impression that the rounding was imposed after their exhumation. The domes vary in character from low whaleback rises, just above the surface, to examples of more complex form (Figure 4). This example was

Figure 4. Margin of a low quartzite dome, Daly River area

again of fine-grained quartzitic rock and is characterized by (i) the deep gnamma holes which perforate the mass and (ii) the recessed rim, extending to an overhang, surrounding the dome. These features are not uncommon in Australia in association with igneous rocks, generally granite (Jutson, 1950). Their presence in quartzite is difficult to explain. The gnamma holes may well represent stages in the initial silicification of the rock when it was different in character. There are examples, in the area of the domes, of Cambrian 'limestones' exhibiting solution pavement features but the rock is now quartzitic; only in the centre of large blocks can a faint reaction be obtained with acid indicating the original rock character. If these holes are of this origin then it is probably wrong to use the term gnamma holes for them. At the present, however, they are being extended by processes very similar to those described for gnamma holes.

The recessed margin is, however, probably a feature developed after exhumation. The rim intersects the holes in the mass and occasionally sections of the rim have collapsed. The area around the dome is composed of the same quartzitic material with a rough surface covered by fine white sand grains which would seem to indicate that the quartzite breaks down particularly along the base where moisture would collect after run-off from the dome via the holes. The basal area when examined in the dry season was damp during the morning as a result of dews accumulating on the dome. This weathering, proceeding by the loosening of small powdery grains, was noticeable on the rock in this basal area but would appear to be a very slow process.

Locally these domes and boulder areas provide an element in local relief. Frequently they form the core of small divide areas and are surrounded by low angle ($1°$-$3°$) wash-slopes.

THE WATERHOUSE RANGE

This lies to the south-west of Alice Springs and forms part of the east-west trending fold ridges of the southern part of the Central Ranges. It rises approximately 600 feet above the Missionary Plains between the MacDonnell and James ranges. The basic structure is an anticline with a core of Lower Palaeozoic rock and rims of the Upper Palaeozoic Pertnajara series, which in this area varies from a coarse sandstone to a conglomerate (Quinlan, 1962). The Lower Palaeozoic core is composed of less resistant formations and forms a series of strike vales. The main drainage of the Hugh River is transverse to the range passing from the open plains to the north at about 2,000 feet through the ridges, in gorge sections, to the southern plain at about 1,900 feet. The general pattern of geology and landform is similar to the James Range to the south. The geomorphological evolution of the James and MacDonnell ranges has been discussed by Mabbutt (1961) and the Waterhouse Range is similar in character. The north and south gorges of the Hugh through the rim of the ranges are bordered with 'ridge bevels' and 'rounded ridge crests' of the type that Mabbutt describes and which are probably associated with the main weathered surface of Central Australia. Below this surface, in the higher parts of the strike vales, lies an extensive

Figure 5. Exfoliation dome and slopes on the southern rim of the Waterhouse Range

valley stage capped with silcrete. This is probably analagous to the silcrete caps noted on the margins of the Todd plain. Below this height several valley stages, some with silcrete surfaces, occur before the terrace gravels and alluvium of the Hugh Valley are reached.

Slope profiles and deep weathering features were examined in two localities, one near the southern gorge of the Hugh, another on one of the silcrete cap remnants in the northern strike vale. The first site forms part of the outer rim of the range facing the open plain to the south. The slope (Figure 5) can be divided in a number of sections:

(i) *Dome surface*

This forms part of a rounded ridge crest and extends as a smooth dome to 70 feet below the crest line. The exfoliation jointing of the sandstone-conglomerate series can be seen in section in the Hugh Gorge where caverns emphasize the joint pattern. Minor caverns

F

are present on the dome surface and jagged remnants of former dome surfaces rise above the general level, a form that is evident in several areas on the southern rim of the range. Weathering products in hollows and cavern areas consist of sand grains and small fragments but these are overlain by finer material of a different colour which from its distribution over the whole slope would appear to be aeolian in origin. There is little sign of any active weathering proceeding at present.

(ii) *Rock slope*

This is extremely variable in form and composition, generally consisting of jagged sandstone blocks, possibly part of the solid rock, with fragments ranging in size from 3-feet long axis to ½-inch and under. The hollows in the rugged surface are infilled by the fine material mentioned above which clearly differs from the finer weathering products of the rock. Hollows are occasionally linked by small channels but these are infilled by aeolian material. Weathering appears to be very slow and the scree material is stable at the general angle of 20°.

(iii) *The slope base*

The junction between rock slope and smooth slopes of the plain (5°-2°) is sharp, the zone of fallen fragments being 5 feet wide at a maximum. The finer material from the surface of the plain is being blown on to the slope with small dune forms developing behind loose blocks on the surface.

The whole of this slope is undergoing very slight change at present and it is possible that the more vigorous signs of retreat, e.g. caverns, fallen blocks, may be relict from a period of greater rainfall. It is probable that this slope is an exhumed feature being covered initially by basin infill up to at least the level of the ridge crest, i.e. the main weathering surface. The successive stages in the lowering of the base level are marked by the valley stages within the range but no such evidence exists on the outer rim of the range. In view of the recognized persistence of relief from former periods evident in this area it would be best to regard this slope as being initially of considerable age. It is, however, a very common feature of the landforms in the Central Ranges.

Slopes of a different character are found in the strike vales within the Waterhouse Range. Here the outstanding feature is the silcrete which caps the highest terrace levels only a few hundred feet below the crest line. This terrace exists as mesa forms isolated by later terrace levels and also as a bench adjacent to the main ridges (Figure 6). The slope below the highest silcrete layer

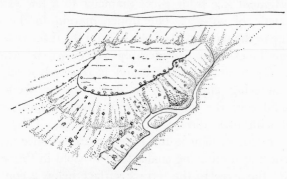

Figure 6. Silcrete-capped bench in the northern part of the Waterhouse Range

is generally the steepest and longest within the ranges except where the main ridge with the crest bevel falls directly to the interior. This, together with the existence of a weathering profile, determined the choice of slope for closer examination. The slopes examined lie around one of the bench features on the northern side of the strike vale. The bench surface, sloping south gently at approximately 1°, is composed of hard white quartzite which from a distance can be seen truncating the dip of strata beneath. The thickness of this silcrete layer can be fixed at only 10 feet + since below the rim a scree slope covers the surface. The rim itself is of interest in two aspects, (i) that blocks are separated by deep cracks at distances of up to 20 feet from the edge in a type of breakaway action, (ii) that the individual blocks, particularly on the extreme rim, are rounded on their upper surfaces. This rounding is evident on large blocks in the scree and would seem to have been imposed by surface weathering. In the case of some of the scree blocks the form is comparable with that of granite core stones.

The eastern slopes of the bench are appreciably steeper than the other sides due to the presence of a stream approaching the bench. Profiles were taken therefore on the southern side, which appeared more characteristic, as well as on the east. The southern profile can best be described as stabilized scree, with a wide variation in fragment size from 4-feet diameter to a few inches, at a general angle of 20°-25°. The upper margin to the bench is convex due to the separation of blocks from the rim moving downhill. Some blocks are considerably overgrown by acacia and sparse eucalypts and the vegetation is relatively dense for the area. Weathering appears to be slow with few fresh surfaces exposed and even the smaller scree fragments appear to be case hardened with little disintegration into grains. This, however, would not be too evident in this parent material since neither the silcrete nor the underlying shales tend to yield in this way. The junction of the scree to the terrace surface below is concave and smooth, with a transition zone from scree slope to a surface of sandy material strewn with fragments of quartzite and hardened shale/sandstone, under 3 inches diameter. This zone shows a few signs of slope wash in the minor ripples of fine material distributed in lobate patterns down the slope. It is probable also that the larger fragments are moved in this way although fragments above 3-inches long axis appeared to have deflected the flow patterns.

The western slope reveals one of the few areas of rapid slope evolution marked by fresh features of breakaway action on the rim and recent falls on to the scree slope. Angles here are higher and clearly related to the presence below the slope of a stream, tributary to the Mueller (itself a tributary of the Hugh). The slope sequence is as follows:

(*i*) *Rim area:* rounded, shattered blocks of silcrete often unstable at edge.

(*ii*) *Scarp face:* varying between 5 and 10 feet and with recent falls determined by cracks in silcrete layer. In a few places an overhang is present but this is not related to a lower weathering horizon and occurs within the main silcrete layer.

(*iii*) *Upper scree slope:* large fallen blocks, 4-feet long axis, often rounded together with finer material down to ½ inch. Above gully areas the rock was probably exposed but owing to the nature of the slope this could not be determined accurately.

(*iv*) *Lower scree slope:* generally smaller fragments distributed by gully forms tributary to the stream. Slope angles on both (*iii*) and (*iv*) vary between 18°-25°.

(*v*) *Stream slope:* this often directly merges to (*iv*) with the stream itself being dry and revealing a great mixture of bedload. Characteristic of this stream (and others in the area) is the irregular long profile with alternations of fine material and large blocks, up to 2 feet, probably related to the irregular régime. Where the stream diverges from (*iv*) the intervening slope is concave, with fragments strewn over the slope. Despite the presence of spinifex clumps of 18 inches or more the wash patterns were again visible in broad channels sweeping between the spinifex.

The gully forms of this slope appear to be characteristic of other features in the range. The gully heads are steep, approaching vertical, and lie in an area of tumbled larger blocks. Percolation through the scree is evident in the washing out of finer material. The lower parts of the gully are irregular in long profile and flatten generally towards the stream. Bed load is extremely irregular but with a preponderance of fragments of 18 inches. In one gully on this slope and on others in the area infilling is taking place and this frequently occurs where there is no main stream to remove the outwash of material from the gully. It would seem that for this process to operate it is necessary to remove the material produced by the gully which, with its limited catchment, tends to deposit the material in its lower course or as a fan adjacent to the scree slope. Where this is not removed gullies appear to infill and merge with the main slope. The possibility also exists that the origin of these gullies lies in a former wetter period and only those especially favoured by the proximity of a stream have persisted.

The two profiles discussed above on the bench near the River Mueller provide an interesting contrast to one another. The southern slope is similar in some ways to that described on the south rim of the range; the same pattern of jagged rock on the main slope with few signs of weathering or water action and a general impression of stability. The main difference occurs below the scree slopes where the northern bench profile exhibits slope wash and removal of material from the slope. This would, however, appear to be very slow and may well be present beneath the wind-blown material of the southern rim profile. The eastern slope of the bench illustrates that where conditions are suitable, i.e. where a stream channel approaches closely to the foot of a scree slope, then retreat can occur with the development of gully forms. This enables some subjective measure of the relative effectiveness of slope-wash and concentrated flow as a removal agent. Clearly under the conditions obtaining in the Waterhouse Range, and probably also over much of Central Australia, slopes depending on slope wash as an agent for removal develop slowly. The supply of material from the upper slopes is small due to the low intensity of weathering; even so the tendency is towards accumulation rather than removal. It is possible that on these slopes wind action in the accumulation or removal of debris may be a significant factor.

In the two areas described above the existing processes are operating upon comparable landforms. The progressive, although not necessarily regular, fall in base-level has seen the establishment of mesa residuals produced by slope retreat and other slopes determined by exhumation of earlier features. Apart from the exhumed landforms the sequence of planed summits, scree slopes and low-angle slopes interposing between scree and stream, is common to both the Daly River area and the Waterhouse Range. The lack of available relief causing rapid slope retreat to end in stabilized scree slope is also noticeable. However, much of this landform sequence must be regarded as having been produced under earlier climatic conditions. In the Daly River area these may have been very similar to those of the present since the processes in operation are competent to produce the landforms examined below the main weathering horizon. This is not true for the Waterhouse Range where both weathering and erosion are operating at a slow pace and where active slope formation is restricted to localities with optimum conditions. Under such conditions persistence of relief rather than denudation is likely to result.

ACKNOWLEDGEMENTS

I wish to record my gratitude to the Imperial Relations Trust for the bursary which made my visit to Australia possible, and to the officers of the C.S.I.R.O. Land Research Division, Soils Division and Bureau of Mineral Resources for their help and hospitality.

REFERENCES

DAVID, T.W.E. (1950) *The geology of the Commonwealth of Australia.*

FOLEY, J.C. (1957) 'Droughts in Australia', *Australian Bureau of Meteorology, Bulletin, 43.*

HILL, D. and DENMEAD, A.K. (1960) *The geology of Queensland.* Melbourne.

IVANAC, J.F. (1954) 'The geology and mineral deposits of the Tennant Creek Goldfield, Northern Territory', *Bur. Min. Resour. Aust. Bull., 22.*

JUTSON, J.T. (1950) 'The physiography of Western Australia', *Geol. Surv. Western Australia, Bulletin, 95.* (Third edn.)

KING, L.C. (1962) *Morphology of the earth.*

MABBUTT, J.A. (1961) 'The deeply weathered land surface in Central Australia', *C.S.I.R.O. Division of Land Research and Regional Survey, Tech. Mem.* 61/20.

— (1962) 'Geomorphology of the Alice Springs area', *C.S.I.R.O. Land Research Series, 6.*

MALONE, E.J. (1961) Darwin : 1 : 250,000 geological series and explanatory notes, *Bur. Min. Resour. Aust.*, D52/8.

NOAKES, L.C. and TRAVES, D.M. (1954) 'Survey of the Barkly Region, Northern Territory and Queensland, 1947/48', *C.S.I.R.O. Land Research Series, 3.*

PERRY, R.A. (1960) 'Pasture lands of the Northern Territory, Australia', *C.S.I.R.O. Land Research Series, 5.*

QUINLAN, T. (1962) 'An outline of the geology of the Alice Springs area', *C.S.I.R.O. Land Research Series, 6.*

RANDAL, M.A. (1962) Fergusson River : 1 : 250,000 geological series and explanatory notes, *Bur. Min. Resour. Aust.*, D52/12.

SLAYTER, R.A. (1960) 'Agricultural climatology of the Katherine area, Northern Territory', *C.S.I.R.O. Division of Land Research and Regional Survey, Tech. Paper, 13.*

— (1962) 'Climate of the Alice Springs area', *C.S.I.R.O. Land Research Series, 6.*

STEWART, G.A. (1956) 'Soils of the Katherine–Darwin region, Northern Territory', *C.S.I.R.O. Soil Publication, 6.*

TWIDALE, C.R. (1956) 'Chronology of denudation in north-west Queensland', *Bull. Geol. Soc. Amer., 67.*

WALPOLE, B.P. (ed.), (1962) *Tectonic Map of Australia (with geological notes).*

WRIGHT, R. (1961) Personal communication. Since published, (1963) 'Deep weathering and erosion surfaces in the Daly River Basin, Northern Territory', *J. Geol. Soc. Aust., 10,* 151.

Annual, seasonal and monthly rainfall over Moçambique

THE Portuguese province of Moçambique occupies the larger part of the coastal tropical belt of eastern Africa south of the Equator, from 11° South to 26½° South (Figure 1). It is an area where meteorological and climatic conditions have received little detailed analysis. Upper-air data, to link with those which are now being obtained in both the Republic of South Africa and in former British East Africa, are limited in amount and began only in 1957. On the other hand, Moçambique does possess a network of climatological stations, containing a relatively large number which have been continuously recording for two decades or more. Although by western European standards both the density of the network and the length of the records are slight, by standards of much of the inter-tropical world the reverse is true. As a result, by the application of suitable statistical techniques to allow for the short period of the records, and by the use of available theoretical concepts to facilitate the interpolation of conditions between recording stations, a reasonably accurate picture of climatic conditions can be constructed.

This essay presents the results of the analysis of one major climatic element – rainfall. Within an environment such as that of Moçambique, temperatures are high throughout the year. A monthly mean of below 18° C occurs in only one or two months in the far south and in the western hills. Therefore it is the variation of rainfall, from year to year at any one place and from place to place at any one time, that forms the major feature of climatic conditions. The following maps and text represent a more detailed and systematic description of the distribution of annual, seasonal

81

and monthly rainfall over Moçambique than exists at present, either in Portuguese (Azevedo, 1947) or in English (Peres, 1930; Schulze, 1947; Boleo, 1948; Jackson, 1951). An analysis on this scale should also have practical value especially, but not only, in the field of agriculture, as has been shown when such rainfall studies have been made in other tropical areas.

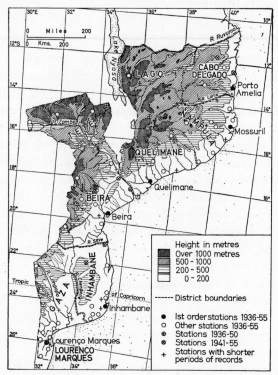

Figure 1. Relief, drainage and rainfall stations of Moçambique

The frequency and intensity of rain over this area is related to the atmospheric circulation over the whole of Africa south of the Equator and the western Indian Ocean, the broad features of which have been presented by S. P. Jackson (1947), A. G. Forsdyke (1948), P. R. Crowe (1949), J. J. Taljaard (1953) and P. A. MacGregor (1955), and summarized recently by G. T.

Trewartha (1961). A deep anticyclone is common over the plateau throughout the year (Figure 2). During the dry (winter) season this is a dominant feature, its subsidence characteristics being intensified by the upper air pattern. Coastal rains occasionally occur during this period, especially in the southern half of Moçambique, sometimes from trailing cold fronts associated with the

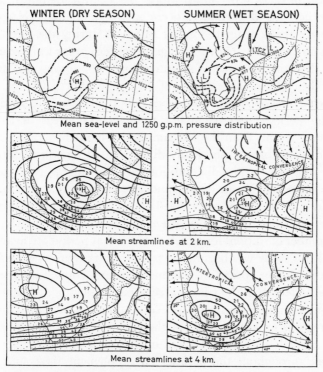

Figure 2. Mean surface and upper air pressure patterns for the wet and dry seasons (after Taljaard, 1953)

Westerlies to the south, and sometimes from isolated storms within the tropical Easterlies. The latter are possibly associated with wave forms within this airstream, perhaps initiated by fluctuations in the position and strength of the anticyclonic centre over the Indian Ocean.

The plateau anticyclone is less permanent during the wet

(summer) season, as it contracts in size and intensity and is periodically replaced by rain-producing atmospheric disturbances. These usually occur as belts of instability within the tropical Easterlies, on either side of the Inter-tropical Convergence Zone, or as disturbances along the zone itself (Thompson, 1957). This I.T.C.Z. establishes itself in January and February in a mean position of *c.* 15°-16° South along the central Zambezi. These rain-producing disturbances occur at irregular intervals, so that there are spells of up to four or five days during the wet season when no rain falls. They impinge on western areas less frequently than they do the coast, for anticyclonic conditions still persist over the interior for much of the time. Furthermore, these characteristics of occurrence and distribution are locally intensified by the periodic encroachment upon coastal areas of tropical revolving storms from the Moçambique Channel.

Across the broad, physically-differentiated terrain of Moçambique (Figure 1) rainfall conditions are thus highly variable and complex, especially in detail, and any pattern that can be discerned must be a very generalized one at best. The initial problem was to maximize both the length of the record being analysed and the number of stations for which data for that period are available. When this study was begun, the twenty years 1936-55 were found to give a better spread of stations than any comparable period, while the length of the period is reasonably adequate. There were forty-four stations that provided continuous, or virtually continuous, records for this period; of these, the six coastal sites specifically named on Figure 1 were officially classed as 'first order' stations throughout the period. To supplement these forty-four stations in areas lacking in data, ten other stations each with fifteen years of records were considered, two of these being for 1936-50 and eight for 1941-55, i.e. the first and last fifteen years of the overall period. Finally, when their situation was obviously critical for any particular map, some or all of ten other stations with no more than ten years of continuous records were also considered. In all these cases the data were extracted from either the *Relatório do Observatório Campos Rodrigues em Lourenço Marques*

(Lourenço Marques, 1936-55), or various numbers of the *Boletim Mensal das Observações Meteorológicas Organizado Pelo Serviço Meteorológico* (Lourenço Marques). The data coverage is nevertheless still highly irregular. The following rainfall maps must therefore be regarded as provisional and exploratory in character, but the broad patterns shown coincide in a general way with those defined elsewhere for neighbouring areas (Federal Surveys, 1958; *Atlas of Tanganyika*, 1948; *Union of South Africa National Atlas*, 1949).

ANNUAL RAINFALL

Mean annual precipitation varies between more than 1,600 mm over the higher uplands in the west to less than 400 mm along parts of the Limpopo valley (Figure 3). In preparing isopleths to display this pattern a choice had to be made concerning the magnitude of the *interval* between isopleths. If the mean value shown here is regarded as only a *sample* mean from a longer period of records, it will possess a sampling error (or standard error) related to the length of the record and the standard deviation of the data. In the light of this, numerous tests were made of the validity of the difference between the sample means of different stations, to obtain an indication of the degree of difference necessary for a 95 per cent level of significance to apply. Despite the difficulties introduced by stations with similar means having differing standard deviations or differing lengths of records, and hence differing standard errors, it was found that an isopleth interval of 200 mm was sufficient to establish statistical significance in nearly all cases. It was therefore adopted as the standard isopleth interval. This means that although it is not possible to assume that there is necessarily a long-term difference between places in adjacent shading categories (although in many, if not most, cases this will be so), it is possible to assert that a significant long-term difference does exist between at least alternate shading categories.

The regional contrasts in Figure 3 seem largely to reflect the presence or absence of uplands and their spatial position relative to the coast. On the other hand, the location of the wettest coastal stretch between Beira and Quelimane cannot be adequately explained in terms of relief; nor can the contrasting dry zone south of Porto Amelia. The explanation of both these and other

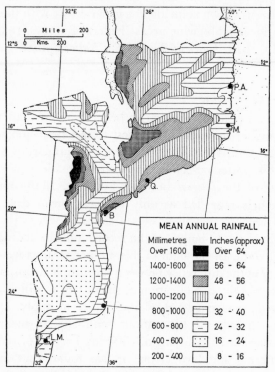

Figure 3. Mean annual rainfall

areas must lie, in large measure, in the atmospheric circulation systems briefly outlined earlier, and their relative frequency and intensity in different latitudes, although the orientation of the coastlines coupled with the pattern of relief may well be contributory differentiating factors.

Individual yearly conditions vary considerably from the values shown here, although the pattern displayed is relatively consistent. This scatter about the mean can be expressed by the standard, or root mean square, deviation. Its magnitude is in part influenced by the magnitude of the mean itself (the correlation coefficient between annual mean and standard deviation values for all the stations is $+0\cdot71$), and purely spatial contrasts are thus minimized. These limitations are largely overcome by the use of the

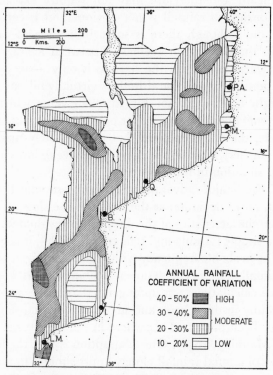

Figure 4. Annual rainfall coefficient of variation

coefficient of variation (V), when the standard deviation is expressed as a percentage of the average (Figure 4). These values are mainly between 20 and 40 per cent, with few areas having values outside these limits. It would be dangerous to overstress any differences that are shown, however, because with only a twenty-year record the standard errors of $V = 40$, 30 and 20 per cent are $6\cdot3$, $4\cdot8$ and $3\cdot2$ per cent respectively. This means that the difference between 20 and 30 per cent barely reaches a level of 'probably significant', while the difference between 30 and 40 per cent does not reach this level.

As is usual with variability, this distribution pattern is not easy to explain, and many of the apparent differences are not statistically significant and therefore may not require explanation. A clear relationship to rainfall is not obvious and is certainly not universal, and although there is some indication of an inverse relationship the correlation coefficient between average and coefficient of variation for all the stations is only −0·25. Furthermore, relationship to relief or altitude is virtually nil, save possibly for this slight inverse relationship to mean value which is itself related to relief in some areas. As for possible influences of location and latitude, the only comment that can be safely made is that perhaps a northerly situation is more conducive to low values than is a central situation in the country.

One of the major advantages in using standard deviation rather than mean deviation as the basis for assessing variability is that further characteristics of the data can be evaluated. Thus by the use of a simple formula and reference to tables, it is possible to calculate the probable frequency with which any given amount of annual rainfall may occur (Glover, Robinson and Henderson, 1954). Such calculations rest upon general assumptions, not all of which are fully justified here, and many of the discussions on this theme have been presented elsewhere in relation to East African data (e.g. Manning, 1956). One assumption is that the frequency distribution of annual rainfall closely approximates to the normal curve. The extent to which this is justified varies from station to station, and for the majority the skew element in the distribution is very slight. For a few stations there is a greater element of skewness, but only rarely is it excessively large. Bearing in mind the scale of the map, the limited density of stations and the question of observational error, the inaccuracies introduced by slight skewness are of marginal relevance. In the choice of isopleth intervals it is again necessary to ensure a statistically significant difference. It was found that an interval of 20 per cent probability was the

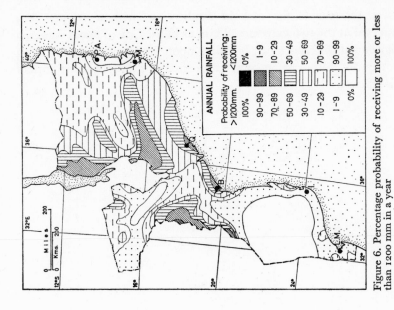

Figure 6. Percentage probability of receiving more or less than 1200 mm in a year

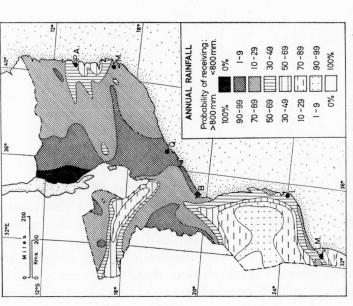

Figure 5. Percentage probability of receiving more or less than 800 mm in a year

G

most serviceable for general application, with a 10 per cent interval at the two extremes. Thus, as in the case of mean values, a significant difference can be relied upon between *alternate* shading categories, although in some cases smaller differences are in fact significant.

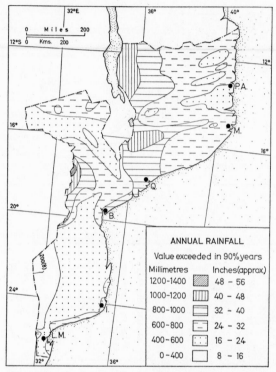

Figure 7. Annual 'reliable' rainfall

Maps showing the percentage probability of receiving more than, or less than, given annual falls of rain were obtained by calculating probabilities not only for the actual observing stations but also for numerous 'derived' stations, obtained by super-imposing the map of average conditions on that of variability (Gregory, 1957). The distributions shown in Figures 5 and 6, which are largely self-explanatory, help to expand and make more specific the impressions presented by the mean and variability maps. The implications of such conditions are numerous and varied, much depending on the amount of rainfall considered critical for any particular problem.

It is also useful to have some indication of the rainfall that can usually be relied upon. Thus, values will equal or exceed those shown in Figure 7 in 90 per cent of the years, and any plant growth or agricultural activity that requires a given rainfall in nearly all years for its effective development will therefore respond to the pattern and quantities shown here, rather than to those of mean conditions. The degree of difference between the wetter and drier areas is less for reliable rainfall than for average rainfall. Nevertheless the difference is still a marked one, and in terms of its implications it may be more significant, for a decrease from 600 mm to 400 mm may be far more effective in changing conditions than a drop from 1,600 mm to 1,200 mm. The pattern is akin to that of average conditions, but the quantitative aspect of it is markedly different. Whereas about two-thirds of the country receive an *average* fall of more than 800 mm, the area that can rely on this amount nine years out of ten is only 20-25 per cent of the country. Equally, almost half the country receives an average fall of at least 1,000 mm but in terms of a reliable fall half the country receives less than 600 mm.

SEASONAL INCIDENCE OF RAINFALL

The prime feature of the seasonal incidence of rainfall over the whole country is the division into a wet and a dry season. The problem is one of defining when the change-over from one season to the other usually occurs and the length and intensity of those seasons. Possible criteria for grouping months together into categories of wet and dry are varied. A visual assessment of either tabulated or graphed data, without any rigid criteria, seems to have been applied to the area north of Moçambique in the *Atlas of Tanganyika* (1948). Alternatively, specified amounts of rain may be expected before a wet month is defined, but this means that in

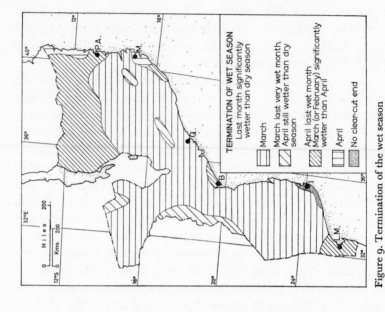

Figure 9. Termination of the wet season

TERMINATION OF WET SEASON

Last month significantly wetter than dry season

March

March last very wet month. April still wetter than dry season

April last wet month. March (or February) significantly wetter than April

April

No clear-cut end

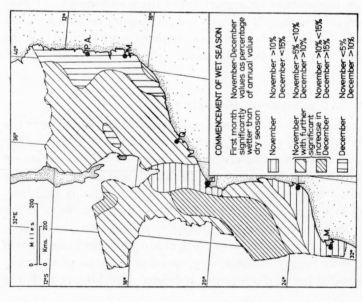

Figure 8. Commencement of the wet season

COMMENCEMENT OF WET SEASON

First month significantly wetter than dry season

November

November with further significant increase in December

December

November-December values as percentage of annual value

November >10% December <15%

November >5% <10% December >10%

November >10% <15% December >15%

November <5% December >10%

dry areas few if any months may be classified as being in the wet season, despite an obvious seasonal variation in the rainfall. To obviate this, the definition of a wet or dry month or period can be related to the conditions of each individual area and not to an arbitrary numerical value. Thus H. B. S. Cooke (1946), for the Union of South Africa, defined wet season months as those with more than 10 per cent of the annual fall and dry season months as those with less than 5 per cent.

In the present essay attention has been focused on those pairs of months between which the change in mean values is statistically significant, while the percentage of the year's rain falling in the individual months was a secondary supporting criterion. The significance of the difference between adjacent months was tested by Student's *t* test, and only those differences that reached at least the 5 per cent level of significance were accepted. Over a long period the particular change, either up or down, could therefore be expected to occur roughly nineteen years out of twenty. The characteristics so defined occur with sufficient frequency for the term 'régime' to be legitimately applied to the pattern of seasonal change.

Over most of the country the first significant increase of rainfall (i.e. the beginning of the wet season) occurs between October and November. Along the north-east coast and over the upper Lurio basin, however, November is still dry and December is the first wet month (Figure 8). Furthermore, the areas where November is the first wet month can be sub-divided. In some places the December rainfall does not differ significantly from that of November, while elsewhere the October–November increase is followed by another significant increase from November to December. In the former case November is clearly the beginning of the wet season, but in the latter case the onset of the wet season appears to be a more prolonged and progressive event. Other explanations for this second case also offer themselves, for example, that the wet season really begins in the second half of November so that December is the first full month within the wet season; that the onset of the wet season fluctuates between these two months from year to year; or that this simply reflects variations between months *within* the wet season that begins in November. On re-examination of the records in terms of the percentage of the annual rainfall occurring in the critical months, a clear relationship was found between the percentage values and the changes already outlined (Figure 8).

The end of the wet season can be defined in the same way (Figure 9) although the percentage investigation does not show so complete a relationship with the changes based on statistical significance as in the case of the beginning of the wet season. Over the larger part of the country March is the last month of the wet season and April the first of the dry season, although in limited north-eastern areas the dry season does not begin until May. There are again other areas with transitional characteristics, where a significant decrease in rainfall from March to April is followed by another significant decrease from April to May. In some of these latter areas March is the last really wet month. In the south is the major anomalous area, the coastal strip of southern Inhambane District, where no clear-cut termination to the wet season is apparent. From March to June each month has a mean value lower than the previous one, but never significantly so. The first statistically significant break is between June and July, the percentages of the annual rainfall occurring in each of the five months March to July at Inhambane being successively 11·4, 8·2, 6·9, 6·4 and 3·9 per cent. If any earlier termination to the wet season were to be chosen, then the change between April and May is nearest to a significant change, i.e. comparable to conditions in Lourenço Marques District to the south.

Regional differences in the length and time of occurrence of the wet season, and therefore by inference of the dry season too, can be obtained by superimposing Figure 8 upon Figure 9. For simplification in Figure 10, however, both categories in which the onset of the wet season occurred with significant increases in both November and December have been grouped together. Apart from the details of actual commencement and termination of the wet season, Figure 10 also shows that the most common length is

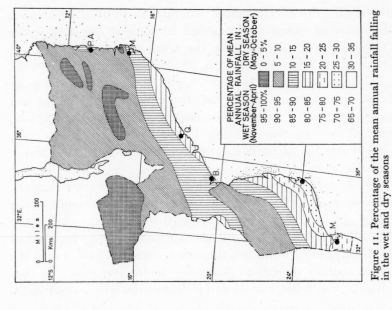

Figure 10. Duration of the wet season

Figure 11. Percentage of the mean annual rainfall falling
in the wet and dry seasons

five months, this affecting more than three-quarters of the country. November to March is the period for most of this area, while December to April obtains in the north-east. A six-month wet season, from November to April, affects the Ruvuma basin in the north and Lourenço Marques District in the south. Along the Inhambane District coastal belt the indistinct end to the wet season means that up to eight months could be classified as wet, for only four months are truly in the dry season. In contrast, limited areas in the north-east have only a four-month wet season from December to March.

Discussion has been centred on the wet season rather than the dry season, though the length and period of occurrence of the latter can be inferred from Figures 8-10. Thus the dry season typically commences in April, though locally it may be deferred until May, and it continues through to include October over the whole country as well as November in the north-east. It thus varies in length between six and eight months, with seven months being most common, though the anomalous characteristics of coastal Inhambane District must be remembered. Moreover, the intensity of the drought tends to increase as the season progresses, for in many areas the last two to four months are significantly drier than the first part of the season. There is thus a much sharper change from dry to wet conditions than there is from wet to dry, for rains continue intermittently but with decreasing frequency during the first few months of the dry season (see Figures 22, 23).

In presenting the quantitative aspects of rainfall during these two contrasted seasons it seems desirable that a given series of months be accepted as the wet and dry season for all stations, rather than varying the period from one area to another. As all the six months November to April form part of the wet season somewhere, and as all the six months May to October are dry season months everywhere, these two periods have been chosen to form the wet and dry seasons respectively. Only a very small element of misrepresentation is introduced by the occasional inclusion of a dry season month within the wet season, while the

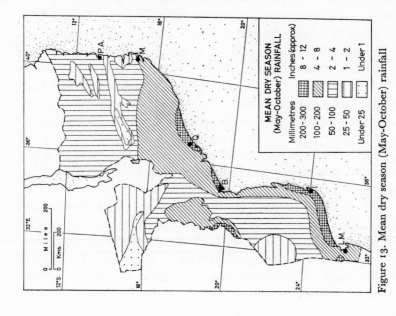

Figure 13. Mean dry season (May-October) rainfall

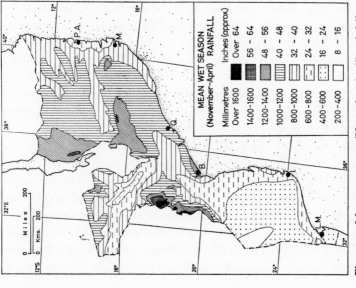

Figure 12. Mean wet season (November-April) rainfall

actual amount of change involved can be readily assessed from the monthly maps (Figures 20-23).

The broad characteristics of the wet and dry seasons are reflected in Figure 11. This shows that in general the proportion of the annual rainfall occurring in the wet season increases both inland and northward. Thus the dry season proportion of the annual rainfall is highest in the south-east, where it forms a third of the total in one area, and lowest in the north-west where at one station it is only 1 per cent. The one anomaly is west of Beira, where the hills experience, and perhaps generate, a relatively high dry season rainfall.

The average rainfall in the November–April wet season (Figure 12) is but little different from that of the year as a whole. No area has changed by more than one shading category as compared with the annual picture (Figure 3), and very few areas display even minor differences of pattern. Dry season (May–October) rainfall presents a markedly different picture, not only because the total values are so much lower but also because the distribution pattern has radically changed (Figure 13). The highest falls of more than 200 mm are either along parts of the coast or over some of the highlands. Nowhere does the total mean fall exceed 300 mm, while over half the country it is below 100 mm. These maps (Figures 12, 13) combined with Figure 11, thus epitomize both the markedly seasonal character of the rainfall of the whole of Moçambique and the regional contrasts in the intensity of this seasonal character. Variations occur from year to year for each of these seasons, however, so that some consideration of variability and probability is desirable.

The coefficient of variation of wet season rainfall (Figure 14) presents a simple and systematic picture, most of the country experiencing values between 20 and 40 per cent. The main contrasts between this and the annual map are the absence of low variability values over the drier areas of the north-east and south-east, and conversely the absence of very high variability over the dry areas of the Zambezi and Limpopo valleys. Thus the pattern displays far more regional coherence during the wet season, the

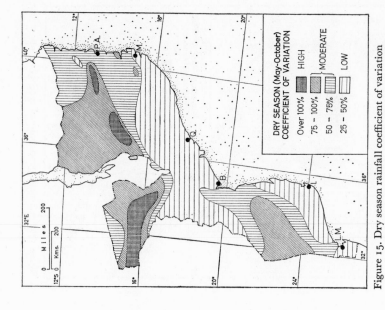

Figure 15. Dry season rainfall coefficient of variation

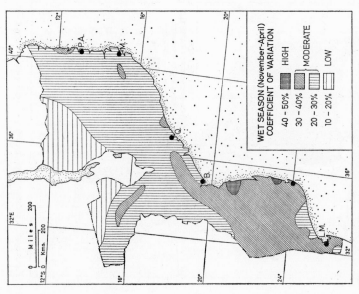

Figure 14. Wet season rainfall coefficient of variation

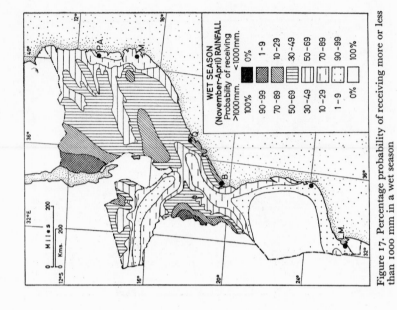

WET SEASON
(November–April) RAINFALL
Probability of receiving:
>600mm.   <600mm.

100%		0%
90–99		1–9
70–89		10–29
50–69		30–49
30–49		50–69
10–29		70–89
1–9		90–99
0%		100%

Figure 16. Percentage probability of receiving more or less than 600 mm in a wet season

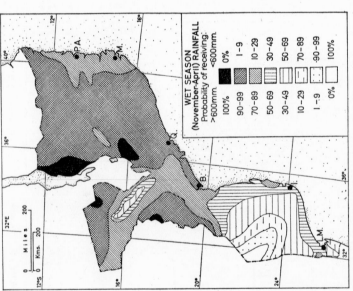

WET SEASON
(November–April) RAINFALL
Probability of receiving:
>1000mm.   <1000mm.

100%		0%
90–99		1–9
70–89		10–29
50–69		30–49
30–49		50–69
10–29		70–89
1–9		90–99
0%		100%

Figure 17. Percentage probability of receiving more or less than 1000 mm in a wet season

irregularities of the annual map being induced by the greater variability of the dry season conditions (Figure 15).

These dry season values are very much higher than those for either annual or wet season conditions, for they nowhere fall below 30 per cent and at times are more than 150 per cent. This results, in large measure, from the truly variable character of the dry season rains, but it is also a function of low mean values and of frequency curves which are often exceedingly skew. Thus predominantly very low values are interspersed with the occasional 'wet' dry season. Bearing these limitations in mind, it is clear from comparing Figures 13 and 15 that the variability of the dry season rains has an inverse relationship with mean values, the patterns of the two maps being very similar but the magnitude of the values changing in opposite directions. With the limited validity of the variability index during the dry season, however, conclusions should not be pressed too far.

These interacting mean and variability patterns can again be analysed in terms of the percentage probability of receiving given rainfall values. For the wet season, the probability maps of 600 mm and 1,000 mm (Figures 16, 17) are presented as illustration, and for comparison with the annual maps (Figures 5, 6). So also is the map of reliable rainfall, i.e. the amount that can be expected at least nine wet seasons out of ten (Figure 18). The pattern defined shows the reliable growing-season rainfall and it is this amount which gives the potential for permanent commercial agriculture, rather than the very much higher mean annual or mean wet season conditions. With low variability in the north, reliable rainfall is some 400 mm lower than the average in the wetter areas and some 200 mm lower in the drier areas. In the south, however, with higher variability, the reliable fall in the drier areas is as much as 300 mm below an already low average, thus partially intensifying areal contrasts.

The considerable skewness of so many of the frequency curves for the dry season means that the chance of receiving more than any given amount is overestimated by this method, and that of receiving less than a given amount is underestimated, the amount

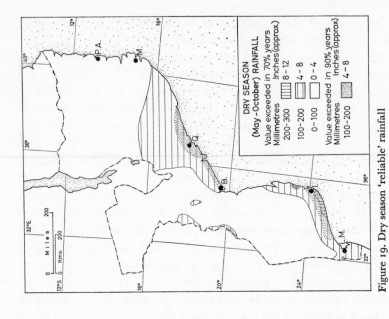

Figure 18. Wet season 'reliable' rainfall

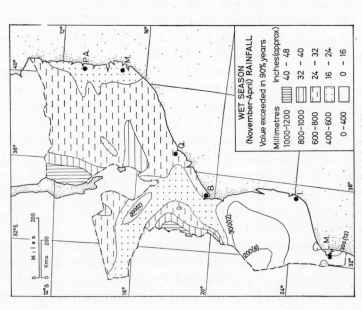

Figure 19. Dry season 'reliable' rainfall

of over- and under-estimation varying from one locality to another. Only the map of 'reliable' rainfall is therefore presented, simply as a general guide to dry season conditions (Figure 19). It is in but a few small areas of the south-east that more than 100 mm can be relied upon at the 90 per cent level of probability. Therefore this map also shows those values that are likely to occur at least seven years in ten, but even in this case about three-quarters of the country can still not expect as much as 100 mm of rain during the dry season.

MONTHLY RAINFALL

Further characteristics of seasonal rainfall can be discerned in the monthly rainfall maps (Figures 20-23). These are arranged in four sets of three months each, such that the first two sets cover the wet season and the last two sets the dry season. The order therefore reflects the rainfall year rather than the calendar year. For each month three maps are presented. The first shows average conditions, while the second shows variability as expressed by the coefficient of variation. During the dry season months especially, the skewness of the frequency distribution curve renders these quantitative values of variability highly suspect, but the relative pattern remains valid. The third map is of isomers, whereby the mean rainfall of the month is expressed as a percentage of the amount of rain which would fall in that month if the mean annual rainfall were evenly distributed throughout the year. Thus in a thirty-day month 8·2 per cent of the year's rain might be expected. If only 4·1 per cent of it falls on average, this is represented by the 50 per cent isopleth, i.e. only half the expected fall occurs. These maps help to provide a more detailed picture of the seasonal rainfall, clearly indicating month-by-month changes.

Detailed accounts of these maps need not be given, especially as they mainly stress again aspects of seasonal conditions that have already been outlined. The earlier onset of the rains in the south is clear, not only from the higher values in November, but also

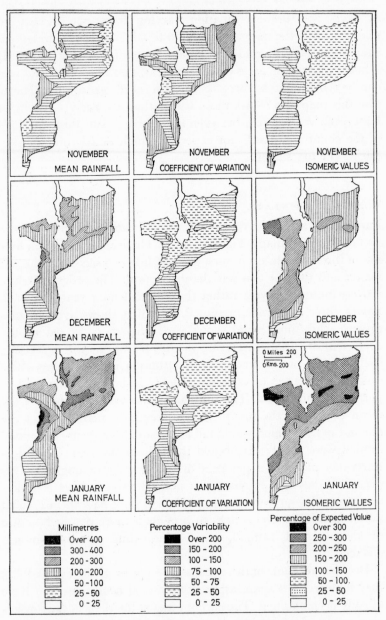

Figure 20. Monthly rainfall conditions – November, December, January

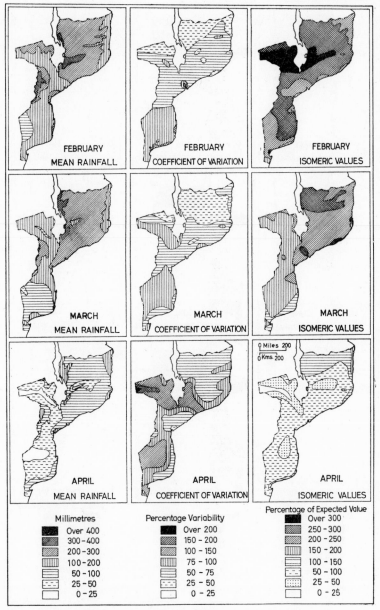

Figure 21. Monthly rainfall conditions – February, March, April

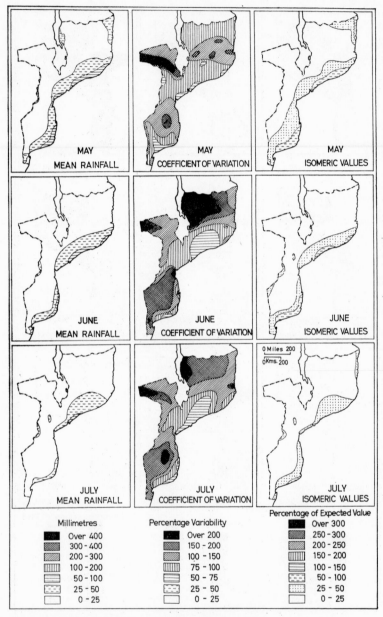

Figure 22. Monthly rainfall conditions – May, June, July

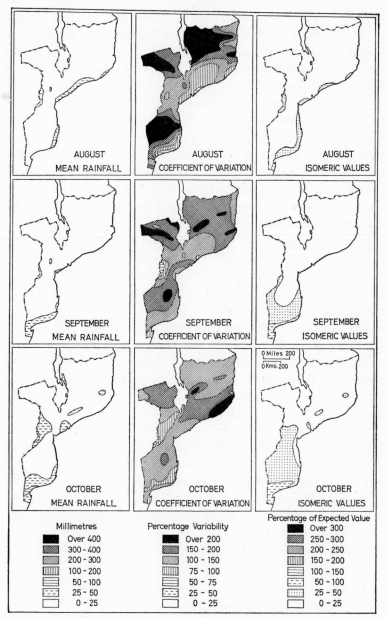

Figure 23. Monthly rainfall conditions – August, September, October

from the slighter increases recorded during the last two months of the dry season. By December this south-north contrast is no longer apparent, while in January and February the height of the wet season is reached and the north is clearly the wettest area. A significant difference often exists between one or both of these months and the rest of the wet season. Moreover there is only *one* period of maximum rainfall, even along the north-east coast, for which area suggestions of a double maximum have been made in some general textbooks on climate. As the dry season becomes established, so both the later arrival of dry conditions in the north-east and the contrast between the coast and the interior become clear in the monthly maps, while the Inhambane District coastal strip remains distinctive in all months.

Seasonal contrasts are thus observable both latitudinally and in relation to coastal or inland situation, the latter being especially marked during the dry season. Latitudinal contrasts are reversed between the seasons, the north being the wettest area in the wet season and the driest in the dry season, while variability is greater in the south than in the north during the wet season and lower in the south in the dry season. These conflicting tendencies are also reflected in the monthly maps, but certain areas maintain a given characteristic for relative wetness or dryness throughout. Thus the valleys of the Zambezi, the Limpopo, the Chengane and the Lurio, as well as the north-east coast, are invariably amongst the driest areas. Conversely the coastal belt from Beira to beyond Quelimane as well as the hills of western Beira District are always amongst the wettest areas. In contrast, the south-eastern coastlands are *relatively* dry in the wet season and wet in the dry season, while the hills of the north-west display the seasonality of rainfall most clearly. Any valid explanation of these regional and local characteristics, however, requires detailed synoptic analyses which have not yet been carried out.

REFERENCES

Atlas of Tanganyika (1948) Dar es Salaam.
AZEVEDO, A.L. DE (1947) *O clima de Moçambique e a agricultura.* Lisbon.

BOLEO, J. DE O. (1948) 'General picture of the climatic conditions in Moçambique', *S. Afr. J. Sci.*, *44*, 99.

COOKE, H.B.S. (1946) 'Some observations on rainfall distribution in South Africa', *S. Afr. geogr. J.*, *28*, 34.

CROWE, P.R. (1949) 'The trade wind circulation of the world', *Trans. Inst. Brit. Geogr.*, *16*, 37.

Federal Surveys (1958). *Average rainfall map of Southern Rhodesia*. Salisbury.

FORSDYKE, A.G. (1948) *Synoptic analysis in the Western Indian Ocean*. Memorandum of the East African Meteorological Dept., *2*, 3.

GLOVER, J., ROBINSON, P. and HENDERSON, J.P. (1954) 'Provisional maps of the reliability of annual rainfall in East Africa', *Quart. J. R. Met. Soc.*, *80*, 602.

GREGORY, S. (1957) 'Annual rainfall probability maps of the British Isles', *Quart. J. R. Met. Soc.*, *83*, 543.

JACKSON, S.P. (1947) 'Air masses and the circulation over the plateau and coasts of South Africa', *S. Afr. geogr. J.*, *29*, 1.

— (1951) 'Climates of Southern Africa', *S. Afr. geogr. J.*, *33*, 17.

MACGREGOR, P.A. (1955) 'The development of the theories of the circulation of the atmosphere over South Africa', *S. Afr. geogr. J.*, *37*, 41.

MANNING, M.L. (1956) 'The statistical assessment of rainfall probability and its application in Uganda agriculture', *Proc. Roy. Soc. B.*, *144*, 460.

PERES, M.A. (1930) 'Preliminary investigations of the rainfall of Lourenço Marques', *S. Afr. J. Sci.*, *27*, 132.

SCHULZE, B.R. (1947) 'The climates of South Africa according to the classifications of Köppen and Thornthwaite', *S. Afr. geogr. J.*, *29*, 32.

TALJAARD, J.J. (1953) 'The mean circulation in the lower troposphere over Southern Africa', *S. Afr. geogr. J.*, *35*, 33.

THOMPSON B.W. (1958) *Some reflections on equatorial and tropical forecasting*. East Afr. Meteorol. Dept. Technical Memorandum, no. 7.

TREWARTHA, G.T. (1961) *The earth's problem climates*. New York. Chaps. IX and X.

Union of South Africa National Atlas (1949) 'Mean annual rainfall map'. Pretoria.

VORSTER, J.H. (1957) 'Trends in long range rainfall records in South Africa', *S. Afr. geogr. J.*, *39*, 61.

JOAN M. KENWORTHY

Rainfall and the water resources of East Africa

WATER resources are a vital factor in practically every aspect of land use in East Africa, and are a limiting factor to development. In Kenya, Uganda and Tanganyika, despite their situation in equatorial latitudes on the eastern side of a continent, there are wide areas where rainfall is markedly restricted in season and drought is a regular occurrence. That East Africa is mainly a dry region frequently occasions surprise and the widespread deficiency of rainfall is described by G. T. Trewartha (1961) as undoubtedly the most impressive climatic anomaly in Africa.

East Africa is also distinguished from much of equatorial Africa by its high altitude. Wide expanses of plateau country at 3,000-4,000 feet are broken by two arms of the Great Rift Valley, by upwarped massifs such as Ruwenzori and the Kenya Highlands, and great volcanic outpourings which have formed the mountain peaks of Kilimanjaro, Meru, Kenya and Elgon. The equatorial climate is considerably modified by the fall in temperature with height on the high plateaux and mountains, while orographic effects are seen in the wide variations in annual rainfall from place to place. These variations in temperature and rainfall combine to give striking changes in climate within small areas, and these are reflected to some extent in the vegetation and scenery: in the tropical savannas and semi-arid scrub of the plateaux, the montane rain forests, bamboo forests and alpine moorlands of the highlands, and the permanent snow and ice on the summits of Kilimanjaro, Kenya and Ruwenzori.

Variations in rainfall are not related simply to the topography. The hot humid coastal belt soon gives way to semi-arid areas inland where the rainfall is more erratic, and then, farther west, it increases again. In the west of the Kenya Highlands rainfall amounts are greater than at equivalent altitudes in the highlands flanking the Rift Valley (Trapnell and Griffiths, 1960); in Uganda to the north and west of Lake Victoria rainfall is heavy and

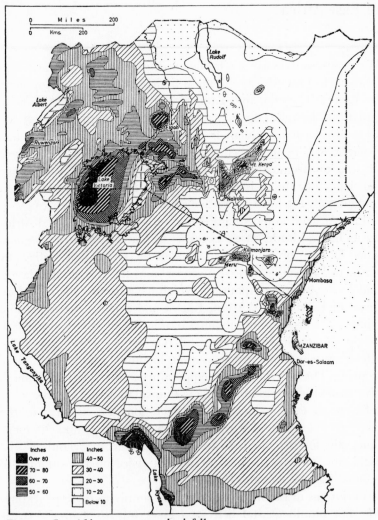

Figure 1. East Africa: mean annual rainfall

reliable, while the Tanganyika plateau becomes steadily wetter westward although there is no well-defined change in the topography.

The short rainy seasons are succeeded by dry seasons when soil moisture is rapidly depleted by high rates of evaporation and when any rain that falls may be of little use to the farmer since it is outside the growing season. Variations in amount of rainfall from year to year are considerable and, because the rainfall is frequently marginal in amount for agriculture and restricted in season, this variability is more critical than in many areas in high latitudes.

The distribution of rainfall is irregular in both time and space, and water is a problem almost everywhere. Only in areas of poor drainage, as in the swamps of Uganda, is excessive water a major difficulty. Planned conservation is essential, particularly as pressure of population on the land in places has resulted in deforestation, over-cultivation and over-grazing that have diminished the usefulness of those moisture resources that are available.

MEAN ANNUAL RAINFALL

The most recent mean annual rainfall map for East Africa (East African Meteorological Department, 1959) is simplified in Figure 1. East Africa may be divided roughly into three regions by the 30-inch isohyet. The coastal belt with over 30 inches mean rainfall is narrow in the north; along the coast itself amounts vary considerably and appear to depend on its alignment. In the drier hinterland the influence of relief is clear and heavy rainfall is confined to the windward slopes of the highland areas. The transition to the wetter western region is gradual in the north and south, but is more complicated in the Kenya Highlands, which are divided by the relatively dry Rift Valley. Heaviest rainfalls occur on south-east and east-facing slopes of the Aberdare Range and Mount Kenya, whereas west of the Rift the wetter areas are on west-facing slopes.

The effects of Lake Victoria on the rainfall of the surrounding

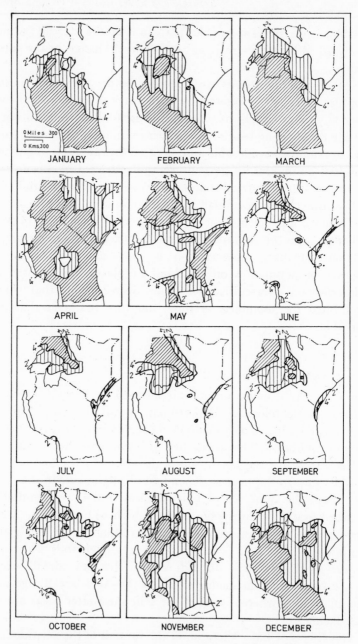

Figure 2. East Africa: mean monthly rainfall, modified to show 2-inch and 4-inch isohyets only

area have never been clearly evaluated. Increased rainfall is evident on the northern and western shores where storms off the lake are concentrated by the prevailing south-easterly winds (Henderson, 1949). There is an associated dry belt on the eastern shores of the lake, possibly intensified by the drying effects of air subsiding off the plateau, but on the other hand, the wetter west-facing slopes of the Mau plateau have also been associated with storms off the lake.

THE SEASONAL DISTRIBUTION OF RAINFALL

The climate of East Africa is characterized particularly by alternating wet and dry seasons, but there are considerable variations in the seasonal régime from place to place that depend not only on latitude but also on location (e.g. coast, hinterland or continental interior) and on topography. In many areas the real explanation of the seasonal pattern is still far from clear.

In general, a belt of rainfall can be said to shift seasonally northward and southward across East Africa. This is illustrated by the mean monthly rainfall charts (Figure 2), although the picture is complicated by the wide variations in amount with topography (Walter, 1952). Local relief may affect the seasonal régime as in the Usambara Mountains where maximum rainfall may be received during the season of the north-east monsoon on north-facing slopes and during the season of the south-east monsoon on south-facing slopes.

The concept of an oscillating belt of rainfall was shown to be over-generalized when the simple association of rainfall with movements of the Inter-Tropical Convergence Zone proved useless for practical forecasting in East Africa (Thompson, 1957). Streamline charts show that the pattern of air flow varies widely within any one month, while the evolution of patterns of rainfall occurrence from day to day is frequently untypical of seasonal trends (Johnson, 1962).

During May to September, instead of a steady movement of the rains away to the north, a rain area remains concentrated over

Uganda and the Kenya Highlands west of the Rift Valley. Rainfall increases in the highlands to the east of the Rift Valley in November and December following the breaking up of this rain area in the west. The effect can be seen in local contrasts in the seasonal régime (Figure 3). In the western Kenya Highlands one

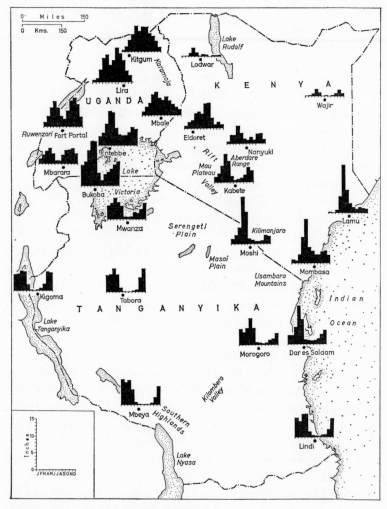

Figure 3. East Africa: seasonal rainfall régimes

long rainy season is characteristic in contrast to the long and short rains pattern east of the Rift Valley, and most of the rain falls from April to August, although there is a secondary and unreliable maximum in November. Along the Rift Valley and the Aberdare Range a transition zone can be distinguished towards the long and short rains pattern as June becomes drier on average, and on the eastern slopes of the Aberdares a small increase in August rainfall may partially bridge the gap between the two rainy seasons.

Other variations in the seasonal régime can be seen in Figure 3. In Uganda, for example, the earlier of the two wet seasons is the more important in the east but in the west the so-called 'short rains' from September to November may equal, if not exceed, the 'long rains'. The two seasons merge in northern Uganda despite the low latitude and present a wet-and-dry-season régime, which is the reverse of that in southern Tanganyika.

The value of rainfall amounts can be properly appreciated only in relation to its seasonal distribution. Examples of the way in which varying seasonal patterns affect local differences in agricultural economy abound. The contrast between the rainfall pattern of the western and eastern Kenya Highlands has a clear effect on agricultural practice. Maize is grown everywhere as a staple food crop, but little is grown commercially east of the Rift Valley, since a longer wet season is required for good and reliable yields. Occasional heavy rains in November west of the Rift may be disastrous for a ripening wheat crop, while east of the Rift, where there is little rain from May to October, the short rains are anxiously awaited.

Since much of the land available for development in East Africa lies in regions of low and variable rainfall, where crop risk is considerable, it is particularly foolish to accept generalized notions of the seasonal régime. Yet despite the differences in régime from place to place, reference to the 'long rains' and 'short rains' is common in many areas where it is not strictly appropriate. H. L. Manning (1956*b*) pointed out that 'the use of the Kenya colloquialism in Uganda is confusing and in the western part of the territory positively misleading'.

The seasonal régime is not necessarily reliable and may vary from year to year. Where the distinction between the seasons is not pronounced, the seasonal pattern may be very variable, as at Nanyuki where over 5 inches were recorded at least once for every month except January during a period of fifteen years. Variations in the seasonal régime may have serious consequences as in 1961, when failure of the long rains brought widespread drought to Kenya, followed by equally disastrous floods during exceptionally heavy short rains, which continued well into the early months of 1962. In this connection it is interesting to notice that heavy rain storms during late January or early February are quite a frequent occurrence, but they may be commonly regarded as exceptionally early rains or freak dry season rains.

The 'typical' pattern has often been too readily accepted as a basis for assessing the climate, and this has led to disillusionment when the equatorial climate proved less regular and less reliable than had been expected. Published accounts have not over-emphasized the regularity of the climate (East African Meteorological Department, pamphlet no. 7). Nevertheless, comments that the weather is 'not what it used to be' are heard in East Africa as frequently as in the British Isles. They imply that the rainfall distribution once conformed to a single pattern of clearly distinguishable wet and dry seasons, but is becoming increasingly unreliable in its time of occurrence. This view was expressed in the Report of the Department of Agriculture, Uganda, 1953: 'Gone seem to be the days when the rainfall followed some sort of pattern throughout the year; in recent times no one year's rainfall seems to have borne any relationship to another.' E. Weigt (1955) has made the interesting suggestion that the settler in East Africa often over-simplified his concept of the seasonal variations in the climate in order to satisfy a need for security when seeking to understand a strange environment.

CROP MOISTURE REQUIREMENTS

Optimum rainfall is difficult to define, since there is seldom a simple relationship between crop yield and rainfall. Nevertheless from detailed study of variations in the yield of maize in the west Kenya Highlands, J. Glover (1957) has shown that the average yield in sub-districts within the region is markedly affected by changes in seasonal rainfall. While yield increased with increasing rainfall in the drier areas where rainfall was less than 25 inches in the season April to August, the yield decreased with increasing rainfall in wetter districts with seasonal rainfall of 35 inches or over. Thus an optimum of about 30 inches of rainfall in the season was demonstrated (equivalent to approximately 40-50 inches annually) and where this occurred a reasonably stable yield was obtained. In Uganda, Manning (1956b) has shown that cotton yield falls off rapidly with rain either more or less than 25 inches in the growing season.

A possible explanation for the indication of optimum rainfall levels can be found in studies of soil fertility in East Africa. The effects of climate and soils are closely inter-related: H. F. Birch and M. T. Friend (1956) have shown, for example, that rainfall is the main factor governing the amount of organic matter and nitrogen in soils, and E. Griffiths (1961) has described the significant release or 'flush' of available nitrate observed to occur in East African soils after heavy rainfall following a dry period. More particularly, recent work in Kenya by R. Scott (1962) has shown that at low levels of annual rainfall leaching of bases increases with increasing amounts of rainfall, but with over 30 inches mean annual rainfall factors related to the increased plant growth gain significance, and percentage saturation of bases rises to an optimum at a mean annual rainfall of about 45 inches. With further increases in rainfall base saturation falls as leaching again becomes dominant. The optimum rainfall level shows a marked coincidence with that noted by Glover to affect maize yields.

While yields are clearly dependent on many factors other than water availability, crop moisture requirements are of prime significance and these depend largely on evapotranspiration rates. The only maps of potential evapotranspiration use Thornthwaite's method (Sansom, 1954 and Carter, 1954). Evaporation pan records are available, but estimates using Penman's formula (Penman, 1948), relating evaporation to net radiation, atmospheric humidity and wind speed, are generally preferred by agricultural physicists. There is little consistency in the rates of evaporation suggested by different methods, and various regional and seasonal contrasts are indicated (Kenworthy, 1960). From the point of view of water storage the importance of lower rates of evaporation at higher altitudes has been stressed (Pearsall, 1957). Nevertheless on plateau areas higher maximum temperatures give greater evaporation rates than at equivalent altitudes on mountain slopes, while the greater wind speeds experienced at high altitudes may counteract the effects of decreasing temperatures. Even so it has been concluded that the close correlation with air temperature ensures a general decrease in potential evapotranspiration with increasing height above sea-level (McCulloch, 1961).

Measurements of water use under different plant covers have been made in a series of catchment experiments. Conditions for full potential transpiration throughout the year are seldom obtained, and actual transpiration varies with rainfall, soil water storage capacity and the extent of the plant cover. Natural vegetation will generally root deeply enough to use all the rain that seeps into the soil profile and is held within the rooting range, provided that this is less than the potential evapotranspiration. It is suggested that indigenous vegetation can transpire from up to 90 inches in the coastal lowlands to 45 inches at altitudes around 8,000 feet. Ley farming can be dangerous in dry regions since a long-rooted ley can dry the soil profile to wilting point during the dry season (Pereira and McCulloch, 1962).

The suitability of seasonal patterns of rainfall varies with the crop. It is particularly difficult to produce an even yield of tea when there are marked seasonal variations in rainfall but no resting period. Experiments in artificial stimulation of rain during dry months over tea estates in Uganda were accepted as a 'proved success' since even a slight increase may have a favourable effect on yield (Sansom, Bargman and England, 1955).

Contrasts in the ability of crops to resist drought are significant. For example, maize and sorghum are able to withstand short droughts, but whereas sorghum can survive drought for a fortnight or more and still produce further growth, many varieties of maize cannot do so.

ASSESSMENT OF THE AGRICULTURAL POTENTIAL

There are scope and need for much detailed assessment of optimum conditions for various crops and for different soil types and rainfall régimes. In broad terms it would seem, however, that optimum rainfall for annual crops is probably between 40 and 50 inches in the year, remembering that it is the seasonal rainfall that matters in each specific case, and that poorly distributed rains could still be critical.

Below 30 inches water is a definite limiting factor and areas with a mean annual rainfall of 20-30 inches in the year must be regarded as marginal, although good crops of sisal are grown with less than 30 inches, groundnuts can do well with an annual rainfall of 25 inches, and agriculture will no doubt continue to be important in many such areas, at least as a subsistence economy. The variability of rainfall in amount from year to year is highly critical and evapotranspiration rates are high. Misuse of the land may threaten the available water resources, but supplementary irrigation may be worthwhile.

Most areas with over 50 inches, and certainly those with over 60 inches in the year, are sources of water-supply for wider regions. Formerly forested, these are the areas under increasing pressure of population and agricultural development. In these areas increasing rainfall does not necessarily increase productivity and it may even be a factor encouraging the leaching of soils and accelerating erosion where protective measures are inadequate. Conservation of water resources is essential for the maintenance of fertility as well as for the benefit of the surrounding lowlands.

THE DESICCATION OF MARGINAL AREAS

In the areas of marginal rainfall, bad land-use practices can create a state of effective aridity. In the Serengeti Plains of Tanganyika, the home of the Masai and their cattle and also the breeding ground of hundreds of game animals whose preservation has become a world-wide concern, W. H. Pearsall (1957) has shown that the combined pressure of cattle and wild game threatens to reduce the natural grazing to desert-like conditions. Because the game ranges widely when grazing, it would seem that a heavier stocking of wild life than of domestic cattle can be maintained without disrupting the ecological balance.

Severe over-grazing by domestic cattle in Karamoja, in north-eastern Uganda, has left a hard compacted surface, so that when rain does fall, usually in intense, sporadic showers, little is able to penetrate into the soil. Soil moisture storage is restricted to a depth of about 18 inches and flash floods sweep down to the river beds along the usually dry drainage channels or sand rivers. Progressive destruction of the vegetation has resulted from the increasing pressure of population and cattle, and ecological surveys have shown that plant species usually associated with arid conditions are well established in areas with a mean annual rainfall of 30 inches (Kerfoot, 1962). The quality of the grazing has undoubtedly deteriorated, and cattle are undernourished. Attempts to persuade the people to reduce the numbers in their herds are only slowly taking effect, but controlled grazing experiments are in progress in an attempt to encourage greater moisture seepage into the soil and to control stream flow.

It has often been suggested that destruction of the natural vegetation, accompanied by increasing run-off and the acceleration of soil erosion, may also result in a drying-up of the climate, so that rainfall becomes more limited in its distribution and more torrential, thus increasing its destructive power. E. P. Stebbing (1937) presented an impressive thesis of increasing intermittency of rainfall in the Sudan, but it is difficult to support his contention that intermittent rainfall is abnormal, when full reference is made to the geographical situation and the meteorology of the areas in question.

Attempts to illustrate trends in rainfall in East Africa (Sansom, 1952) have not been statistically very significant, while the concept of increasing aridity is not simple to judge from the ecological standpoint. In few parts of Africa does the existing form of natural vegetation represent a true climatic climax after a long history of biotic interference by grazing and burning, and H. C. Dawkins (1954) showed that there are few uninhabited areas in Uganda where the forest is not spreading or colonizing.

Whether the destruction of forest can itself result in increasing intermittency of rainfall and in decreasing amounts depends on the significance of local moisture supplies and, although this is not always easy to assess, meteorologists rarely attribute much significance to local sources of humidity. Turbulence and cooling over forested hills are sometimes thought to produce more rainfall, but the local effects of occult precipitation are probably more important (Hursh and Pereira, 1953). It is clear that the vegetation cover plays an important part in utilizing available water to maximum advantage, and J. Glover and M. D. Gwynne (1962a, 1962b) have shown how maize can intercept light rain during prolonged dry spells and concentrate it around the stem base in sufficient quantity to be of value, while the rosette formation of many plants in dry areas facilitates the accumulation of water after rain or the deposit of dew.

THE CATCHMENT AREAS

A consequence of the uneven geographical distribution of rainfall is that agricultural development in many low-lying areas is dependent on stream flow from the afforested catchments at high levels. As a result of cutting down forests, burning bush, over-grazing and over-cultivation along watersheds, rates of run-off are increased, the wet-season flood-flow of streams is exaggerated and soil erosion is accelerated. Experiments at the Perkerra irrigation scheme in the Kenya Rift Valley showed that growing crops on moisture stored from a single flooding is not successful, and emphasized the dependence on an even stream flow during the dry season (Pereira, 1958).

Referring to conditions in the Serengeti National Park, Pearsall (1957) commented that 'the manner in which human settlement and woodland clearance are taking place on the collecting grounds of the main permanent waters is appalling to anyone interested in conservation and contrary to all the experience obtained in India and in other parts of the world with similar climates'. Nevertheless pressure on the land is increasing and it is the highland areas that offer the more suitable climates and more fertile soils to an expanding population. The question that arises is what form of land use will allow maintenance of a water balance so that losses in evapotranspiration are at least restricted to those found under the natural vegetation cover, soil moisture is retained, run-off is controlled, and an even stream flow is preserved. Dry-weather flow can be sustained and the acceleration of erosion prevented, provided a high infiltration rate can be maintained at the soil surface, although as Pereira (1959) pointed out 'the concentration of rainfall into the tropical wet season is so acute that not even the combination of heavy forest and deep porous soils can succeed completely in the even regulation of stream flow'.

In 1956, an East African Catchment Area Research Committee was set up, and experimental catchment areas selected for investigating the effects of changes in land use, by measuring the response of stream flow and soil moisture storage to rainfall both before and after changes took place. The changes that have been studied are from natural bamboo forests to softwood plantations in the Aberdare Range in Kenya, the clearance of large areas of indigenous forest for tea plantations on the Mau plateau, and the introduction of peasant cultivation in the Mbeya Range of the Southern Highlands of Tanganyika.[1] Reference has been made to the catchment studies in Karamoja to assess the effects of controlled grazing experiments on run-off and stream flow.

[1] The mean annual rainfall is 60-100 inches in the Aberdares, 70-80 inches on the Mau plateau and over 60 inches in the Southern Highlands.

Interim conclusions drawn from these catchment experiments (Pereira, 1962) have shown, as might be expected, that dense forest is unsurpassed in ensuring maximum infiltration, reducing surface run-off to a minimum, and regulating stream flow. Although transpiration rates for forest are high, long-rooted Kikuyu grass can transpire as much moisture (Pereira and McCulloch, 1962). The replacement of bamboo forest in the Aberdares by softwood plantations, in which clean weeding was practised, gave a net saving of water, although it is possible that moisture requirements will increase with maturity, and that rotational felling will be essential for maintaining maximum water yields from afforested catchments.

Under softwood plantations there was no marked change in the response of stream flow to rainfall incidence, but under tea plantations on the Mau plateau storm run-off was considerably increased. Slightly reduced transpiration rates from the areas planted with tea resulted in an increase in total stream flow of 15 per cent. In the Southern Highlands the effect of cultivation has been to increase the sediment load of the streams, indicating that soil stability is inadequate and off-setting any saving in water through reduced transpiration rates.

Even in forested catchments the ratio of wet-season flow to dry-season flow may be considerable and storage structures are needed if dry-season water supplies are to be properly safeguarded. It may be many years, however, before such structures can be afforded on an adequate scale (Pereira, 1962) and the effects of natural vegetation and land-use patterns on stream flow, about which there is still much to be learned, will remain critical.

THE RELIABILITY OF RAINFALL

No assessment of the rainfall of East Africa can be meaningful without some appreciation of its variability in amount from year to year, for there are few areas where variability is not significant. Almost everywhere rainfall is restricted in its seasonal distribution, and variations in the total amount of rainfall in a given season depend on its distribution in the year. One of the frustrating characteristics of tropical rainfall for the farmer is its extreme localization, so that neighbouring areas may experience good and bad rainfall conditions in the same season. But it is in the wide areas where average rainfall is marginal in amount that variability is most critical.

For considerable areas in the Sudan, Stebbing (1937) suggested that 'both African chief and African peasant will admit that there is something wrong with his rainfall – that it is not as it was, perhaps even in his father's day and that it cannot be depended upon'. But there is little evidence in East Africa that it has ever been otherwise in recent historical times; poor crops through failure of the rains have been a constant threat to the African farmer. In recognition of the risk of drought and crop failure, many tribes have a compulsory levy of grain for use in famine.

The peasant farmer runs the risk of hunger if the rains fail. Provided he and his family survive, the misfortunes of one season may be forgotten with the successful harvest of the next, although an undernourished family works badly on the land and yields may fall again in consequence. If drought is widespread a whole region may face famine and it has been said that the resources of a peasant community are severely overstrained if this happens more than once in twenty years. It has been estimated that the European or African farming on a commercial scale can afford only one crop failure in three years (Glover, Robinson and Henderson, 1954). Failure of rainfall to meet expectation in two successive seasons may kill a farming enterprise.

A perennial crop is more able to withstand variations in the seasonal régime than an annual crop, provided soil moisture is maintained above wilting point, but nevertheless if a crop such as tea or coffee is killed by a severe drought heavy financial loss is involved and several years elapse before a re-established crop reaches maturity. The failure of the groundnut scheme in Tanganyika was so notorious that it is hardly necessary to stress how seriously unreliable rainfall may affect a large-scale enterprise involving heavy capital expenditure, particularly if combined with other setbacks.

The significance of variations in amount of annual rainfall from year to year is difficult to assess unless these are related to defined minimum requirements. This can be done by estimating the probability of specified amounts of rain being obtained within a year or a season. An alternative method is to indicate the range

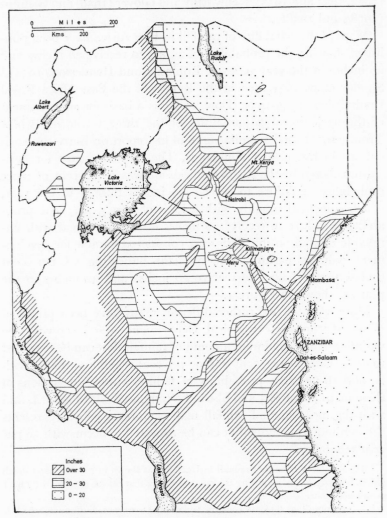

Figure 4. Annual rainfall : 30 per cent probability

of values likely to occur within certain confidence limits, so that the rainfall is unlikely to exceed or fall short of those values in a certain percentage of the years. Particular attention has been drawn to the value of such analyses in East Africa by the work of Manning (1949, 1950, 1956a and 1956b), Glover and Robinson (1953, 1954 and 1955), Kenworthy and Glover (1958) and Griffiths (1958a and 1958b).

Maps of the reliability of rainfall in East Africa have been published showing the probability of failing to receive 20 inches and 30 inches in the year (Glover, Robinson and Henderson, 1954).[1] Similar maps were used in the Report of the East Africa Royal Commission, 1953-1955 (Dow, 1955) as a basis for an assessment of the agricultural potentialities of the three territories, whilst Troup (1953) used a similar map in his report on European agriculture in the Kenya Highlands. The limiting factor for agriculture chosen by the Royal Commission was 30 per cent or more probability of failure to receive 30 inches rainfall in the year, which coincided roughly with a limit of over 5 per cent probability of failure to receive 20 inches of rainfall. Areas with unreliable rainfall on this basis were considered suitable for development only as pasture. The isopleths indicating 30 per cent probability of failure to receive 20 inches and 30 inches in the year are shown in Figure 4.

More recently two rather different maps have been prepared (East African Meteorological Department, 1961) showing the variation in the minimum amount of rainfall that can be expected to occur with 80 per cent and 90 per cent reliability, that is with 20 and 10 per cent probability of failure. Simplified versions of these maps (Figures 5 and 6) can be compared with Figure 4, and with the mean annual rainfall map (Figure 1) which represents the minimum amounts that can be expected to occur with 50 per cent reliability.[2]

[1] The reliability of annual rainfall in Uganda was shown in rather greater detail (Manning, 1956b), by indicating the range of values that can be expected with 9 : 1 confidence limits.

[2] i.e. assuming that the data conform to a normal frequency distribution, which is assumed in all of these maps.

The reliability of seasonal rainfall

It is the variability of seasonal rather than annual rainfall that is really critical for the cultivation of annual crops. Estimates of the reliability of seasonal rainfall can be made but the mapping of

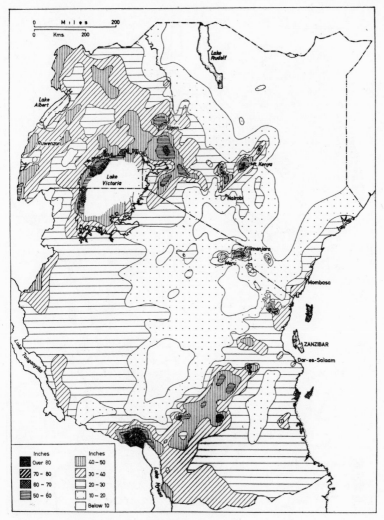

Figure 5. Annual rainfall: 20 per cent probability

these values is complicated by variations in the length of the wet season from place to place and in the length of the growing season required by various crops. Such maps have been attempted for the period from October to May in Tanganyika (Glover, 1956) and for the long rains in Kenya and adjacent parts of Tanganyika

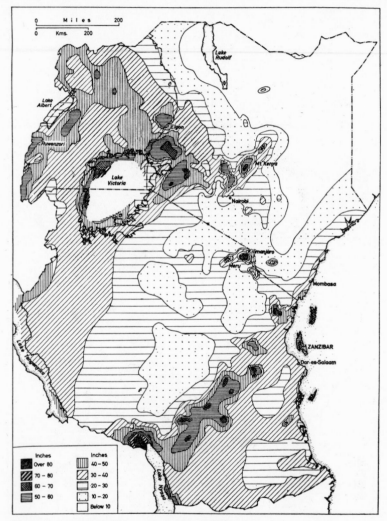

Figure 6. Annual rainfall: 10 per cent probability

(Kenworthy and Glover, 1958). Rainfall totals cannot be compared readily for seasons of different lengths, but for Kenya the analyses emphasized the more favourable conditions in the west Kenya Highlands where there is a greater likelihood of satisfying crop requirements in the longer rainy season.

Analyses of the pattern of rainfall within the growing season
The actual pattern of rainfall in any one season cannot be predicted with accuracy and the choice of planting date will always be a gamble. It may be necessary to wait for a critical build-up of moisture in the soil (Pereira, 1956), although planting just before the rains ensures that an annual crop can benefit from the release of available nitrates associated with rainfall following a prolonged dry period (Griffiths, 1961).

Nevertheless the most useful application of probability analyses has been in the detailed study of the reliability of the pattern of rainfall within the growing season. Thus later planting dates have been recommended in Tanganyika, to avoid unreliable rainfall in November (Evans, 1955), or to avoid the coincidence of the peak demand of a crop with a frequent dry spell during February (Glover and Robinson, 1953).

In a similar way, H. L. Manning (1949 and 1950) suggested improved planting dates in Buganda, so that the maximum requirements of the cotton crop would coincide with a period of reliable rainfall. Cotton is grown on the second rains, but Manning has shown that in some areas planting on the decline of the first rains in early June is necessary to ensure an adequate growing season. Even so early sowing runs the risk of loss at picking through heavy rains likely to occur in November once in ten years.

It was also shown that maize could be planted a month earlier than was customary. An increase in rainfall in early March, before the onset of the main rains, was recognized by Africans as the 'fool's rains' since they were of little value to the banana and coffee crops. The value of these rains for early planting of the more recently introduced maize crop had not been appreciated (Manning, 1956*b*).

CONCLUSION

A reasonable comparison of the situation in the three territories can be made from the maps included here. In Kenya, the areas with good reliable rainfall are confined to the narrow coastal belt and to the highlands. The transition from humid to drier areas is particularly sharp and is related to the equally sharp changes in the topography. East of the Rift Valley, where two distinct wet seasons are characteristic, conditions are more often marginal for grain crops, although where rainfall totals are adequate good yields of coffee and tea are obtained on deep Kikuyu loams. The longer rainy season of the highlands west of the Rift Valley offers a more reliable growing season for annual crops and this area has long been the nucleus of agricultural production in Kenya.

In Tanganyika, the north-east may be compared with the east Kenya Highlands in that sharp contrasts in rainfall amount are evident and depend largely on the topography. The wetter areas, in the Usambara Mountains and south of Mount Meru and Kilimanjaro, have been intensively developed for African and European agriculture. Elsewhere in Tanganyika many areas with a fairly good rainfall have not as yet been fully developed, although these areas are small. Examples are the Kilombero valley, to which the Royal Commission drew particular attention, and the Southern Highlands where development has been limited partly through inadequate communications.

The western part of the Tanganyika plateau has a distinctly better rainfall than the plateau to the east, but marked topographical contrasts are lacking and areas with over 40 inches of rainfall are few. The area with over 30 inches on the map of mean annual rainfall rapidly dwindles when 80 and 90 per cent reliability tests are applied (Figures 5 and 6). Moreover, most of the rainfall is concentrated in the season from November/December to April/May, and during the severe drought of the remaining six months streams dry up, soil moisture is depleted and pasture deteriorates. It has often been suggested that the tsetse fly, by hindering development, has preserved this area from all too easy exhaustion through the depredations of man and his cattle.

Uganda has the better rainfall conditions of the three territories. Higher and more reliable rainfall totals are received in the west, the east and the lake areas, with a falling off in amount and reliability in the centre and south-west. Despite the distribution of rainfall in two seasons, the intervening dry season is less severe than in the east Kenya Highlands. In the north rainfall is concentrated in one season and offers less possibility for obtaining two crops in the year. Dry conditions prevail in the north-east and in parts of the western Rift, but these are less extensive than the dry areas of Kenya and Tanganyika and form only a small proportion of the total area.

Detailed local analyses of rainfall conditions are plainly the most useful and to correlate agricultural potentialities with the reliability of annual rainfall over-simplifies the climatic factors concerned. Other reservations must also be borne in mind. The Royal Commission pointed out that in areas where rainfall is too unreliable, according to their selected criteria, to allow the economic development of agriculture, farming is not impossible and is practised.

While rainfall remains the chief factor limiting agricultural and livestock potential, the picture of rainfall conditions which has been presented is only part of the story. Potentialities for irrigation, to open up dry areas or to supplement rainfall in dry months, have been exploited on only a limited scale in the three territories. Their assessment depends not only on water supplies but on knowledge of the economics of irrigation for different crops. More widespread in significance, the organization of water supplies from bore-holes, tanks and dams plays a vital part in the rural economy of all areas. Nevertheless the amount of rainfall and its effective use largely determine the distribution of potential water supplies.

Perhaps the most striking feature of rainfall in East Africa is the complexity of its distribution. The wide regional variations in rainfall amount make all aspects of water conservation of vital importance. F. Debenham (1948) selected control of the rate of run-off as a factor of prime importance. Perennial rivers are indeed almost literally the life-blood of those areas unlikely to receive 30 inches of rainfall in the year, and water is one of the most valuable crops that can be harvested from the small areas with higher rainfall (Russell, 1962).

Appreciation of the seasonal distribution of rainfall and its variability in amount and in distribution from year to year is not only important for overall assessments of agricultural potential, but also for improvements in farming practices as much in areas with good rainfall as in areas with marginal rainfall. During the last half-century or so mistakes have been made in pioneer developments through inadequate understanding of the climatic conditions. There is still a long way to go before the dynamics of the climate are fully understood, but detailed analyses of rainfall records in particular localities are beginning to provide the 'weather lore' that has previously been lacking.

ACKNOWLEDGEMENT

I should like to thank Dr E. W. Russell, Director of the East African Agriculture and Forestry Research Organization, for the guidance and working facilities given to me during 1956-8 when I held a Leverhulme Overseas Research Scholarship in East Africa.

REFERENCES

BIRCH, H.F. and FRIEND, M.T. (1956) 'The organic-matter and nitrogen status of East African soils', *J. Soil Sci.*, 7, 156-67.

CARTER, D.B. (1954) 'Climates of Africa and India according to Thornthwaite's 1948 classification', Johns Hopk. Univ., Lab. of Clim., *Publications in Climatology*, 7, 4.

DAWKINS, H.C. (1954) 'Timu, and the vanishing forests of N.E. Karamoja', *E. Afr. agric. J.*, *19*, 164-7.

DEBENHAM, F. (1948) 'Report on the water resources of the Bechuanaland Protectorate, Northern Rhodesia, the Nyasaland Protectorate, Tanganyika Territory, Kenya and the Uganda Protectorate', *Colon. Res. Publ.*, 2.

DOW, SIR HUGH (Chairman) (1955) *East Africa Royal Commission 1953–1955 Report*. H.M.S.O. Cmd. 9475.

East African Meteorological Department (n.d.) 'The weather of East Africa', *Pamphlet no. 7*.

— (1959) Mean annual rainfall map of East Africa, based on all available data at 1955.

— (1961) 10% and 20% probability maps of annual rainfall of East Africa.

EVANS, A.C. (1955) 'A study of crop production in relation to rainfall reliability', *E. Afr. agric. J.*, *20*, 263-7.

GLOVER, J. (1956) 'Tanganyika. The probability of receiving less than 15 and 20 inches of rainfall in a season'. *East African Agriculture and Forestry Research Organization*. Unpublished.

— (1957) 'The relationship between total seasonal rainfall and yield of maize in the Kenya Highlands', *J. agric. Sci.*, *49*, 285-90.

GLOVER, J. and GWYNNE, M.D. (1962a) 'Light rainfall and plant survival in East Africa, I. Maize', *J. Ecol.*, *50*, 111-18.

GLOVER, P.E., GLOVER, J. and GWYNNE, M.D. (1962b) 'Light rainfall and plant survival in East Africa, II. Dry grassland', *J. Ecol.*, *50*, 199-206.

GLOVER, J. and ROBINSON, P. (1953) 'A simple method for assessing the reliability of rainfall', *J. agric. Sci.*, *43*, 275-80.

GLOVER, J., ROBINSON, P. and HENDERSON, J.P. (1954) 'Provisional maps of the reliability of annual rainfall in East Africa', *Quart. J. R. Met. Soc.*, *80*, 602-9.

GLOVER, J., ROBINSON, P. and TAYLOR, J. (1955) 'Assessing the reliability of rainfall if monthly falls are not independent', *J. agric. Sci.*, *46*, 387-8.

GRIFFITHS, E. (1961) 'Seasonal fluctuations in the microbial populations of the soil', *Aspects of Soil Climate*, Mem. 4., Dept. of Geogr., Univ. College of Wales, Aberystwyth, 32-5.

GRIFFITHS, J.F. (1958a) 'An initial investigation of the annual rainfall in East Africa', *E. Afr. Met. Dept.*, Mem. Vol.. III, no. 5.

— (1958b) 'Annual rainfall distribution in East Africa', *Nature*, Lond., *181*, 1331.

HENDERSON, J.P. (1949) 'Some aspects of climate in Uganda, with special reference to rainfall', *E. Afr. Met. Dept.*, Mem. Vol. VI, no. 5.

HURSH, C.R. and PEREIRA, H.C. (1953) 'Field moisture balance in the Shimba Hills, Kenya', *E. Afr. agric. J.*, *18*, 1-7.

JOHNSON, D.H. (1962) 'Rain in East Africa', *Quart. J. R. Met. Soc.*, *88*, 1-19.

KENWORTHY, J.M. (1960) 'The variability of rainfall and of rainfall effectiveness in East Africa'. Unpublished. B.Litt. thesis, University of Oxford.

KENWORTHY, J.M. and GLOVER, J. (1958) 'The reliability of the main rains in Kenya', *E. Afr. agric. J.*, *23*, 267-72.

KERFOOT, O. (1962) 'The vegetation of the Atumatak catchments', *E. Afr. agric. J.*, *27*, 55-8.

135

McCULLOCH, J.S.G. (1961) 'The Penman equation for estimation of open water evaporation and transpiration'. *East African Agriculture and Forestry Research Organisation.* Cyclostyled.

MANNING, H.L. (1949) 'Planting date and cotton production in the Buganda Province of Uganda', *Emp. J. exp. Agric.*, *17*, 245-58.

— (1950) 'Confidence limits of expected monthly rainfall'. *J. agric. Sci.*, *40*, 169-76.

— (1956*a*) 'Calculation of confidence limits of monthly rainfall', *J. agric. Sci.*, *47*, 154-6.

— (1956*b*) 'The statistical assessment of rainfall probability and its application in Uganda agriculture', *Proc. Roy. Soc. B.*, *144*, 460-80.

PEARSALL, W.H. (1957) *Report on an ecological survey of the Serengeti National Park, Tanganyika, 1956.* Fauna Preservation Society, Zoological Society, London.

PENMAN, H.L. (1948) 'Natural evaporation from open water, bare soil and grass', *Proc. Roy. Soc. A.*, *193*, 120-45.

PEREIRA, H.C. (1956) 'Soil moisture at planting time'. Paper to East African Agriculture and Forestry Research Organization, 4th Forestry Course and Kenya D.F.O.s Conference, Cyclostyled.

— (1958) 'The limited utility of flood-water in the Perkerra River irrigation scheme, Kenya', *E. Afr. agric. J.*, *23*, 246-53.

— (1959) 'A physical basis for land use policy in tropical catchment areas', *Nature, Lond.*, *184*, 1768-71.

— (1962) 'Hydrological effects of changes in land use in some East African catchment areas', *E. Afr. agric. J.*, *Special Issue*, *27*, 1-131.

PEREIRA, H.C. and McCULLOCH, J.S.G. (1962) 'Water requirements of East African crops' in E. W. Russell (ed.), *The Natural Resources of East Africa*, 88-91.

RUSSELL, E.W. (1962) Foreword to Pereira (1962).

SANSOM, H.W. (1952) 'The trend of rainfall in East Africa', *E. Afr. Met. Dept., Technical Mem.*, 1.

— (1954) 'The climate of East Africa (based on Thornthwaite's classification)', *E. Afr. Met. Dept. Mem. Vol. III*, no. 2.

SANSOM, H.W., BARGMAN, D.J. and ENGLAND, G. (1955) 'Report on experiments on artificial stimulation of rainfall at Mityani, Uganda', *E. Afr. Met. Dept. Mem. Vol. III*, no. 4.

SCOTT, R. (1962) 'Exchangeable bases of mature, well-drained soils in relation to rainfall in East Africa', *J. Soil Sci.*, *13*, 1-9.

STEBBING, E.P. (1937) *The creeping desert in the Sudan and elsewhere in Africa, 15°-13° Lat.*

THOMPSON, B.W. (1957) 'Some reflections on equatorial and tropical forecasting', *E. Afr. Met. Dept. Technical Mem.*, 7.

TRAPNELL, C.G. and GRIFFITHS, J.F. (1960) 'The rainfall-altitude relation and its ecological significance in Kenya', *E. Afr. agric. J.*, *25*, 207-13.

TREWARTHA, G.T. (1961) *The earth's problem climates.* New York.

TROUP, L.G. (1953) *Inquiry into the general economy of farming in the Highlands.* Govt. Printer, Nairobi.

WALTER, M.W. (1952) 'A new presentation of the seasonal rainfall of East Africa', *E. Afr. agric. J.,* *18,* 11-20.

WEIGT, E. (1955) *Europäer in Ostafrika, Klimabedingungen und Wirtschaftsgrundlagen.* Kölner Geog. Arbeit, Doppel-Heft 6/7.

K

PAUL WHEATLEY

The land of Zanj: exegetical notes on
Chinese knowledge of East Africa
prior to A.D. 1500*

WESTERN scholars have for long been predisposed to seek connections between China and Africa. The germ of such ideas seems
to have sprung from the superficial resemblance between Egyptian
hieroglyphs and certain archaic Chinese graphs, and to have been
nurtured by the biblical notion that Asia had been peopled by the
sons of Ham. As early as 1614 an atlas of maps by Peter Kaerius
referred to some white natives of Madagascar 'supposed to have
been transplanted out of China' (1).† In 1654, in a work entitled
Œdipus Ægyptiacus, Athanasius Kircher propounded the view that
Chinese civilization derived from that of Ancient Egypt, a thesis
that was fully developed a century later by M. de Guignes of the
French Academy. In his *Mémoire dans lequel on prouve que les Chinois
sont une colonie égyptienne* this author equated events and personages
of legendary Chinese history with similar happenings and rulers
in the early Egyptian dynastic period. The stimulation afforded
to such studies by the alleged discovery in 1834 of Chinese bottles
in a Theban tomb ceased abruptly when it was shown that the
bottles were unlikely to be older than the Tao-kuang period,
1821-51 (2). The final chapters in this genre of historical specula-
tion more nearly concern East Africa. In 1853 Charles de Paravey
(3) proposed that the Hsi-wang-mu[1] of the *Bamboo Annals* – now
thought to have been a Central Asian tribe, but whose name can

---

* I take pleasure in expressing my thanks to Mr Ellis Anderson-Ahl for a great deal
of general assistance in the preparation of this paper, and particularly for the execution
of Figure 1.

† Figures in brackets in the text refer to Notes and References (see p. 169); Superscript figures, e.g.,[1] refer to names and terms translated in the text (see p. 184).

be translated to mean 'the Queen-Mother of the West' – was in fact the biblical Queen of Sheba (*Saba'*). Fifty years later A. Forke refurbished this bizarre notion and, as his imagination took wing, discovered a transcription of the K'un-lun Mountains,[2] home of [the] Hsi-wang-mu, conveniently to hand in the *qolla* of Abyssinia (4). Other theories in this genre were propounded from time to time, and as late as 1938 a writer sought in all seriousness to derive Hottentot physical characteristics from an infusion of Mongoloid blood when 'millions of Chinese' swarmed over Africa between A.D. 900 and 1200 (5). These extravaganzas need detain us no longer, though perhaps we should mention Albert Herrmann's advocacy of another and almost equally impossible theory. This related to a well-known passage in the *Annals of the Former Han* (6) which told how, in the reign of the Emperor Wu (140-86 B.C.), Chinese envoys sailed to the country of *Huang-chih*.[3] Half a century later, during the reign of the usurper Wang Mang, this same kingdom was cajoled into sending a live rhinoceros as tribute to the Chinese court. A. Herrmann considered that *Huang-chih* denoted Abyssinia, the graphs being a transcription of *Ag'āzi[yān]*, the name of a people living on the Somali coast (7). Despite the efforts of a succession of scholars (8), we still know only one thing about *Huang-chih* – that it could not have been located anywhere in the African world. It is mentioned here only as an example of the readiness with which historians, even in comparatively recent times, have welcomed the opportunity of linking China and Africa, and because of the distressing frequency with which Herrmann's identification is still being cited as established fact.

THE NATURE OF THE EVIDENCE

Before proceeding to resurrect authentic Chinese references to East Africa, it may be as well to interpolate a few words of warning. In the first place there is no reason to believe that Chinese visited the African coast before Ming times, so that the information which they undoubtedly possessed in earlier periods must have been acquired at second-hand. So far as the dynastic histories were concerned, a preponderance of their information derived from the records of the Hung Lu,[4] an office which, in T'ang times and later, interrogated foreign envoys and tribute-bearers concerning the geography and customs of their homelands. The clerks in this office subsequently transcribed personal and place-names according to the phonology of the *kuan hua* or official language, usually with a fair degree of accuracy – though, as the following pages show, they were on occasion capable of creating virtually impenetrable disguises for some toponyms. This administrative information was supplemented after the seventh century, but especially during the Sung and Yüan dynasties, by unofficial works based on information provided by the Arabo-Persian merchants who frequented the ports of South China. Only in the early Ming do we encounter personal observations by Chinese who had visited the African coast.

The second caveat that needs to be entered concerns the rendering of place-names into Chinese. Generally speaking, the versions which occur in Chinese writings fall into three categories: descriptive names coined by Chinese sailors, translations of local words, and transcriptions of native names. So far as can be determined at present, all the East African place-names occurring in Chinese works belong to the third category, and here we encounter the crux of the problem. The Chinese language comprises only just over 400 different monosyllables, whose combinations are incapable of reproducing accurately the range of sounds employed in East African languages. The use of tones, which in ordinary speech goes far to reduce the excessively large number of homophones in the language, brings no advantage to the transcription of foreign place-names into Chinese. For a name such as Juba the transcription *Chu-pu*[5] is reasonably accurate. Mogadishu is likewise easily recognizable in its Chinese garb of *Mu-ku-tu-shu*[6], and Brava is only slightly more obscure as *Pu-la-wa*,[7] but *Chung-li*[8] and *Ts'eng-pa*,[9] for example, are considerably more cryptic (pp. 150 and 152 below). It should be remembered, of course, that for periods earlier than the fifteenth century, such names are usually not so much direct transcriptions into Chinese as Chinese forms of Arabic versions of East African (including Arabo-Persian) words. Generally speaking, the unofficial transcriptions of private individuals were less accurate and less scholarly than those of the Hung Lu clerks in the canonical histories. In the following pages the established, but debatable, custom of romanizing names according to the slightly modified adaptation of Wade's *Syllabary* used in the *National Language Dictionary* has been followed, in the belief that it is more readily intelligible to those unfamiliar with the Chinese language than is the Gwoyeu Romatzyh.

THE T'ANG PERIOD

The Chinese exploration of South-east Asia and the Indian Ocean is a saga yet to be related in detail, but the outlines are clear enough. As early as the first century B.C. personal emissaries of Emperor Wu were undertaking voyages of several years' duration into the southern seas. In A.D. 413-14 the monk Fa-Hsien[10] returned to his homeland from India by sea, and by the second half of the seventh century the voyage from China to India had become a comparatively commonplace, albeit adventurous, episode in the lives of Buddhist monks. At the turn of the eighth and ninth centuries Chia Tan, Duke of Wei and Prime Minister under Emperor Te-tsung, collated the received geographical knowledge of his time in a series of itineraries, including one from China to India, but made no mention of Africa. Although Alexandria may feature in earlier records (9), not for another half-century do we encounter the earliest known reference to East Africa. It occurs in the *Yu-yang Tsa-tsu*[11] (*The Miscellany of the Yu-yang Mountain*), compiled by the scholar Tuan Ch'eng-shih[12] in A.D. 863 (10). From internal evidence it appears that this author derived at least part of his information about South-west Asia from priests of the Roman Orient and Magadha (11), but so far as East Africa was concerned, it is more than probable that his informants were Arabs or Persians.

The passage in question (chap. 4, f. 3 verso) relates to the coastal region of Somaliland, under the orthography *Po-pa-li*[13] (*pi̯wɒt b'wat li̯ək*), by Chinese standards an adequate transcription of Berbera. Tuan Ch'eng-shih had ferreted out enough facts to be able to present an outline of the country that would not disgrace a modern travel book. As he saw it, Berbera was a country of half-naked and feuding pastoralists who owed allegiance to none, but which yielded certain valuable products. Tuan's description clearly refers to the countryside rather than to the port of Berbera, an important emporium since at latest the first century A.D. (12), and it may be accounted strange that his Arab informant, whose experience would have been restricted to the cosmopolitan life of the towns, should have laid such emphasis on the very different economy of the countryside.

Tuan Ch'eng-shih had discovered, vicariously, the extreme eastern tip of the broad zone of desert and low-grass savanna that stretches across Africa between latitudes 15° and 30° North, and which is the home of peoples with predominantly pastoral economies. He knew that agriculture was unimportant on the Berbera coast and remarked that 'the five grains were not eaten'. Instead the inhabitants depended on a meat and milk diet, together with, significantly, blood freshly drawn by inserting a needle into the veins of cattle. This is an important passage because, to members of the Ishaak tribal-family and the Mijertein sub-confederacy who inhabit the coastal tracts today, the practice of drinking fresh blood is unknown. Among the Somali, only the Sab and the Bararetta adhere to this custom (13), and it is extremely unlikely that they were ever a dominant group along the Berbera coast. It is virtually impossible that Tuan Ch'eng-shih could have fabricated such a culture trait, which is in fact endemic to East Africa. Neither is it at all probable that the Ishaak and Mijertein would have abandoned such a distinctive custom during the last thousand years except under a strict and pervasive alien interdiction, and of this there is no evidence. The resolution of this apparent inconsistency appears to reside in the ethnic history of the region. According to Murdock's reconstruction of East African culture history (14), during the ninth or tenth century the

Afar and Galla, hitherto agriculturalists supplementing their livelihood with animal husbandry, elaborated the pastoral aspect of their economy so that they were able to migrate from the uplands of south-eastern Abyssinia down to the steppes and deserts of the Horn. The drinking of blood is a trait characteristic of the pastoral Galla (15) who presumably occupied at least part of the coast in T'ang times. As Tuan Ch'eng-shih was writing in 863, it may be prudent to antedate the Galla migration by a few years – to, say, the seventh or eighth century. Subsequently the Somali, who had adopted Islam as a result of their trading relations with coastal ports on the Gulf of Aden, replaced the Galla in this region, as later they were to occupy territory as far south as the Tana River (15a).

Hereditary slavery is today a prominent institution of Galla society, and something of this nature is hinted at by Tuan Ch'eng-shih when he says that the natives were given to seizing their own women and selling them to foreign traders.[14] Presumably these unfortunates were either members of outcaste groups or, perhaps, were Bushmanoid hunters of Stillbay culture who may have continued to exist in the interior. Tuan also adds some information about the procedures adopted by one group of these foreign merchants, the Persians.[15] As the compilers of the *Hsin T'ang Shu* misunderstood this passage (16), it should occasion no surprise that Friedrich Hirth failed to interpret it adequately (17). For the correct elucidation we are indebted to J. J. L. Duyvendak (18). Apparently the Persian merchants opened proceedings by presenting gifts of cloth to the assembled tribesmen (several thousand strong in the text), after which the Africans swore oaths of good faith in their own blood. Only then did trading begin. In this connection it is pertinent to note that Persian merchants are thought to have maintained a dominant interest in Azanian commerce from about A.D. 550 to 900, after which they were supplanted by Arab traders. The commodities in special demand in this trade were ambergris (*a-mo* [*hsiang*][16] = Arabic '*anbar*[17]) and ivory (*hsiang ya*[18]). The former was introduced into China by Arabo-Persian traders towards the end of the T'ang dynasty, and

Tuan Ch'eng-shih's reference to it must be one of the earliest in Chinese literature. Ambergris itself is a solid, fatty, inflammable substance occurring as a biliary concretion in the intestine of the sperm-whale (*Physeter macrocephalus*), which frequents the seas off the Horn of Africa. Whereas in the Muslim world ambergris was used as a cosmetic and as a culinary spice, in addition to its role in the preparation of incense, in China it was used only as an ingredient to be mixed with other perfumes in the belief that it induced permanence in floral odours which were themselves evanescent (19). Ivory, the second product known to Tuan Ch'eng-shih, was presumably obtained mainly from the African elephant (*Elephas africanus*, Linn.), though evidence will be presented below (p. 149) suggesting that, in Sung times at least, some tusks were obtained from what appears to be a small race of elephants inhabiting Somaliland, namely *E. a. orleansi*, Lyd.

The only other T'ang account of East Africa occurs in the *Hsin T'ang Shu* and relates to the country of *Mo-lin*[19] (*muâ liĕn*) [i.e. Malindi] (20), which was believed to be 'the old *P'o-sa*'[20] (*b'uâi' sât*). If this was meant, as seems likely, to be a transcription of the *Paza* (modern Faza) of the Swahili annals of Pate (21), the statement is apparently erroneous, for the two places are separated by more than 100 miles of coast. Conceivably, however, the passage implies that hegemony over this stretch of coast had passed from Faza to Malindi, but of this there is no independent confirmation. The semi-desert nature of much of the coast was, however, known to the Chinese authors, who characterized it as 'pestilential, and lacking herbs, trees and cereals' (22). Apart from this last remark, the text makes no mention of agricultural practices but claims that the *hu-mang*[21] (23), which it defines as 'the Persian jujube', the date, featured prominently in the local diet. If this were so, it must have been imported, for the southern limit of the date (*Phoenix dactylifera*) reaches only to the latitude of Zeila.

The text goes on to describe the inhabitants of *Mo-lin* as 'black and of fierce disposition', presumably referring to the north-east coastal Bantu who had displaced Bushmanoid hunters in the interior of the Azanian coast probably between the sixth and ninth centuries A.D., or possibly remnant groups of these hunters themselves. The port cities such as Malindi had from early times been inhabited by a mixture of Megalithic Cushites, Persians, Arabs and Malays, and the omission of such groups from the Chinese text might be held either to imply that the Bantu element was already prominent in the towns or, perhaps more probably, that the Arab or Persian informants were referring to the hinterland of Malindi rather than to the city itself. Of one or more of these ethnic groups the T'ang history adds: 'In the seventh moon they rest completely, neither dispatching nor receiving [merchandise] in trade. All night long they sit drinking.' Presumably this refers to Muslim behaviour during Ramaḍān, the month of daily fast from sunrise to sunset, and implies that the inhabitants of Malindi were Muslim. This was true enough of the urban populations of the coast, but it is a moot point whether it applied to the Bantu of the countryside at this early date. Actually the fast occurs in the ninth (not seventh) month of the Muslim calendar (was *ch'i*[22] a mislection for *chiu*[23]?), when tradition has it that the Qur'ān was revealed (*sūr.* 2, 181). As the Muslim year is purely lunar, the months do not correspond to particular seasons in the sense implicit in the Chinese text.

Another curious sentence runs *Pu ch'ih cheng-pao*,[24] which Duyvendak rendered as 'They are not ashamed of debauching the wives of their fathers or chiefs' and, continuing the translation, added 'they are (in this respect) the worst of the barbarians. They call this: to seek out the proper master and subject' (24). It is true that, in its Chinese context, *cheng* does have the special meaning of 'to commit incest with someone of an older generation', and Duyvendak has cited a *Tso-chuan* example of *pao* apparently used in a similar sense [Duke Hsüan III] (25), but I interpret the phrase as an attempt to describe either some social custom such as that of the levirate or, more probably, the specifically African manifestations of queenship. In the sub-Saharan parts of the continent the institutions of queen-mother, queen-consort and queen-sister are widespread, such women often enjoying extraordinary prestige and even outranking the king himself. Not infrequently queens, particularly queen-sisters, although forbidden to marry, are sexually promiscuous, as are the women that they take as 'wives' (26).

This is the meagre sum of T'ang knowledge of East Africa which, as far as I have been able to ascertain, has been both preserved and identified. Whether it is a fair summary of Chinese knowledge of the time, or whether it is even representative of the sort of information which filtered into China, I do not know. It seems unlikely, however, that much new evidence will come to light. Probably the best hope is that the identification of some hitherto elusive toponym may add a significant fact to what will almost certainly remain an incomplete account.

THE SUNG PERIOD

Chinese maritime trade reached its apogee under the Southern Sung dynasty (A.D. 1127-1279). Having lost their northern territories, including the gateways to central and western Asia, the Chinese turned perforce towards the southern seas. As early as 960 T'ai-tsu regulated the conditions of this trade (27), and succeeding emperors observed them as dynastic rules. By the early years of the Southern Sung, maritime commerce was yielding some two million strings of cash, or about a fifth of the total cash revenue of the state (28). As the exchequer became increasingly dependent on these profits, the Government endeavoured to foster the trade by every means in its power. In 987 four missions were dispatched with credentials under the imperial seal to induce foreign traders to visit China on promise of special import licences (29). The maritime customs service was reorganized (30), successful merchants were rewarded with official rank (31), hostels were constructed for the convenience of visiting factors (32), a welfare service was instituted for the benefit of shipwrecked seamen (33), a programme of harbour clearance and construction initiated along the South China coast (34), and the principle of extra-territoriality (already long-established in the ports of East Asia) interpreted in liberal fashion (35). In Hang-chou, Ch'üan-chou,

Kuang-chou and other large ports, for example, Middle Eastern Muslims resided in special quarters[25] characterized by mosques and *suqs*, were ministered to by their own *qāḍīs* and governed by their own sheikhs. These trade relations brought the Chinese a great deal of new information about the shores of the Indian Ocean, which we might expect to find recorded in the elegant prose of the Sung dynasty, the more especially as the art of printing had made rapid advances under the Five Dynasties (A.D. 907-60). That such a development did not take place must be ascribed to the 'Confucian' ethic.

However great the profits of trade might prove to be, ideologically it was an inferior, if not sordid, activity. As F. Hirth and W. W. Rockhill put it, the knowledge of foreign countries was 'an obscure, unprofitable hobby . . . which in no way appealed to the public fancy' (36). Apart from the official Sung history, only two works have preserved formal descriptions of East Africa. The first is the *Ling-wai Tai-ta*[26] (*Information on what lies beyond the Passes*), written in ten books by Chou Ch'ü-fei,[27] the Assistant Sub-Prefect at Kuei-lin, in 1178. Although professing to be supplementary to the *Kuei-hai Yü-heng Chih*[28] (*Topography and products of the southern provinces*) by Fan Ch'eng-ta,[29] the *Ling-wai Tai-ta* incorporates summary outlines of numerous foreign countries. In its pages we catch a glimpse of the geographical notions entertained by a cultivated official in South China in the twelfth century. He was fairly well informed about South-east Asia (though only by hearsay), and he was not unfamiliar with conditions round the shores of the *Sea of Ceylon*[30] (the Bay of Bengal). Beyond stretched the vast *Eastern Sea of the Arabs*[31] (the Arabian Sea), the western shores of which constituted the extreme limit of Chou's oecumene.

The second of the Sung topographies containing material relating to East Africa is the *Chu-fan-chih*[32] (*Gazetteer of Foreigners*), compiled by Chao Ju-kua[33] in 1225. Chao was Superintendent of Maritime Trade at Ch'üan-chou (37), where he enjoyed exceptional opportunities for discussion with Arabo-Persian mariners and merchants who frequented that port. His book is divided into two parts. The first comprises descriptions of foreign countries as far west as the African coast and the Mediterranean, the second takes the form of a systematic survey of the principal commodities entering into Chinese maritime trade. In both sections Chao Ju-kua drew largely on his store of knowledge acquired by means of personal association with overseas traders, supplemented by borrowings from the *Ling-wai Tai-ta* and, to a smaller extent, by obsolete material from the *Yu-yang Tsa-tsu*, the *T'ung Tien*[34] and dynastic histories.

Prominent among the countries known vicariously to Chao was Berbera [*Pi-pa-lo*[35] (38)], which he characterized as the home of a Muslim populace (39), of whom a portion were grouped in four departmental cities[36] (40) and the rest were scattered through the countryside in warring villages, where they followed a pastoral mode of life. Their herds were composed of camels and sheep (*mien-yang*[37]), and their normal food was camel meat and milk, supplemented by baked cakes (41). This account certainly implies the salient characteristics of Somali nomads (42), but Chao Ju-kua, as would be expected of a Superintendent of Maritime Trade, was better informed about the commercial products of the region than about the ethnic background of the inhabitants. Berbera did, in fact, feed three important commodities, ivory, ambergris (43), and rhinoceros horn (44), into the Arab-dominated trade of the Indian Ocean. Chao added appreciably to Tuan Ch'eng-shih's account of the first of these commodities. African tusks, he noted, with their delicate streaking on a pure white ground, were superior to any from Asia. Large specimens from the Berbera coast might exceed 100 *chin* in weight.[38] As this is by no means excessive for good African ivory, which *averages* about 150 pounds, it appears that some of the Berbera tusks at least were obtained from the small *Elephas africanus orleansi* [Somali = *marodi*] (45). Other products recorded by Chao included puchuk (46), sweet oil of storax (47), tortoise shell and myrrh (48), while he listed the camel-crane [ostrich (49)], the giraffe (50) and the zebra (51) among the local fauna. His concluding remarks noted that the tribesmen from time to time[39] hunted this game with 'medicated arrows'[40]. G. Ferrand (52) and G. Révoil (53) described such hunts with the use of poisoned arrows late in the nineteenth century in terms almost identical with those of the Chinese and, moreover, made the point, which escaped Chao, that noble Somali do not themselves hunt, but delegate that privilege to outcaste *sab* or adopted slaves. Chao was, however, correct in regarding hunting as a seasonal activity. Specifically it is all but restricted to the dry season, when both game and tribesmen gather round water-holes, when other food tends to be depleted, and when caravans are too infrequent to provide profitable loot.

The *Chu-fan-chih* (*1*, 59-60) also incorporates a notice of a country under the orthography *Chung-li*[41] which, as far as I have been able to ascertain, is a *hapax legomenon* in Chinese topographical writing. The *chung* in this name has sometimes been held to represent the sound *zəndʒ* [Arabic.[42] Cf. Persian[43]], by which medieval Arabs referred to negroes in general (54). Phonetically this is just possible, but it is probably significant that elsewhere Chao Ju-kua apparently transcribed this sound by *ts'eng*[44] (55), which is phonologically more acceptable. So far no one has been able to establish the precise location of *Chung-li*, but several items of information discussed below, notably its association with the frankincense trade, leave little doubt that it was situated somewhere on the Horn of Africa. In this connection it is tempting to read *Chung-li* as a not unreasonable transcription of *Shungwaya*, the legendary home of the coastal tribes of the North-eastern Bantu (56). The consensus of tradition, Portuguese documents and early European cartography point to a site for this emporium on the southern Somali coast in the neighbourhood of Pate, but the limits of its territory are completely unknown (57).

In the accounts of his informants Chao discerned a two-class society, which probably reflected at least in part an ethnic duality. On the one hand there were bareheaded and barefooted *hoi polloi* who, 'as they dared not wear jackets, wrapped cloths around themselves' (58); on the other hand there were the *élite*, specifically ministers and the king's courtiers, who 'wore jackets and turbans on their heads as insignia of distinction' (59). Moreover, whereas the former lived in dwellings of thatch and palm fronds, the king's residence was built of large bricks and slabs of stone (60). Cattle, sheep and camels were plentiful, and provided the chief dishes on special occasions (cf. note 41); cakes of baked flour, together with camel and sheep's milk, constituted the every-day fare. Towards the end of spring this was supplemented by 'countless migrant birds which alighted outside the suburbs . . . the inhabitants trapped them in nets for food; their taste was delicious.' At the onset of summer these migrants departed (lit. were interrupted[45]). The bird referred to can hardly have been other than the harlequin quail, *Coturnix delegorguei Delegorgue*, Vög., whose true home is in equatorial Africa but which migrates northward to Somalia when the *gu* rains of May bring an abundance of insect life to the plains. Today these birds are still trapped in thousands in many parts of Africa by means of decoys which call them up through snared runs (61).

The products of *Chung-li* as recorded by Chao Ju-kua afford some confirmation of our proposed location on the Somali coast. Prominent among them was 'the nipple incense' (62), or frankincense, a gum-resin produced by several members of the genus *Boswellia*, all of which are endemic to South Arabia and Somalia. In the latter region both *B. Carterii* and *B. Frereana* occur on the slopes of the maritime range and again farther inland on the plateau. It is interesting to note that, although Chao had a fair idea of the method of extraction of the gum (*2*, 97), knew that it was transported from the Somali coast to the great staples at Murbat, Shihr and Dhufar on the Hadhramaut coast, and was able to describe no less than thirteen commercial grades of frankincense, he was in error in supposing that it was carried to the coast on elephants. Slips such as this serve to remind us that his knowledge of East Africa was at best at second-hand.

Chao Ju-kua was also better informed than his predecessors about the role of the whale in the economy of the East African littoral (63). He noted that although the inhabitants of *Chung-li* made use of its oil in lamps and, mixed with lime, as a means of caulking boats, and although the poorer folk employed its ribs for rafters, its backbone for door-leaves and the vertebrae for mortars, none of them ate its flesh. This is surprising since today the coastal folk prize whale flesh as food, which, incidentally, counts as fish so that it is not necessary to *halal* the creature. Despite this acquaintance with whales, neither Chao nor any other contemporary Chinese author connected them with ambergris. In fact Chao stated explicitly that the provenance of ambergris was unknown: lumps of from 3 to 10 *chin* in weight were either driven onshore by the wind or run across at sea.

Finally Chao interpolated a few remarks on a *shan*[46] that was situated on the confines of Berbera.[47] Duyvendak read this phrase as 'mountains which are contiguous with Berbera' (64). But *shan* in medieval texts sometimes means 'island' and this is the connotation that I believe it probably has in the present instance (65). Among its products as enumerated by Chao was a variety of aloes (66) which he described specifically (*2*, 130) as resembling the tail of a king crab in appearance.[48] This is, in fact, a reasonable description of *Aloe Perryi* (67), a plant endemic to Socotra, which bears its fleshy leaves towards the end of a long stem. From these leaves was expressed the drug known as hepatic aloes. Other products attributed to the *shan* or its neighbouring seas, namely tortoiseshell (68), ambergris (69) and dragon's blood (70), do not conflict with this interpretation. This last was the resin of *Dracaena cinnabari*, Balf. f. (Arabic *damm al-'ahwein*), a tree of some 20-30 feet in height, stands of which clothe the slopes of Jebel Haggier at elevations above 1,000 feet.

Turning his attention southward, Chao Ju-kua was able to provide a sketchy account of the neighbourhood of Zanzibar, which he transcribed as *Ts'eng-pa*[49] (pt. 1, p. 55). Situated in the ocean to the south[-west] of Gujerat (*Hu-ch'a-la*[50]), the country, according to Chao, comprised a succession of forested hill ranges[51] culminating at its western boundary in 'a great mountain' that inevitably suggests itself as Kilimanjaro. Chao correctly observed that temperatures were always high, with no really cool season. It is instructive to note that his Arab informants had apparently told him only of their own co-religionists, so that he described the inhabitants of Zanzibar as of 'Arab [*Ta-shih*[52] (71)] type and following the Arab religion [Islam].' They wound imported, drab-coloured cotton cloths about themselves and wore red leather shoes. Their daily fare consisted of meal, cakes of baked flour and mutton. Local products included ivory, native gold (72) ambergris and sandalwood. This last must have been the product of *Pterocarpus santalinus* or perhaps of some allied species, not of the true sandalwood tree (*Santalum album*), which is confined to parts of southern Asia. In return for these commodities, Gujarati and Arabo-Persian merchants, arriving on the northerly monsoon, traded red cottons (73), white cotton cloth, porcelain (74) and copper.

Both Chao Ju-kua (*1*, 74) and Chou Ch'ü-fei (*3*, 6a) described another country 'in the sea to the south-west and adjacent to a large island where there are regularly found great *p'eng*[53] birds which, when they take to the air, momentarily [*i kuei*,[54] an elliptical expression implying "the time needed for the sun to shift the shade on the sundial"] obscure the sun. . . . If a *p'eng* bird encounters [a camel], it swallows it up (75). If one chance to find a feather of the *p'eng*, one can fashion a water-jar from the quill.' This fabulous bird is certainly the *rukh* of medieval romance, about which similar tales were told round all the shores of the Indian Ocean (76), and whose presence sufficiently identifies the large island as Madagascar, the home of the now extinct *Æpyornis* or *rukh* (77). The legendary quills of the *p'eng* have been identified by Ferrand as a fanciful interpretation of the *langanå*, a Malgash name for a large bamboo much used by the coastal tribes of Madagascar as water vessels (78).

The mainland territory which led Chao Ju-kua and Chou Ch'ü-fei into these asides was known to the Chinese as *K'un-lun-ts'eng-ch'i*[55] (79), a name that itself deserves a brief excursus. The term *K'un-lun* has a fascinating but obscure history. It seems that originally it denoted the arched vault of the heavens and was etymologically associated with the word for 'chaos'.[56] When it first appeared as a place-name in Chinese literature it was applied to the mighty K'un-lun mountains of Tibet which, to the Chinese

L

of the Chin dynasty [A.D. 265-420 (80)] and later, were still half legendary and an appropriate locale for the domain of the Hsi-wang-mu (p. 139). Nor is it surprising that Buddhism, with its elusive mythological topography, should have availed itself of the vagueness associated with this place-name, suitably remote but yet of attested authenticity, to identify the K'un-lun with the Anavatapta mountain and the Sumeru in India (81). From these Buddhist conceptions probably derived the East Asian tradition of religious cosmography in which circular maps were centred on Mount K'un-lun (82). With the passage of time the term not unnaturally often came to mean nothing more precise than the peoples of distant and exotic lands, especially those inhabiting the fringe of the Chinese oecumene in South-east Asia. In particular it did duty as a transcription of an ethnonym of type KROM/ PROM/PRUM which, although perhaps best known in the form 'Khmer', occurred widely in peninsular South-east Asia (83), but the term was also pressed into service as an almost standard rendering of nasalized words beginning with an unvoiced velar. Hence we find the Kundur [islands] referred to in this way, as well as the Old Khmer style *kuruṅ*, meaning 'ruler' (*T'ai-p'ing Yü-lan*, 788). In China itself *k'un-lun* seems to have been used as an epithet applicable to dark skins. The priest Tao-an[57] (A.D. 314-85), for instance, although a North Chinese, was known alter-natively as 'the K'un-lun fellow'[58] or 'the lacquered monk'[59] on account of his swarthy features (84), and a brunette consort of Emperor Chien-wen[60] (A.D. 371-2) attracted the sobriquet *k'un-lun* by virtue of her dark complexion (85).

As the Chinese pieced together a coherent geography of the Indian Ocean, they extended the application of *K'un-lun* to include the dark-skinned peoples who lived at the extreme western limits of their known world, that is on the coast of Africa. This usage was perhaps induced, or at least encouraged, by the presence of an ethnonym on the KROM/PROM/PRUM model with which the Chinese had already become familiar in South-east Asia. The linguistic affiliations of this word are unknown, but it passed into Arabic as *Qamar*, meaning 'moon' (later apparently corrupted to *Qumr*[61]), so that we find medieval Arab authors writing of both the Mountains of *Qamar*[62] (where the Nile was supposed to take its rise) and the Island of *Qamar*[63] (86). By Sung times the name *K'un-lun* had become firmly attached to the negro or negroid inhabitants of East Africa whenever they figured in Chinese writings (87).

There is little doubt that the second element in the place-name *K'un-lun-ts'eng-ch'i* was a transcription of *Zanj*, the Arabic term for negroes (88), so that the complete toponym comprised a Chinese term which had come to denote negroes joined to the transcription of an Arab synonym. In this connection it has been suggested that the element *zanj* may also be at the origin of another toponym, *Seng-chih*.[64] *Chih* is, in fact, a frequent mislection for *ch'i*[65] (89), a homophone of the graph[66] used by Chao Ju-kua to represent *ts'eng-ch'i* above. As early as A.D. 613 Javanese envoys presented four *Seng-chih* slaves as tribute to the imperial court, and a century later emissaries from *Śrī Vijaya* offered two dwarf women, together with two *Seng-chih* women (90). It is tempting to think that we have here a record of China's first encounter with Africans who, as in so many other parts of the world, made their début in the role of slaves. Whether or not this argument be accepted, both Chou Ch'ü-fei and Chao Ju-kua leave us in no doubt that the East African coast was a source of slaves. In the *Ling-wai Tai-ta*, under the rubric *K'un-lun-ts'eng-ch'i*, Chou remarked that 'many savages, with lacquer-black bodies and frizzy hair, were enticed by [offers of] food and then captured', a version of incidents mentioned in Idrīsī's description of the Zanzibar coast, where Arabs of 'Umān were reputed to entice children into slavery by offering them dates (91). When we next meet these unfortunate negroes they are employed as door-keepers far away in China, whither they have been shipped as one of the costliest wares of Arab merchants. The *P'ing-chou K'o-t'an*,[67] compiled by Chu Yü[68] in 1119, contains this description of them (*Shuo-k'u* edition, p. 7b):

In Kuang-chou (Canton) most of the wealthy people rear[69] devil-slaves (92), who are very strong and can lift [weights of] several hundred *chin*. Their language and tastes are unintelligible [to the Chinese]. Their nature is simple and they do not abscond. They are also called 'wild men' (93). They are as black as ink, their lips are red, their teeth white, and their hair curly and yellow [*sic* (94)]. There are both males and females [among these creatures (the numerary adjunct for animals is used here)]. They live on islands beyond the sea. In their natural state they eat their food raw. If, in captivity, they are fed on cooked food, after several days they suffer from diarrhoea, which is called 'changing the bowels'.[70] For this reason they sometimes fall ill and die. If they do not die, one can rear them, and after a long time, they begin to understand people's language (i.e. Chinese), although they themselves cannot speak it. There is one kind of wild men [living] near the sea, who can enter the water without closing their eyes. They are called *K'un-lun* slaves.

tr. Duyvendak (1949), mod.

In another place Chu Yü noted that these slaves were employed on shipboard to caulk leaking seams below the water-line from the outside, as they were expert swimmers who did not need to close their eyes under water.

One other African kingdom of the Sung period merits brief discussion here. In 1071 (fourth year of *Hsi-ning*) a tribute (95) mission reached the Chinese court from the country of *Ts'eng-t'an*,[71] as a result of which a description of this state was incorporated in the official Sung history (96). The exact site of this merchant city, which the Chinese text locates twenty *li* (97) from the sea, has not been established, but E. H. Schafer has suggested that *Ts'eng-t'an* may represent an original form something like *Zangistan* [the country of the *Zanj*' (98)]. Such a form must almost certainly have underlain the *Zanghezin* (and allied forms) which early cartographers located on the Tanganyika mainland (99) in contradistinction to the *Zamzibar* (etc.) of the islands. According to the Chinese, the ruler of the country had adopted the style *A-mei-lo A-mei-lan*, which Hirth and Rockhill have restored as Persian *Amir-i-amiran*[72] (100), together with an almost certainly spurious dynastic genealogy extending over 500 years. Stronger testimony to the stability of this state is the record that its officers were paid official Government salaries and, particularly, that trade was conducted with the mandatory aid of a Government-issued coinage, consisting of three parts of a gold-and-copper alloy to a fourth part of silver. It has sometimes been claimed that the only sub-Saharan African state to strike its own coins in the Middle Ages was Kilwa (101), but this port, whether located at Kilwa Kisiwani, Songo Mnara or elsewhere in that neighbourhood, does not meet the exigency of an inland location demanded by the Chinese evidence.

The rest of the passage throws a little light on the ethnology and economy of the port. The wealthier classes wore turbans of *yüeh[-no]*[73] cloth (102) and dressed in robes of flowered brocade or *po-tieh*[74] cloth (103). Their speech sounded similar to that of the Arabs. Fish constituted an important item in the people's diet, and they partook of three main beverages, *mi*[75] (104), *sha*[76] (105) and *hua*[77] (106). Padi, millet and wheat (107) comprised the products of the district. The same text includes a list of exports including puchuk, dragon's blood, myrrh, borax (108), asafoetida (109), frankincense, pearls (110) and glass, but most of these commodities seem to have been re-exports rather than strictly local products. The drugs are characteristic of both South Arabia and the Somali coasts. Borax, an evaporation product of alkaline lakes, also indicates a predominantly arid climate, while pearls are fished in the Red Sea.

There is no reason to believe that the Sung Chinese acquired any part of their knowledge of the geography of East Africa from personal experience. As far as we can tell they learned it at second-hand from Arabo-Persian merchants and sailors, and it suffered from the defects common to information obtained in this fashion. But although emphasis was often misplaced, the miraculous was restricted to a few forgivable instances and, generally speaking, the information was factual and reliable. Nor must we underestimate the difficulties facing a sophisticated Chinese of the Sung period, especially one lacking first-hand knowledge of any country beyond his own frontiers, who set out to write about a country and a culture on the far side of the world.

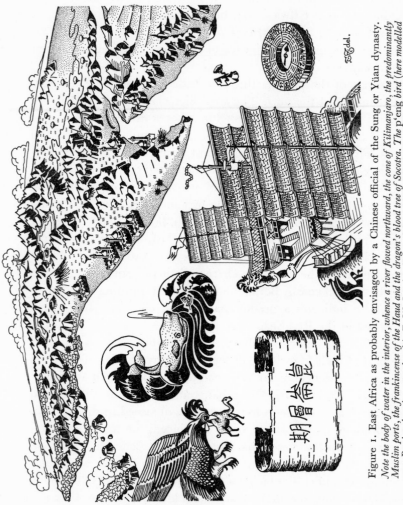

Figure 1. East Africa as probably envisaged by a Chinese official of the Sung or Yüan dynasty. Note the body of water in the interior, whence a river flowed northward, the cone of Kilimanjaro, the predominantly Muslim ports, the frankincense of the Haud and the dragon's blood tree of Socotra. The p'eng bird (here modelled on a Persian drawing reproduced in E. W. Lane's edition of the Arabian Nights) and the whale both featured in Chinese accounts of the coast. The representation of the junk follows contemporary drawings, and the direction indicator approximates to a bronze floating-compass of the Ming period, as illustrated by Wang Chen-to (1951)

THE YÜAN PERIOD

The next Chinese topographer to mention East Africa was Wang Ta-yüan.[78] This author travelled in the South Seas during the thirteen-thirties and -forties but, needless to say, had no first-hand experience of Africa. His *Tao-i Chih-lioh*,[79] compiled in 1349, is a description in 100 sections of ninety-nine countries, ports and noteworthy localities ranging from the Moluccas to Arabia and, in at least one instance, the African coast (ff. 17 verso-18 recto). This latter country, situated to the south-west of the *Tājik* lands (note 71), was known to Wang as *Ts'eng-yao-lo*.[80] 'There were no trees along the coast, the soil was mostly saline and the fields infertile, so that there were few cereals of any kind. Instead [the inhabitants] grew mainly yams.' This description accords fairly well with the southern Somali coast, as does Wang's remark that '[the inhabitants] net both birds and beasts for food'. Puccioni, for example, has described the use of nets by Hober, Iantar and Helai in the hunting of dik-dik (111). Nevertheless, the *Tao-i chih-lioh kuang-cheng*[81] amends *yao* to *pa*,[82] thus transcribing the name as *Ts'eng-pa-lo*, which Rockhill construes as a version of Zanzibar (112). This interpretation is possible but the phonetic equivalence of even the amended version falls short of that achieved by Chao Ju-kua more than a century before. On the other hand, the mention of red sandalwood as one of the chief products of the country bespeaks a location in the neighbourhood of Zanzibar, or farther south, rather than on the Somali coast. Other exports included ivory, ambergris, native gold, sugar-cane and duck-bill copper sulphate (113), but it is impossible to be certain whether all or any of these were indeed local products or re-exports. The trade goods that Wang Ta-yüan recommended for this coast were ivory boxes, trade silver, coloured satins and, above all, rice. As a result of the inhospitable environment which prohibited cereal cultivation, 'if any ship voyaging thither in search of trade carry a cargo of rice, it makes very large profits'.

One other of Wang Ta-yüan's toponyms may also relate to East Africa. From Quilon, 'riding the wind with all sails set, within two months one reaches the country of *Kan-mai-li*,[83] famous for its sewn-boats designed specifically for the transport of horses. [Skin bags?] of frankincense are stowed very compactly in the bottom of the hold[84] and several hundred head of horses stabled above.' The reference to sewn boats is reminiscent of the craft[85] that the *Periplus* (§ 15 and 16) associated with *Rhapta*,[86] the last trading port of the continent of *Azania*, some two days' sail beyond the island of *Menuthias*[87] (114). Consequently Rockhill (1915, 623-4) tentatively identified *Kan-mai-li* with the Comoro Islands. The name may very well incorporate the element *qamar/qumr* discussed above, but if so, why should it not refer to Madagascar, the *Qamar* of the medieval Arabs, which Yāqūt in his *Mu'jam* (Wüstenfeld's edition, *4*, 172) characterized as the largest island in the Sea of the *Zanj*, and which was so described and depicted by early European travellers and cartographers (115)? However, the reference to horses would seem to relate to the Somali country rather than to any more southerly region, an impression strengthened by the inclusion of the so-called puchuk (116) and ambergris among the products of the region. It is, moreover, unlikely that frankincense would have been available in such large quantities outside the Arabian or Somali peninsulas. All other commodities available in *Kan-mai-li*, Wang noted, derived ultimately from *Fo-lang*,[88] the country of the Franks. Despite his scrappy treatment of this emporium, Wang Ta-yüan leaves us in no doubt as to its importance in the trade of the Indian Ocean. 'Generally speaking, no ships carry out with them goods one-tenth as valuable as those they bring back.' The trade commodities which brought the best returns were cloves (117), nutmegs (118), musk (119), sapanwood (120), blue satins and floral prints from Su-chou and Hang-chou, red beads, porcelain jars and iron bars.

Despite the lively intercourse between East and West which obtained during the century or so of Mongol dominance over Asia, and which must have brought to China a great deal of new factual information, it cannot be claimed that Wang Ta-yüan's brief and ambiguous references to East Africa add anything of significance to the account of Chao Ju-kua. This is the more surprising when we remember that on a map incorporating data from the period round about 1300 Chu Ssŭ-pen[89] (1273-1337) depicted in unambiguous outline the triangular shape of Africa (121). Working beyond the authoritative restraints of the Ptolemaic tradition, the Chinese cartographer was under no compulsion to distend southern Africa in an easterly direction, as was the custom on contemporary European and Arab maps. A large river flowing northward through the length of the continent was presumably meant to represent the Nile, and an extensive body of water in the interior was probably inspired by tales of the African lakes. In the matter of place-names we cannot pretend that Chu Ssŭ-pen was well informed (122). Zanzibar (*Sang-ku-pa*:[90] the *ku* presumably deriving from the gutteral remarked on above, p. 156), the only name which can be identified with certainty, was relegated to a position on the west coast. Farther south on the same coast *Che-pu-lu-ma*[91] may have incorporated a transcription of Arabic *jebel*,[92] meaning 'mountain'. In the eastern half of the continent the only name on the mainland was *Ha-na-i-ssŭ-chin*,[93] the ford of *Hanais*, which W. Fuchs suggests – though without conviction – may possibly be a transcription of the Abyssinian *Abai*, applied to the Blue Nile. Off the east coast was located an island labelled *Ti-pa nu*.[94] The first two characters are apparently a transcription of the Arabic *dīb*[95] (123), so that the legend can be read as 'Island slaves', a phrase reminiscent of the devil-slaves discussed above.

In 1402 two maps incorporating much the same information (though belonging to a different technical tradition) and compiled by the Chinese cartographers Li Tse-min[96] (*fl.* 1330) and Ch'ing-Chün[97] (1328-92) respectively (124), were combined in a single map by Li Hui[98] and Ch'üan Chin,[99] both working in Korea. A copy of this map, entitled *Map of the territories of the one world and the capitals of the countries in successive ages* (125) and dating from *c.* 1500, has been described by T. Ogawa (126) and S. Aoyama (127). I have not seen this map nor a reproduction of it, but Joseph Needham (1959, 555) reports that there are about thirty-five largely unidentified place-names on the south-pointing triangular continent of Africa. Currently W. Fuchs is engaged in a study of the western sectors of this map.

THE MING PERIOD

With the Ming dynasty we come to the first authenticated voyages of Chinese missions to the African coast. The desire of the imperial court for foreign luxuries, coupled with the need to re-establish the prestige of the Empire abroad, induced the Yung-lo Emperor, third of the Ming dynasty, to dispatch a series of naval expeditions to the Indian Ocean. Between 1405 and 1433 at least seven fleets sailed southward and westward, of which both the fifth and the sixth, in 1417-19 and 1421-2 respectively, reached as far as the African coast. All were under the direction of a Muslim court official named Cheng-Ho. The official reports of these voyages were subsequently destroyed and even the *Veritable Records of the Ming Dynasty* distorted, but descriptions of a few African countries have been preserved in the *Ming Shih* and, particularly important for our present purpose, in a work by Fei-Hsin, a junior officer in the entourage of Cheng-Ho. This book, compiled by Fei-Hsin[100] in 1436, is entitled *Hsing-ch'a Sheng-lan*[101] [*Triumphant vision of the starry raft* (128), that is, a ship carrying an imperial ambassador] and includes notices of three African countries. Fei-Hsin himself never ventured much beyond the Persian Gulf, certainly not to the African coast, but unlike his predecessors, he did acquire his information from *Chinese* who had been that far.

In order to convey some flavour of the original, there follows a full translation of Fei-Hsin's description of Brava, which appears under the orthography *Pu-la-wa*[7] (edition of *c.* 1450, folios 4 verso-5 recto).

Going southward from *Pieh-li-lo*[102] (129) in *Hsi-lan*[103] [Ceylon], one can reach this country [of Brava] in twenty-one days and nights. It is a continuation of the mountainous land of *Mu-ku-tu-shu*[6] [Mogadishu] and borders the coast [of the Azanian Sea]. The town walls are built of piled rocks, the houses of ashlars. The locality is devoid of herbs and trees, and the countryside presents an extensive saline waste. There is a salt lake into which one has only to throw branches and trees and when, after a period of time, one lifts them out, they have become covered with white salt. The customs [of the people] are simple. They do not till the soil but support themselves by fishing. [Both] men and women dress their hair in rolls. Some wear a short skirt, others wrap themselves in a length of cotton [cloth]. The married women wear gold coins in their ears and pendant fringes around their necks. [Of vegetables] they have only onions and garlic, but no brinjals (130). Local products include *ma-ka* beasts[104] (131), which resemble musk-deer; *hua-fu-lu*[105] [zebras], which are like piebald donkeys; leopards[106] (132), deer, [107] rhinoceroses, myrrh, frankincense, ambergris, ivory and camels. The goods traded [there] include gold, silver, satins, silks, rice, beans and chinaware. The ruler [of *Pu-la-wa*], in appreciation of the Imperial bounty, offered local products as tribute at the Chinese court.

Fei-Hsin's sections relating to Juba (folio 5 recto) and Mogadishu (folio 5 recto et verso) are cast in a similar mould. The port cities, with their walls of piled rock and their houses of cut stone, are typical of those which archaeology is bringing to light at sites ranging from Zeila to Songo Mnara (133). The four- and five-storey houses of Mogadishu attracted particular attention. Beyond the towns, so far as the Chinese were concerned, there stretched an unattractive, and largely uncultivated, expanse of country characterized by yellowish-red soils. Farther inland, 'towards the foot of the mountain [the granite upland stretching from the Shebelle basin to Bur Meldak in the Juba valley] the country is a desert of brown soil and stones [the *arra gudud* of Somali physiography]' (134). The use of *noria* for raising water[108] was recorded at both Juba and Mogadishu. Fishing was an important activity, apparently mainly among the poorer folk, and in Brava at least seems to have been the basis of the economy (135). Some rather precise notions of the dress and appearance of the inhabitants of these ports have filtered into the Chinese accounts. In both Brava and Juba, for example, both sexes allegedly wore their hair in rolls (136), whereas in Mogadishu this style was restricted to the men, and the women adopted a sort of chignon, at the same time smearing a glistening yellow varnish on the crown of the head.[109] Clothes seem to have consisted of short skirts or lengths of cotton cloth wound about the body, and for both Juba and Mogadishu there is a reference to the use of hoods for outside wear. Perhaps the most interesting of the comments is the ethnocentric statement that the natives were excitable and obstinate,[110] a remark which might have come — as it often did — from the lips of later colonial administrators in Somaliland (137).

The Chinese court was always intrigued by strange animals, which were conceived of as beneficent cosmic creations born of the superabundant goodness generated by an harmonious reign (138), so that it is not surprising that Fei-Hsin included a list of the large Somali game animals in his account. To those enumerated under Brava should be added lions and ostriches in the hinterland of Juba. Other local products included frankincense, myrrh, ivory, ambergris and golden amber (139); this last was probably copal, a gum which is found buried in recent sands on the East African coast, and which is usually lighter in colour and clearer than amber. Recommended trade goods included a variety of silks, porcelain, pepper, rice and, in the case of Juba, vermilion. Finally, there are notices in the official Ming history that Juba dispatched frequent 'tribute' missions to China during the reign of the Yung-lo Emperor and that Mogadishu sent an embassy in 1416 (140).

These three descriptions provide no more than a glimpse of conditions on the East African coast during the early years of the fifteenth century, but they are supplemented by a set of combined marine charts and sailing directions which are believed to show the tracks of the Ming fleets between 1405 and 1433. These charts were incorporated in a work entitled *Wu-pei-chih (Notes on Military Preparation)*, written before 1621 by a certain Mao Yüan-i,[111] and offered to the throne in 1628 (141). Their African material is to be found on folios 19 recto to 20 verso of Chapter 240. The chart itself takes the form of a cartogram which adopts the ancient device of running the coast as a continuous, irregular line horizontally across the page, thus compressing several divergent sailing tracks within a frame of manageable dimensions. Estuaries are represented by sinuous indentations in the coastline, and coastal hills and offshore islands are depicted in crude perspective. The scale varies to suit the convenience of the cartographer, but along the East African coast it averages about 120 miles to the inch.

The Chinese versions of identified toponyms on the East African coast, together with their present-day forms, are listed below in order from north to south:

Hsü-to-ta[112]   Perhaps Arabic *Suk Qāṭir* = 'dragon's-blood mart', possibly a rationalized corruption of some Prākrit form of the Skr. [*Dvīpa*] *Suk-hādhāra* that was attested by Agatharchides of Cnidus in the second century B.C.

called by foreigners

Su-ku-ta-la[113]   Socotra.

Ha-pu-ni[114]   *Opone*[115] of the *Periplus Maris Erythraei*, §13; *Ḥāfūnā*[116] of Ibn Saʿīd (folio 3 recto); *Khāfūnā*[117] (erroneously) and *Jāfūnā*[118] (erroneously) in Abū'l-Fidā' (*Taqwīn al-buldān*, 2, 206) and Masʿūdī (*Kitāb murūj al-dhahab*, 1 232) respectively; present-day [Ras] Hāfūn. It has been suggested that this may be the *Poen-at* of Egyptian inscriptions and the *Panchaia* of Virgil's *Georgics*, 2, 139[119] [Schoff, W. F. (1912), *The periplus of the Erythraean Sea*, 87]. On eighteenth-century European maps this name was often rendered as *Opin*.

Mu-ku-tu-shu[120]   Mogadishu.

Shih-la-wa[121]

an obvious mislection for

Pu-la-wa[122]   Brava.

Man-pa-sa[123]   Mombasa.

Men-fei-chʿih

probably a mislection for

Men-fei-i   *Monfiyeh*, an older form of present-day Mafia.

Ko-ta-Kan   possibly Kitoka, but if so the legend is misplaced with respect to both Malindi and Mafia.

Ma-lin-ti[124]   Malindi.

There are several other legends and unidentified place-names on the African section of the *Wu-pei-chih* cartogram, as well as directions for both coastal and ocean sailing. Not the least interesting of these latter is a voyage of 150 watches[125] (142) direct from Ceylon to Mogadishu. Apart from Duyvendak's introductory remarks in *Monumenta cartographica Africae et Ægypti* (143), this section of the chart has been little studied (144). From a superficial

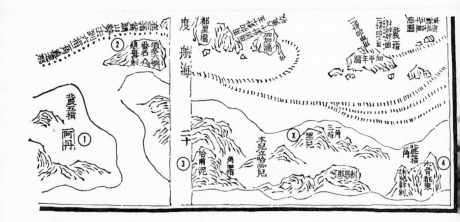

inspection it would seem to have been compiled hastily, possibly from a corrupt source. Recognizable errors include careless copying of the place-name *Pu-la-wa* and the omission of the last character of *Mu-ku-tu-shu* in the sailing directions. In addition Malindi is misplaced with respect to Mombasa. I have found no evidence in support of P. Pelliot's suggestion (145) that the chart was based on an Arab prototype [in any case, no Arab chart of the period has so far been discovered and such materials as are available suggest that Arab nautical lore was mainly memorized, often in doggerel verse (146)]; but there is a strong indication that the *information* incorporated in the chart had an Arab provenance. Important place-names are accompanied by the altitude of the Pole Star in *chih*,[126] a direct translation of the Arabic *iṣba'*[127] (147). This practice was absent in the more easterly sectors of the chart (148), which distinguishes the Afro-Arabian folios from those of the Bay of Bengal and South-east Asia, where, although both Chinese and Arab sailing directions appear to derive from a common original, there are few, if any, traces of mutual borrowing. This is to be expected. In each realm the Chinese mariners relied on informed local opinion: in the East on Malay seamanship, in the West on Arab nautical lore.

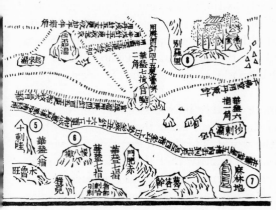

Figure 2. Folios 19 recto—20 verso of chap, 240 of the *Wu-pei-chih* (*c.* 1628), depicting part of Arabia and the African coast from Cape Guardafui to Malindi. *Circled Arabic numerals denote the following toponyms: 1. 'Aden. 2. Socotra. 3. [Ras] Hāfūn. 4. Mogadishu. 5. Brava. 6. Mombasa. 7. Malindi. 8. Belligam (Ceylon). X denotes the ethnonym 'the Blacks', presumably a translation of ez-Zanj. For a general description of this chart see p. 164*

It will have become apparent from the foregoing remarks that Chinese knowledge of East Africa prior to the age of Western exploration compared favourably with that possessed by contemporary European peoples. In part this reflected the intensity of intercourse between Europe or China on the one hand and the Muslim world of the Middle East on the other. Whereas the latter was separated from Western Europe by an ideo-religious barrier, across the eastern half of Eurasia Arabs, Persians and other Muslims not only travelled freely back and forth but also on occasion achieved high office in the Chinese bureaucracy. In fact, it is hardly an exaggeration to say that the Chinese viewed the far south-western fringe of their oecumene through Arabo-Persian spectacles. The episodic and fragmentary knowledge obtained in this way was perhaps formalized under the influence of Persian astronomers, particularly the Marāghah astronomer Jamāl al-Dīn, who brought to Peking in 1267 a terrestrial globe that probably depicted *inter alia* the western shores of the Indian Ocean (149). It is interesting to note that, in the earlier centuries of this period, when the Chinese were wholly dependent on Arabs and Persians for their knowledge of the African coast, their geographical coverage was considerably more extensive than that which accrued from the first-hand observations of Cheng-Ho's captains. Although some information relating to Berbera had filtered into China as early as the ninth century A.D., that coast was ignored in the descriptive reports derived from the voyages of the Ming fleets; and although Zanzibar, and possibly regions farther south, featured in the accounts of Chao Ju-kua and Wang Ta-yüan, Fei-Hsin made no mention of the coast beyond Malindi.

The Chinese were more reliably informed about the environment and ethnology of the African coast than they were about society in that part of the world. This is not surprising in view of the attitude of conscious superiority that they adopted towards other nations. The formal patterns of gregarious existence devised by unclothed tribal peoples ignorant of the Confucian proprieties could hardly be matters of intellectual concern to members of the Chinese mandarinate, who regarded respect for the five relationships as part of the genetic make-up of the *chün-tzŭ*. As far as the texts permit an opinion, the Chinese seem to have considered African society to be wholly unstructured. Yet these random jottings culled from Chinese literature do reflect something of East African realities, even though seen through – a neologism coined on traditionalistic principles – double filters (150). There was, too, reason for a material interest in that ragged selvedge of the world, whence came not only devil-slaves to grace the portals of the stately homes of Ch'üan-chou but also the *chi-lin*, 'the noblest form of animal creation, the emblem of the highest good, the incarnate essence of the five elements' (Ts'ai Yung), whose manifestation signified a reign of perfect benevolence and felicity.

NOTES AND REFERENCES

Note: Superscript letters, e.g.ᵃ, refer to names and terms transliterated in these notes and references. See p. 186.

1. Reproduced in *Tanganyika Notes and Records, 3* (1937), opp. p. 1.

2. HIRTH, F. (1890) *Chinesische Studien*, 46-7. This ludicrous episode is neatly summarized by J.J.L. Duyvendak (1949) in his published lectures given before the University of London, *China's discovery of Africa*, 6.

3. DE PARAVEY, C. (1853) 'Archéologie primitive. Traditions primitives conservées dans les hiéroglyphes des anciens peuples . . .', *Annales de philosophie chrétienne*.

4. FORKE, A. (1904) 'Mu Wang und die Königin von Saba', *Mitteilungen des Seminars für Orientalische Sprachen*, 7, 117-72. For comments on the term *K'un-lun* see p. 153.

5. SCHWARZ, E.H.L. (1938) 'The Chinese connection with Africa', *Journ. Roy. As. Soc. Bengal*, Letters *4*, 175-93.

6. Chap. 28, pt. 2, ff. 32*a* and *b* [*Ssŭ-pu pei-yao* edition].

7. HERRMANN, A. (1913) 'Ein Seeverkehr zwischen Abessinien und Süd-China zu Beginn unserer Zeitrechnung', *Zeitschrift der Gesellschaft für Erdkunde zu Berlin*, 553-61.

8. Including, in addition to Herrmann, Paul Pelliot, Berthold Laufer, Gabriel Ferrand, Gordon Luce, Fujita Toyohachi, R. Hennig and J.J.L. Duyvendak: details in Wheatley (1957), 'Possible references to the Malay Peninsula' in 'The Annals of the Former Han', *J. Malayan Branch Roy. As. Soc., 30*, 115-21.

9. PELLIOT, P. (1915) '[Li-kien, autre nom du Ta-ts'in', *T'oung Pao, 16*, 690-1 and (1926) 'Les anciens rapports entre l'Egypte et l'Extrême-Orient', *Comptes rendus du Congrès international de Géographie, 5*, 21-2], for example, has claimed to recognize the name of Alexandria in both *Li-hsüan*ᵃ [*Shih Chi*, Chap. 123, p. 4, Ku Chieh-kang's edition, and *Wei-Lüeh*,ᵇ quoted in commentary in *San Kuo Chih*, Chap. 30; but variously as *Li-kan*ᶜ (*Ch'ien Han Shu*, Chap. 96A, p. 27*b*, Wang Hsien-ch'ien's edition) and *Li Chien* ᵈ (*Hou Han Shu*, Chap. 88 and *Chin Shu*, Chap. 97)] and *Hsien-tu*ᵉ [*Wei Lüeh*,ᶠ quoted at end of Chap. 30 of *San-Kuo Chih*. Cf. (1921) 'Sur les anciens itinéraires chinois', *J. asiatique, 172*, 145]. With a rather greater degree of probability, Friedrich Hirth has also identified the [*Wu-*]*ch'ih-san*ᵍ of the *Wei Lüeh* with the same city (*China and the Roman Orient*, 1885, 182).

10. The *Yu-yang Tsa-tsu* was published in the *Chin-tai Pi-shu*ʰ by Mao Chin,ⁱ who lived from 1598 to 1657, but the antiquity of its substance is guaranteed by the inclusion of an abridged extract in the *Hsin T'ang Shu* (Chap. 221B,

M

p. 13*b*: Chin-ling edition), completed in 1060. Mao Chin's edition comprises a nominal twenty chapters with a ten-chapter supplement. An edition of 1608 by Li Yün-hao[j] was reprinted in both the *Hu-pei Hsien Cheng I-shu*[k] and the *Ssŭ-pu Ts'ung-k'an*.[l] A fragmentary version in only two chapters is reproduced in the *I-yüan Chün-hua*,[m] the *Lung-wei Pi-shu*,[n] the *Shuo K'u*[o] and the *T'ang-t'ai Ts'ung-shu*,[p] and an abridged edition is included in the *Shuo-fu*.[q] Hirth also mentions a fairly reliable edition in Chang Hai-p'eng's[r] collection *Hsüeh-chin T'ao-yüan*[s] of 1805 [*J. Amer. Orient. Soc.*, *30*, 17-18. See also Duyvendak, *China's discovery of Africa*, 13 and Pelliot, 'Autour d'une traduction sanscrite du Tao Tö King', *T'oung Pao*, vol *13* (1912), 373-5].

11. *Vide* HIRTH, F. (1909-10) 'The mystery of Fu-lin', *J. Amer. Orient. Soc.*, *30*, 18-19.

12. As most authors have done previously, I am locating the *Malao* of the *Periplus Maris Erythraei* on the site of present-day Berbera on the basis of the diagnostic feature of the anchorage, 'an open roadstead, sheltered by a spit protruding from the east'—(*Periplus* § 8). It is not certain when the name *Berbera* was first used, but it appears[u] in the *Periplus* § 2-12 (material from first half of third century A.D.) where, significantly, the Emporium and Cape of Perfumes[v] (C. Guardafui) were located 'at the very end of the Berbera coast toward the east' (§ 12). Ptolemy's Barbaric Gulf,[w] by contrast, apparently lay beyond the Cape of Perfumes (Bk. 4, Chap. 8). Arab authors varied in their opinions as to the limits of Berbera.[x] Mas'ūdī (*Kitāb murūj al-dhahab*, Bk. 3, Chap. 33, 2) regarded the inhabitants of this region as basically a tribe of *Zanj* (note 55) with a strong admixture of Abyssinian blood, a point of view later adopted by Yāqūt (Wüstenfeld's edition, *4*, 602). To Abū'l-Fidā' (*Taqwīn al-buldān*, 159) Berbera was also a country of the *Zanj*. Ibn Baṭṭūṭa described Zeila as 'the city (sc. capital) of the *Barbara*'— [GIBB, H.A.R. (1962) *The Travels of Ibn Baṭṭūṭa*, Vol. 2, 373]. Generally speaking, Arab authors seem to have regarded *Barbara* as synonymous with the Hamitic tribes of the Horn. Cf. Ibn Khaldūn: 'To the south of Zeila on the western coast of the Indian Ocean are the villages of Berbera, which extend one after the other all along the southern coast [of the Indian Ocean] to the end of the sixth section. There, to the east, the country of the *Zanj* adjoins them' [ROSENTHAL, F. (1958) *The Muqaddimah*, Vol. 1, 123].

13. LEWIS, I.M. (1955) *Peoples of the Horn of Africa*, passim; PAULITSCHKE, P. (1888, second edition) *Beiträge zur Ethnographie und Anthropologie der Somâl, Galla und Harari*, passim and (1893-6) *Ethnographie Nordost-Afrikas*, 2 vols.; and DRAKE-BROCKMAN, R.E. (1912) *British Somaliland*. A practice similar to that mentioned by Tuan Ch'eng-shih is illustrated in SIMOONS, F.J. (1961) *Eat not this flesh*, fig. 6; MURDOCK, G.P. (1959) *Africa: its peoples and their culture history*, 334; and JENSEN, E. (1959) *Altvölker Süd-Äthiopiens*, Tafel 37, 2.

14. MURDOCK, *Africa*, Chaps. 2, 41 and 42.

15. WERNER, A. (1914) 'The Galla of the East Africa Protectorate', *J. Anthropological Soc. 13*; DE SALVIAC, M. (1901) *Les Galla*. Huntingford, G.W.B. (1955) *The Galla of Ethiopia* also has some pertinent information.

15a. Since this paper was written H. S. Lewis has re-interpreted the available evidence in an attempt to show that, although both Somali and Galla entered the Horn from the south-west, the Somali expansion preceded that of the Galla, and the Galla have never occupied more of Somaliland than they do at present ['Historical problems in Ethiopia and the Horn of Africa,' *Annals of the New York Academy of Sciences* (1962), *96*, 504-511]. Persuasive though his arguments are in the context of the strictly African evidence, they are not easily reconciled with the Chinese account, for they imply that the Galla never occupied the Berbera coast, and leave unsolved the problem as to who were the blood-letting folk that occupied that area in the ninth century A.D. On the other hand, the hypothesis put forward by I. M. Lewis [op. cit.] and supported by G. P. Murdock [op. cit.] does allow the Galla to occupy the Berbera coast at that time. However, the matter is still far from clear and we can only conclude with a *non liquet*.

16. Chap. 221B, f. 13 verso [Chin-ling edition].y

17. HIRTH, F. (1909-10) 'Early Chinese notices of East African Territories', *J. Amer. Orient. Soc., 30*, 47-9; and HIRTH, F. and ROCKHILL, W.W. (1911) *Chau Ju-kua*, 129.

18. *China's discovery of Africa*, 13-14.

19. KENTARO YAMADA (1955-6) 'A short history of ambergris by the Arabs and Chinese in the Indian Ocean', *Report of the Institute of World Economics, 8*, 1-26 and *11*, 1-32; and WHEATLEY, P. (1959) 'Geographical notes on some commodities involved in Sung Maritime trade', *J. Malayan Branch Roy. As. Soc., 32*, 125-30.

20. Chap. 221B, p. 13*a* [Chin-ling edition. This history was compiled in 1061]. Under this orthography it might be disputed whether Malindi was intended, but the same name occurs again in *Ming shih*, Chap. 304, folio 2 verso-3 recto in the form *Ma-lin*,z where it is clearly an apocope of *Ma-lin-ti*,aa the full version of which occurs in Chap. 326, folio 7 verso.

21. *Akhbar Pate*, passim. Copied in 1903 from a MS. written by Muhammad bin Fumo Omar en-Nabhani. Text and translation by WERNER, A. (1915), *J. African Soc., 14*, 148-61, 278-97, 392-413.

22. The aridity of tropical East Africa, located in a latitudinal and geographical situation normally subject to tropical humid conditions, has been described as the most impressive climatic anomaly in the whole continent, and was inevitably a matter for comment by even the least well informed Chinese author (cp. pp. 162 and 163). The causes of this aridity have not

been wholly explained. Although the negative rainfall anomaly extends southward along the coast to Tanganyika it is best developed on the Horn of Africa, nearly all of which appears as being in the dry category of Thornthwaite's 1948 classification. Large tracts of this area are, in fact, desert, from which the ancient name *Azania* [ab] may have been derived (perhaps = 'the desiccated land': cp. Gr. *azaino* [ac] =I am dry).

23. In the *Yu-yang Tsa-tsu*, Chap. 18, f. 9 recto this word occurs as *k'u-mang*, [ad] which Berthold LAUFER recognized as a transliteration of a hypothetical Middle-Persian **kurmang*, whence presumably derived the New-Persian *xurma*. Cp. Neo-Greek [ae] =date. (*Sino-Iranica*, 385.)

24. *China's discovery*, 15.

25. Duyvendak [*ibid.*] has also pointed out that the phrase 'worst of the barbarians' occurs in Chinese literature in connection with two other cases of allegedly incestuous relations among certain tribes. Cp. CHAVANNES, E. and PELLIOT, P. (1911), 'Un traité manichéen retrouvé en Chine,' *J. asiatique*, 156.

26. A good account of the 'female kings' of the Lovedu is contained in KRIGE, E. J. and KRIGE, J. D. (1943), *The realm of a rain-queen*. See also the first author's 'The place of the North-Eastern Sotho in the South Bantu complex,' *Africa*, 2 (1938), 265-293. For statements on queenship generally in sub-Saharan Africa and for bibliographical materials consult MURDOCK, G. P. (1959), *Africa*, passim.

27. *Hsü Wen-hsien T'ung-k'ao* [af] (compiled by Chi Huang [ag] in 1747), Chap. 14, 144, col. 3—145, col. 1.

28. LI HSIN-CHUAN, [ah] *Chien-yen Ch'ao-yeh Tsa-chi* [ai], Pt. 1, Chap. 15, 17.

29. *Sung Shih*, Chap. 186, folios 15-16 [Chekiang Printing Office edition, 1883] and *Sung Hui-yao*, [aj] *Yüeh-hai Kuan-chih*, Chap. 2. [ak]

30. On this topic see JITSUZO KUWABARA (1923) *So-matsu no Teikyo-shihaku, Saiiki-jin Ho Ju-ko no Shiseki*. The substance of this article had previously appeared in *Shigaku Zasshi*, *26-9*, and subsequently an expanded and amended English translation appeared under the title 'On P'u Shou-keng', *Memoir of the Research Department of the Toyo Bunko*, 2 (1928), 1-79 and 7 (1935), 1-104. There are Chinese translations by Feng Yu [al] (second edition, 1934) *Chung-kuo A-la-po Hai-shang Chiao-t'ung Shih* [am] and Ch'en Yu [an] (1929) *P'u Shou-keng k'ao.* [ao] See also Fujita Toyohachi (1943) 'The superintendency of merchant shipping during the Sung period', *Tosai Koshoshi no Kenkyu*, 281-398.

31. *Sung Shih*, Chap. 185, f. 18.

32. *Sung Hui-yao Kao*, [ap] *Chih kuan*, [aq] Chap. 44, 10 and 15 [Photolithographic reprint by the National Library of Peiping 1936] and *Sung Hui-yao*, 14th year of Chao-hsing.

33. *Sung Shih*, Chap. 491, f. 6.

34. LIU MING-SHU (1945) 'Sung-tai hai-shang t'ung-shang shih-tsa k'ao'[ar] *Bull. of Chinese Stud.,*[as] 5, 52 and IKEDA Shizuo (1940) *Shina Suiri Chiri shi Kenkyu*, Chaps. 6 and 7.

35. Cf., for example, CHU YU (1119) *P'ing-chou K'o-t'an,*[at] Chap. 2.

36. *Chau Ju-kua*, 38.

37. From a brief notice in the *Chih-chai Shu-lu Chiai-t'i,*[au] written by Ch'en Chen-sun[av] in the middle of the thirteenth century.

38. CHAO JU-KUA, *Chu-fan-chih*, p. 57 [edition, with annotations, of Feng Ch'eng-chün,[aw] Shanghai, 1938].

39. His phrase runs: 'They serve Heaven, not the Buddha.'[ax]

40. It is uncertain to which towns Chao Ju-kua is here referring. If Berbera included all the coast from Zeila to Mogadishu, the four towns may have been Zeila, Berbera itself (*Barbara*, which Ibn Baṭṭūṭa described as the regional capital), Mogadishu (*Makdashaw* of Ibn Baṭṭūṭa) and Brava, though this last is not mentioned in strictly contemporary Arab records. On the other hand, if Berbera denoted only the southern coast of the Gulf of 'Aden, the four towns presumably included Zeila and Berbera, and perhaps *Mait*, *Juah*, or some of the other small ports mentioned by early Arab authors. In this connection it may be significant that Leardo's map of 1448 marks four towns (with indecipherable names) on this stretch of coast.

41. In the light of Chao's remarks it is of interest to quote the present-day diet of pastoral nomads (in LEWIS, *Peoples of the Horn*, 74): 'milk, often sour, from five pints to two gallons daily; ghee, bush fruits when available, and meat especially for feasts and entertaining guests'.

42. I am assuming that the Somali migration had reached the Berbera coast by the thirteenth century: it is usually considered to have begun in about the tenth century A.D.

43. Under the name *lung-hsien*[ay] [=dragon spittle], which came into fashion at the time of the Northern Sung dynasty.

44. From *R. bicornis*, Linn. Rhinoceros horn[az] was probably the single most valuable item in the Chinese pharmacopoeia, a veritable apotropaion. For Chao's hierarchy of grades, based on the morphology of the horn, see *Chu-fan-chih*, 2, 138-9.

45. The *chin* was equivalent to 16 ounces on the Chinese scale. Subject to a wide range of local and commodity variations, it was fixed for tariff purposes by the Trade Regulations annexed to the Sino-British Treaty of 1858 at 23⅓ ounces avoirdupois.

46. *Mu-hsiang,*[ba] a term of no botanical value, used in medieval commerce for roots of widely differing plants. True puchuk, regarded as a universal

panacea, was the root of the Himalayan herb *Saussurea lappa*, C. B. Clarke. Presumably Chao's African puchuk was a root similar in properties and appearance to true puchuk.

47. *Su-ho hsiang-yu.*[bb] Obtained by subjecting the bark of *Liquidambar orientalis* to heat and compression.

48. *Mo-yao.*[bc] The Somali recognize two varieties of myrrh, *guban malmal* and *ogo malmal*, both from the *didin* tree, which is usually identified as *Balsamodendron myrrha*, Nées. The best qualities apparently come from central and west Somaliland. Descriptions and illustrations in DRAKE-BROCKMAN, R.E. (1912) *British Somaliland*, 239-50 and 302-5. See also a perceptive study by STEUER, R.O. (1933) *Myrrh and Stakte*.

49. *lo-t'o hao.*[bd] There is an interesting parallel here between this word, the Persian *ushturmurgh* and the Arabic *tir al-jemel*, all of which can be rendered as 'camel-bird'.

50. *tsu-la.*[be]

51. lit. 'a mule with red, white and black stripes wound girdle-like round its body'.[bf]

52. FERRAND, G. (1903) *Les Çomalis. Matériaux d'études sur le pays musulmanes*, 197-9.

53. REVOIL, G. (1882) *La vallée du Darror*, 127.

54. e.g., *Ts'eng-pa* for *Zanj-i-bar* (Pt. 1, 55) and possibly *K'un-lun Ts'eng-ch'i* (Pt. 1, 74).

55. *Zanj* or *zinj* derived ultimately from Persian or Sanskrit, probably through the medium of the lingua franca of the Persian Gulf. It is the Cape *Zinggis*[bg] of Ptolemy (Bk. 4, Chap. 8) and the *Zinggion*[bh] of Cosmas Indicopleustes [Hakluyt Society edition by J. W. McCrindle (1897), 38, 39, 52]. The *Bilād ez-Zanj*[bi] of the Arab authors stretched along the African coast from the Berbera country to the neighbourhood of Sofala, beyond which lay the country of *Wāq Wāq.*[bj] *Yāqūt* (Wüstenfeld, 4, 602) described Mogadishu as the most celebrated town in the realm. Cf. Ibn Khaldūn: 'The name "Zanj" is restricted to those Negroes who live along the Indian Sea.' [ROSENTHAL (1958) *The Muqaddimah*, Vol. 1, 171].

56. A Giryama informant related to Alice Werner that the Pokomo, Teita, Digo and Giryama had migrated from *Shungwaya*, and a Kauma informant claimed that the Kauma, Segeju and Pokomo had all retreated from that country at the time of the Galla invasions. A Mrabai also stated that the Wanyika had come originally from *S[h]ung[w]aya*, and subsequently members of nearly all other sub-tribes among the Pokomo and Nyika have made similar claims. Prins adduces circumstantial evidence that the Teita, too, at one time formed part of a group emigrating from *Shungwaya*. Baker additionally reports that a Segeju elder believed that in their *Shungwaya* homeland,

the Somali, Galla, Barawa and Wakatwa were ruled by a single chief. Information culled from WERNER, A. (1915) 'The Bantu coast tribes of the East African Protectorate, *J. Roy. Anthro. Inst.*, *45*, 326-54; KRAPF, J.L. (1858) *Reisen in Oost-Afrika*, *2*, passim; DAMMANN, E. (1944) 'Zur Geschichte der Digo', *Z.f. eing. Spr.*, *34*, 53-69; BAUMANN, O. (1891) *Usambara und seine Nachbargebiete*; and BAKER, E.C. (1949) 'Notes on the history of the Wasegeju', *Tanganyika Notes and Records*, *27*, 16-41. Much of this and other material is summarized in PRINS, A.H.J. (1952) *The coastal tribes of the north-eastern Bantu*, 8-11 and 43-51. For similar traditions preserved by the Kilindini see GUILLAIN, C. (1856-7) *Documents sur l'histoire, la géographie et le commerce de l'Afrique orientale*, *2*, 237-45.

57. *Shungwaya* appears on early maps under a variety of orthographies:

Battista Agnese's *Charta navigatoria seculi XVI* (plate 24)	. . . *gu.wa*
Bartolomeu Lasso's *L'atlas portugais* (1590)	*Jungaya* and *Jungaia*
Portulan portugais anonyme, probably by Pedro de Lemos (*c.* 1590)	*Jungaia*
Peter Kaerius's *Africae nova descriptio* (1614)	*Iungaya*
Several Blaeu maps from the middle of the seventeenth century	*Tungaya*

Numerous subsequent maps carry versions of the same name in such forms as those below:

Carte du Royaume de Congo . . . (Amsterdam, 1719)	*Mosseguaies*
Jacobus Keizer's *Kaartje van Africa* (Almeloo, 1747)	*Mosseguaias*
Emanuel Bowen's *A new and accurate map of Africa* (*c.* 1747)	*Mosseguaies*
Robert de Vaugondy's *L'Afrique* . . . (1756)	*Mossegayes*
D'Anville's *Kaart van Afrika* (1763)	*Mosseguejos*
George Rollos's *An accurate map of Africa* (1769)	*Mofeguaies* (a patent miselection)
Samuel Dunn's *Africa and its several regions* (1774)	*Mosseguejos*; etc.

After 1780 this toponym appeared on maps of Africa only sporadically, but may possibly persist unrecognized in the name of the *Shimambaya Islands*, better known as the Arlett Islands.

These forms derived from *Mshungwaya*, as did the *Mosungalos* of the Portuguese chroniclers [STRANDES, J. (1899) *Die Portugiesenzeit von Deutsch und Englisch Ost Afrika*]. It is interesting that (if the above identification is correct) both Portuguese and Chinese rendered the velar semi-vowel by a [presumably] dark *l*. In fact, in several Swahili dialects *l* and *w* are virtually interchangeable. Cp. Kiamu (the Lamu dialect) where an initial *l* is often transposed to *y*. The name *Shungwaya* itself occurs in the Swahili *Akhbar Pate* (see note 21) as well as in oral folklore. In the former instance it is clearly associated with the ports of the Benadir coast: *Alikanda kupija zita tangu Kiwayu na Tula na Shungwaya na bandari zote—Barawa, Marika, Mukdishu* (Werner, 159).

58. Presumably a garment similar to the present-day Somali *maro,* though there is evidence that skins were formerly a common form of clothing: cf. PUCCIONI, N. (1936) 'Osservazioni sui Uaboni', *L'Universo, 6,* 1-8.

59. The turban was adopted by African rulers who journeyed to Mecca after the example of the Sultan-Caliphs of Egypt [ROBINSON, A.E. (1939) *Tanganyika Notes and Records, 7,* 104]. Ibn Baṭṭūṭa described the dress of the Sheikh (here =Sultan) of Mogadishu as follows: 'His garments on that day were a large green mantle of Jerusalem stuff, with fine robes of Egyptian stuffs . . . and he was girt with a waist-wrapper of silk and turbaned with a large turban' (Gibb's translation, Vol. 2, 377).

60. This duality of house styles, which contrasts the two-storied Arabian, minaretted, brick-and-plaster type with a light hut may reflect the marked dichotomy between urban and rural conditions that has characterized the East African coast throughout its history. Presumably Chao Ju-kua was then envisaging the *mondullo* of the peasant cultivator, that is a fixed hut with cylindrical walls and conical roof, rather than the *aggal* or bee-hive hut of the nomad. Alternatively Chao may have been contrasting two types of town house, the Arabian style and the *arish,*[bk] a rectangular building with a pointed gable, from 9-12 feet high, which is virtually restricted to the coastal cities. In any case, Chao's 'thatch'[bl] was probably in reality a mat of withies. Rural dwellings of Somali nomads are illustrated in PAULITSCHKE, P. (1893) *Ethnographie Nordost-Afrikas*; PUCCIONI, N. (1936) *Antropologica e etnografia delle genti della Somalia, 3,* tav. 3, 4; CERULLI, E. (1959) *Somalia,* Vol. 2, figs. 41-4 and 53.

61. See, for example, PRAED, C.W.M. and GRANT, C.H.B. (1952) *African handbook of birds: eastern and north-eastern Africa,* Vol. 1, 267 [pictured on plate 20; distribution mapped on p. 266]; and ARCHER, SIR GEOFFREY and GODMAN, E.M. (1937) *The birds of British Somaliland and the Gulf of Aden,* Vol. 2, 309. Cf. ibid., lxxii: 'Both inland and along the shore of the Gulf of Aden the middle of April constitutes the peak period of the northerly migration, and the passage is much more marked and noticeable then than on the southerly migration in September and October.'

62. *Ju-hsiang,*[bm] presumably from the shape of the tears. Cf. Pliny: 'Praecipua autem gratia est mammosó, cum haerente lacrima priore consecuta alia miscuit se' (*Nat. Hist.,* XII, xxxii, 61). For details of Chao Ju-kua's classification of commercial grades of frankincense see WHEATLEY, J. *Malayan Branch Roy. As. Soc., 32,* 47-9. The Somali frankincense localities are defined in some detail by DRAKE-BROCKMAN, *British Somaliland,* 250-60 and 305-6.

63. For the mythology, derived in the main from Arab folklore, which had bedevilled earlier Chinese writings on whales, see WHEATLEY, J. *Malayan Branch Roy. As. Soc.*, *32*, 125-30.

64. *China's discovery*, 21.

65. If Duyvendak's interpretation be accepted, Chao's mountain was presumably the Hadaftimo range in general or, perhaps, Pyramid Peak specifically.

66. *Lu-hui*[bn] < Arabic *alwa* < Greek *alóe*.[bo]

67. Socoteri *tāyif*.

68. Cp. *Periplus Maris Erythraei*, 30.

69. Cp. Marco Polo under the rubric *Of the island of Soccotera*: 'The inhabitants find much ambergris upon their coasts, which is voided from the entrails of whales.'

70. *Hsüeh-chieh*[bp] (*Xi^w et g'iät*), probably directly from Arabic *u qāṭir*[br] as recorded in Yāqūt's *Mu'jam al-Buldān* [WUSTENFELD, F. (1866-70) *Jacut's geographisches Wörterbuch*, Vol. 3, 102]. In Socoteri this resin is known as *idihab*. It was the Indian cinnabar[br] which, according to the *Periplus*, § 30, was gathered as it exuded in tears from trees on Socotra (Dioscorida Island). Cp. Chao's description: 'the resin flows spontaneously without the tree being gashed with an axe'.[bs]

71. *d'âi dᶲ'iək*, from Pahlawi *Tājik*,[bt] modern *Tāzi*;[bu] used for Arabs and Middle Eastern Muslims in general.

72. Cp. Cosmas Indicopleustes, *'Ajā'ib al-Hind*, *al-Qazwīnī*, *Idrīsī* and early Portuguese voyagers. Summarized in DEVIC, L.M. (1883) *Le pays des Zendjs* 168-77.

73. *Hung chi pei*[bv] (=red *kĭĕt-puâi* =cotton), a term first used in the sixth century in describing the dress of the people of Bali (*Liang shu*, 54). PELLIOT, P. (1959) *Notes on Marco Polo*, 433-42 sees in this form a scholarly correction of a primitive *kuo-puâi* < a possible Cham *kupāi* < *kappāi* < *kappāsī* < Skr. *karpāsa*.

74. For the distribution of Chinese porcelain in East Africa see, *int. al.*, MATHEW, G. (1956) 'Chinese porcelain in East Africa and on the coast of south Arabia', *Oriental Art*, *2*, 50-5 and FREEMAN-GRENVILLE, G.S.P. (1962) *The medieval history of the coast of Tanganyika*. For general remarks on the export of Chinese porcelain under the Sung see TAO TSUNG-I (1366) *Cho Keng Lu*,[bw] *29*, 446-7.

75. Cp. Marco Polo: '[the rukh] being so large and strong as to seize an elephant with its talons, and to lift it into the air, from whence it lets it fall to the ground, in order that it may prey upon its dead carcase' [under the rubric *Of the great island of Madagascar*]. Concerning the *p'eng* the *Chuang Tzŭ* says: 'When this bird rouses itself and flies, its wings are like clouds all

round the sky. .... On a whirlwind it mounts upwards as on the whorls of a goat's horn for 90,000 *li*, till, far removed from the vapourous clouds, it bears on its back the blue sky, and then it shapes its course for the south, and proceeds to the ocean there' [transl. J. Legge, mod., *The Texts of Taoism* (1959), 212-13].

76. e.g. Polo (*ibid.*); Shams al-Dīn al-Dimashqī, *Nukhbat al-dahr* (A. F. Mehren's translation), 216; and *Alf Laylah wa Laylah*, night 545. For summary see DEVIC (1883), 236-54. Cp. the *sīmurgh*, which plays an important role in the legend of Zál and his son Rustam, as described in Firdausi's *Sháhnámah* [described on pp. 235-6 of A. G. and E. Warner's edition, 1905] and the gryphon of the European bestiaries. The *rukh* may possibly be connected in some way with Viṣṇu's mount Garuḍa, itself probably a survival of an ancient theriomorphic cult. All possibly not unconnected with the winged bulls of Assyria.

77. Not the dodo, as Hirth and Rockhill (*op. cit.*, 149, note 1) and Duyvendak (*op. cit.*, 22) believed. The dodo, a smaller bird than the *rukh*, was an inhabitant of Mauritius.

78. FERRAND, G. (1907) 'Les îles Rāmny, Lāmery, Wāḳwāḳ, Komor des géographes arabes, et Madagascar', *J. asiatique, 10*, 551.

79. In one of Probsthain's catalogues of Chinese *objets d'art* from the late twenties or early thirties, item 4 in a list of six Sung pictures attributed to Li Lung-mien was entitled *The K'un lun Ts'eng K'i country*. I have not seen this picture and the reference is from INGRAMS, W.H. (1931) *Zanzibar*, 93.

80. When the *Bamboo Annals*, in which this reference occurs, were discovered, purged and edited.

81. According to the *Ch'ien Han shu*, Chap. 61, f. 3*b*, when Chang Ch'ien returned from his diplomatic mission to Bactria, the Emperor consulted ancient sources and decreed that the mountains from which the Huang River took its rise should be called *K'un-lun*.

82. See, *int. al.* for example, YI IK-SEUP (1892) 'A map of the world', *Korean repository, 1* and NAKAMURA, H. (1947) 'Old Chinese world-maps preserved by the Koreans', *Imago Mundi, 4*. The salient characteristics of this cartographic tradition have been summarized by NEEDHAM, J. (1959) *Science and civilisation in China*, Vol. 3, 565-8: an eighteenth-century Korean example illustrated on plate 89. For the *K'un-lun* depicted on a diagrammatic chart from Fu Yin's *Yü-kung Shuo-tuan* of *c.* A.D. 1160, see *ibid.*, fig. 208.

83. STEIN, R. A. (1947) *Han-hiue*, 209-311.

84. PELLIOT, P. (1923) 'Notes sur quelques artistes des Six Dynasties et des T'ang', *T'oung Pao, 22*, 272.

85. KUWABARA (1928), 62.

86. e.g., Ibn Khurdādhbih, *'Akhbār aṣ-Ṣīn wa'l-Hind*, Abū Zaid, Mas'ūdī, al-Bīrūnī, al-Idrīsī, Yāqūt, Ibn Sa'īd, al-Dimashqī, Abū'l-Fidā', Ibn Khaldūn, *et al.* Summarized in FERRAND (1907), 506-38. There is a strong probability that the *Jebel Qamar* of the Arabs is related to (possibly a translation of) the Moon Mountains[bx] of Ptolemy, and that both are not unconnected with the Bantu *U-nya-mwezi* located on the southern shore of Lake Victoria (*u* = locative prefix; *nya* is unexplained; and *mwezi* = 'moon'). See also p. 160.

87. The several phases in the elucidation of the *K'un-lun* problem each has its own exegetical literature. L. DE SAUSSURE, for example, examined 'L'étymologie du nom des monts K'ouen-louen' in *T'oung Pao, 20* (1921), 370-1. In 1919 Gabriel FERRAND produced his massive analysis, 'Le K'ouen-louen et les anciennes navigations interocéaniques dans les mers du sud', *T'oung Pao, 13*, 233-39, 431-92 and *14*, 6-68, 201-41. Most perceptive of all such studies was that of R. A. STEIN, note 83 above. Wolfram EBERHARD has also dealt with this topic in his *Lokalkulturen im alten China, T'oung Pao*, supplement to *37* (1942), 245-8, and A. CHRISTIE has related the term *K'un-lun* to the *kolandio[phonta]* of the *Periplus* in *Bull. School Oriental African Stud., 19* (1957), 345-53.

88. Note 52.

89. PELLIOT, P. (1904) 'Deux itinéraires de Chine en Inde à la fin du VIIIe siècle', *Bull. de l'Ecole française d'Extrême-Orient, 4*, 290-1. This author also gives reasons for accepting *Seng-ch'i* (*Sang g'ịụ*) as the correct version, which reminds us that the Greek form also preserved the guttural (note 55).

90. *Hsin T'ang Shu, 222C*, ff. 6 recto and 8 verso.

91. AL-IDRISI (1154) *Kitāb nuzhat al-mushtāq, 1*, 58.

92. *kuei-nu.*[by]

93. *yeh-jen.*[bz]

94. Possibly as a result of the use of a dye, though I suspect textual corruption.

95. There is no doubt but that the 'offerings' made by 'envoys' (these are technical terms) to the Imperial Court were customarily construed by the Chinese as symbols of submission, but it is not at all clear that the rulers of the tendering countries regarded them as anything more than profitable investments. Protocol decreed that the Chinese Emperor, the apogee of oecumenical superiority, should recompense humble suppliants with gifts several times more valuable (according to a fixed scale) than those offered.

96. *Sung shih*, Chap. 490. Sailing before the monsoon, the envoys from *Ts'eng-t'an* had taken 160 days to reach China, calling at *Wu-hsün,*[ca] *Ku-lin*[cb] (Quilon) and *San-fo-ch'i*[cc] (*Śrī Vijaya*) on the way. *Wu-hsün* has not been identified, but the fact that Quilon lay on the envoys' route implies that they came from a state on the shores of the Arabian Sea, a conclusion with which

their sailing time of 160 days is in accord. Cf. WHEATLEY (1959), 13-14. The *Sung shu* adds: 'The Emperor Shen-tsung, in consideration of the exceedingly great distance that [the envoy] had come, bestowed on him 2,000 ounces of silver, in addition to those presents which had already been given to him.'

97. The *li* has varied with time and place. In the sixth century A.D. it was equivalent to about a quarter of an English statute mile [STEIN, *Han-hiue, 2,* 11-12]. The early Jesuit geographers, on the other hand, reckoned 200 *li* to a mean degree of the meridian, thus equating one *li* with 1,826 feet [PHILIPS, C.H. (1951) *Handbook of Oriental history,* 185-6].

98. SCHAFER, E.H. (1957) 'Rosewood, dragon's blood, and lac', *J. Amer. Orient. Soc., 77,* 133.

99. e.g. Ioh. Matthia Hasio, *Africa secundum legitimas projectionis stereographicae regulas* (1700).

100. HIRTH and ROCKHILL (1911), 127. This style is typical of the titles borrowed by the rulers of East African port cities from the Muslim world. The annals of Pate and Kilwa contain little else.

101. ROBINSON, A.E. (1937) 'The Shirazi colonizations of East Africa', *Tanganyika Notes and Records, 3,* 40; MURDOCK, *Africa,* 308. For accounts of the history of Kilwa based largely on local annals (*Kitāb al-Sulwa fī 'Akhbar Kilwa*) see DORMAN, M.H. (1938) *The Kilwa civilization and the Kilwa ruins,* TNR., *5,* 61-71, and GRAY, SIR JOHN (1951) ibid., *31,* 1-24. Archaeology has recently shown that the supposed Persian antecedents which pervade the indigenous chronicles of this coast were in fact derived from Bahmanī India.

102. * *ji^wat-nâk,* representing some Prākrit form of Skr. *varṇakā* and denoting an unidentified textile, presumably on account of its colour (*varṇā*). [PELLIOT, P. (1959) *Notes on Marco Polo,* 483-4.]

103. i.e. white * *d'iep* = a strip of plain cotton. Rendered as *yüriŋ böz* = 'white cotton stuff' in a Uighur version of the *Suvarṇaprabhāsa* translated from the Chinese. See Pelliot's magnificent exposition, ibid., 442-56.

104. Persian *mei* = wine.

105. Arabic *sharab,* Anglicized as 'sherbet'.

106. Unidentified.

107. Probably an error, though a difficult one to correct.

108. *P'eng-sha.*[cd]

109. *A-wei,*[ce] a gum resin derived from several umbelliferous plants indigenous to arid south-west Asia [*vide* WHEATLEY (1959), 117-8].

110. *Chen-chu.*[cf]

111. PUCCIONI, N. (1936) *Antropologia e etnografia delle genti della Somalia,* Vol. 2, 57.

112. ROCKHILL, W.W. (1915) 'Notes on the relations and trade of China with the eastern archipelago and the coast of the Indian Ocean during the fourteenth century', *T'oung Pao*, *16*, 622.

113. *Ya-tsui tan-fan*[cg].

114. The memory of *Menuthias* may be preserved in the modern name Mafia (*Monfiyeh*), but this passage of the *Periplus* is corrupt and the whole subject is obscure. It is also tempting to discern (as have numerous previous authors) an echo of *Rhapta* in the name Ruffiji; in which case the *Pyralaae*[ch] islands, situated two days' and two nights' sail to the north of *Menuthias*, would accord well with the islands of Pemba and Zanzibar.

115. e.g. Castanheda: 'de là [Pierre de Covilham] se vendit à Sofala et à l'île qu'on appelle à présent de San Lourenço et que les Maures appelaient île de la Lune'. [Quoted in GRANDIDIER, A. and G. (1903) *Collection des ouvrages anciens concernant Madagascar*, Vol. 1, 2.]. Cp. Albert Cantino's map of 1502 where both *Madagascar* and *Comorbimam* occur side by side; also Canerio (1502); Ruysch (1508); Sylvano (1511); and Andrea Vavassore (sixteenth century).

116. Note 46, where the *puchuk* of the Chinese is identified with a Middle Eastern herb.

117. *Ting-hsiang*.[ci]

118. *Jou-tou k'ou*.[cj]

119. *She-hsiang*.[ck]

120. *Su-mu*,[cl] the product of *Caesalpinia sappan*, Linn.

121. This map forms the subject of a monograph by FUCHS, W. (1946) *The Mongol Atlas of China by Chu Ssŭ-pen and the Kuang-Yü-T'u: Monumenta Serica Monograph VIII.* Africa is depicted on plate 44, and the commentary is on p. 14. Biography of Chu Ssu-pen in NAITO Torajiro (1920) *Ti li hsüeh chia Chu Ssŭ-Pên*,[cm] *Geibun*, *11*. Reprinted in *Dokushi Sōroku*[cn] (1929). Chinese translation by Wu Han (1933) in *T'u-shu Ch'i-k'an*,[co] 7. Under the title *Yü-t'u*,[cp] this map existed for some two centuries in manuscript only. In 1541 it was revised and enlarged by Lo Hung-hsien,[cq] and was printed in 1555 with the title *Kuang Yu-t'u*.[cr] Dr Fuchs has both corrected Wang Yung's[cs] assertion [*Chung-kuo ti-li hsüeh shih*[ct] (1938) 91] that the African section of the map was introduced only in Ch'ien Tai's[cu] edition of 1579 and established that the outline of the continent was pointed towards the south even in Chu Ssŭ-pen's original edition, prepared between 1311 and 1320 [personal communication to Joseph Needham, *Science and Civilization*, 552].

122. Chu Ssŭ-pen was himself aware of this and Fuchs (p. 552) quotes him as writing: 'There is no means of investigating [remote foreigners] because of their great distance, although they are continually sending tribute to the

court. Those who speak of them are unable to say anything definite, while those who say something definite cannot be trusted.'

123. < Pāli *dīpa* < Sanskrit *dvīpa*. Cp. Ibn Sā'id's (first climate, 6th section) *ad-Diyāb*[cv] for the Maldives and Laccadives.

124. NEEDHAM (1959), 551-6.

125. *Hun-i chiang-li li-tai kuo tu chih t'u.*[cw]

126. OGAWA Takuji (1920) *Kinsei Seiyō Kōtsū Izen no Shina Chizu ni tsuite, Chigaku Zasshi*, 22. Reprinted in OGAWA (1928) *Shina Rekishi Chiri Kenkyū*, 2 vols.

127. AOYAMA Sadao (1939) 'Ri-chō ni okeru nisan no Chōsen Zenzu ni tsuite', *Tōhō Gakuhō, 9*; and some earlier publications by the same author.

128. The text of the *Triumphant vision* that is usually quoted consists of four chapters in *Ku-chin Shuo Hai* (1544), of one chapter in *Chi-lu Hui-pien* (1617), and again of four chapters in both *Hsüeh-hai Lei-pien* and *Che-ku Ts'ung-ch'ao*. This text does not differentiate between the countries visited by Fei-Hsin himself and those on which he reported by hearsay, but another, of only two chapters, in the *T'ien-i-ko*, does make this distinction. For the complicated relationship between these texts see PELLIOT, P. (1933) 'Les grands voyages maritimes chinois au début du XVe siècle', *T'oung Pao, 30*, 246-339.

129. The correct form of this name is to be found in the *Hsi-yang chao-kung tien-lu*,[cx] written by Huang Sheng-ts'eng[cy] in 1520, and on folio 19 verso of Chap. 240 of the *Wu-pei-chih*[cz] (see fig. 2). It was identified as the district of *Pieh-lo-li*[da] =Belligam, thirteen miles from Galle, by PHILLIPS, G. (1914) *T'oung Pao*, 439.

130. *Kua ch'ieh*,[db] *Solanum melongena*, Linn.

131. A species of antelope: perhaps the oryx (*Oryx beisa*, Rüpp. Somali *be'id*), the commonest of the larger Somali antelopes, or Kirk's dik-dik (*Madoqua Kirkii*, Günth.), commonest in the vicinity of Brava.

132. Leopards are found over the greater part of the African continent. Perhaps here the dwarf race of Somaliland (*Felis pardus nanopardus*) is referred to.

133. MATHEW, G. (1953) 'Recent discoveries in East African archaeology', *Antiquity, 27*, 212-18. [FREEMAN-GRENVILLE, G.S.P. (1962) *The medieval history of the coast of Tanganyika*].

134. The Somali distinguish five physiographic zones in this territory: (i) *ba'ad*, migratory dunes along the coast; (ii) *arra'ad*, consolidated dunes on the landward side; (iii) *arra gudad*, the red flinty steppe referred to in the text; (iv) *doi*, the relatively fertile pastures between the Juba and the Shebelle; and (v) *arra mado*, alluvial valley floors. The Chinese were apparently acquainted, though vaguely, with i, ii, iii and perhaps iv.

135. Cf. GROTTANELLI, V.L. (1955) *Pescatori dell' Oceano Indiano*.

136. Hair styles similar to those mentioned in the Chinese text are attributed by HUNTINGFORD (1955), 69, to women of the eastern Galla. Pictured in CERULLI (1959), Vol. 2, figs. 11, 24, 25 and, for Danakil women, in PAULITSCHKE (1893), figs. 1, 2 and 4. The prevalent Somali coiffure is arranged as a cultivated mop rather than in rolls.

137. Cf. BURTON, R.F. (1857) *First footsteps in East Africa*, 87: 'They have all the levity and instability of the Negro character'; and a series of opinions quoted in DRAKE-BROCKMAN (1912), Chap. 7. Psychological insight into the character of primitive peoples has not been common in either Chinese or West European history.

138. The voyage of 1417-19 escorted home Malindi envoys who had presented a giraffe to the Chinese court. For the role of this creature (whose Somali name *gerrin* approximates closely to the Chinese *k'i-lin* [*ch'i-lin*dc] =unicorn) as a material manifestation of the beneficence of the reign of the Yung-lo Emperor, see DUYVENDAK, J.J.L. (1938). 'The true dates of the Chinese maritime expeditions in the early fifteenth century', *T'oung Pao, 34*, 341-412.

139. *Chin-po.*dd

140. *Ming shih*, Chap. 326, folio 7 verso and 8 recto.

141. For elucidation of the pedigree and authorship of these charts we are indebted to DUYVENDAK, J.J.L. (1933), 'Ma Huan re-examined', *Verhandelingen der Koninklijke Akademie van Wetenschappen te Amsterdam*, Afdeeling Letterkunde, n.r., *32*, no. 3; 'Sailing directions of Chinese voyages' (1938) *T'oung Pao, 34*, 230-7; and (1938) *ibid.*, 341-412. See also PELLIOT, P. (1933) 'Les grands voyages maritimes chinois au début du XVe siècle', *T'oung Pao, 30*, 237-452.

142. A watch lasted for 2 hours 24 minutes and averaged about sixty *li* in distance.

143. YOUSSOUF KAMAL, Prince (1935-9), *4*, fasc. 4, folio 1415.

144. J. V. Mills has a complete analysis of these charts from Jewel-ship Depot, near Nanking, to the African coast currently in the press.

145. PELLIOT (1933) 268.

146. Cp., for example, the sailing directories of Ibn Mājid and Sulaimān al-Mahrī in *MSS. Arabe 2292* and *2559* in the Bibliothèque Nationale at Paris. Arabic text published by FERRAND, G. (1928) *Introduction a l'astronomie nautique arabe*, 3.

147. Cp. Portuguese *pulgado*. The *isba'* was approximately 1° 43'.

148. See, for example, MILLS, J.V. (1937), *J. Malayan Branch As. Soc.*, *15*, 1-48.

149. *Yüan Shih*, Chap. 48, f. 2 verso.

150. Cp. *chung i* = 'double translation', an expression implying extreme remoteness.

NAMES AND TERMS MENTIONED IN THE TEXT.

1 西王母
2 崑崙山
3 黃支
4 鴻臚
5 竹步
6 木骨都束
7 卜剌哇
8 中理
9 層拔
10 法顯
11 西陽雜組
12 段成式
13 撥拔力
14 國人自掠賣
　與外國商人
　其價數倍
15 波斯
16 阿末囤

17 عنبر
18 象牙
19 磨鄰
20 勃薩莽
21 鶻莽
22 七
23 九
24 不恥烝報
25 蕃坊
26 頻外代答
27 周去兆
28 桂海虞衡志
29 范成大
30 細蘭海
31 東大食海
32 諸蕃志
33 趙汝适

34 通典
35 弼琶囉
36 州
37 綿羊
38 象牙有重百餘斤
39 時
40 藥箭
41 中理
42 جبل
43 جبل
44 層絕
45 絕
46 山
47 國有山與弼
　琶囉國隔界
48 其狀如鸞尾
49 層拔

50 胡茶辣
51 山林多障岫層疊
52 大食
53 鵬
54 穆骨
55 崑崙層期
56 渾淪，混淪
57 道安
58 崑崙子
59 漆道人
60 簡文
61 القُمْر
62 جبال القُمْر
63 جزيرة القُمْر
64 僧祇
65 祇
66 期
67 萍洲可談

68 朱彧

69 畜

70 換腸

71 層檀

72 亞美羅亞眉蘭

73 越諾帣

74 白疊毛帣

75 密

76 沙㷟

77 㷟

78 汪大淵

79 島夷誌略

80 層搖羅

81 島夷誌略廣證

82 拔

83 甘埋里

84 下以乳香壓重

85 πλοιάρια ῥαπτά

86 Ῥάπτα

87 Μενουθιάς

88 佛郎

89 朱思本

90 桑骨八

91 這不魯麻

92 جبل

93 哈納亦思津

94 娣八奴

95 دبب

96 李澤民

97 清濬

98 李薈

99 㰚近

100 費信

101 星槎勝覽

102 別里羅

103 錫蘭

104 馬哈獸

105 花福祿

106 豹

107 麀

108 絞車以羊皮袋水

109 黃漆光頂

110 嚻頑

111 茅元儀

112 須多大嶼

113 東古荅剌

114 哈甫泥

115 Ὀπώνη

116 حافونى

117 خافونى

118 جافونى

119 Totaque turiferis
Panchaia pinquis arenis

120 木骨都束

121 十剌哇

122 卜剌哇

123 慢八撒

124 麻林地

125 一百五十更

126 指

127 امبل

N

NAMES AND TERMS MENTIONED IN THE NOTES AND REFERENCES

a 黎軒
b 魏略
c 黎靬
d 黎鞬
e 賢督
f 魏咯
g 〔鳥〕犀散
h 津逮祕書
i 毛晉
j 李雲鵠
k 湖北先正遺書
l 四部叢刊
m 藝苑捃華
n 龍威秘書
o 説庫
p 唐代叢書
q 説郛

r 張海鵬
s 學津討原
t Μαλαὼ
u Βαρβαρία
v Ἀρώματα ἄκρον καὶ ἐμπόριον
w Βαρβαρικός κόλπος
x (الدر)
y 波斯商人欲入此國圉集數千人齎綵布沒老幼共束血立誓乃市其物
z 麻林
aa 麻林地
ab Ἀζανία
ac ἀζαίνω
ad 屈蕁
ae Χουρμᾶς
af 續文獻通考

bm 乳香
bn 蘆薈
bo ἀλόη
bp 血碣
bq (الطلاء)
br κινναβαρι το λεγομενον Ἰνδικόν
bs 脂自流溢不扣斧鑿
bt (كندس)
bu (دردي)
bv 紅吉貝
bw 陶宗儀輟耕錄
bx ὄρη σεληναῖα
by 鬼奴
bz 野人
ca 勿巡
cb 古林
cc 三佛齊

cd 鵬砂
ce 阿魏
cf 真珠
cg 鴨嘴瞻礬
ch πυραλααι
ci 丁香
cj 肉荳蔻
ck 麝香
cl 蘇木
cm 内藤次郎地理學家 朱思本
cn 讀史叢錄
co 吳晗圖書季刊
cp 輿圖
cq 羅洪先
cr 廣輿圖
cs 王庸
ct 中國地理學史
cu 錢岱

ag 毹璸   au 直齋書錄解題

ah 李心傳   av 陳振孫

ai 建炎朝野雜記   aw 馮承鈞

aj 宋會要   ax 事天不事佛

ak 粵海關志遺內侍八人,   ay 龍涎
　　齎敕書金帛分四綱各往   az 犀角
　　海南諸蕃國勾招進奉博買   ba 木香
　　香藥犀牙真珠龍腦每綱空名   bb 蘇合香油
　　詔三道,然所至處賜之

al 馮攸   bc 沒藥

am 中國阿剌伯海上交通史   bd 駱馳鶴

　　 be 俎蠟

an 陳裕   bf 騾子紅白黑三色相間
　　 　　紋如綆帶
ao 蒲壽庚芳   bg Ζίγγιοα ἄκρα

ap 宋會要稿   bh Ζίγγιον

aq 職官   bi بلاد الزنج

ar 劉銘恕,宋代海上   bj الوقواق
　　通商史雜考
as 中國文化研究彙刊   bk عربش

at 朱彧,萍洲可談   bl 葵茆苢蓋

cv الدياب   cz 武備志

cw 混一疆理歷代   da 別羅里
　　圖都之圖
cx 西洋朝貢典錄   db 瓜茄

　　 dc 麒麟

cy 黃省曾   dd 金珀

Continuity and change in African population mobility

POPULATION mobility has been and still is an important feature of African society; it has many varied characteristics with manifestations and implications for a wide range of human affairs. Many studies have been made of different aspects of mobility but there have been few general considerations. This essay takes an overall view in time and space of this phenomenon in Africa, to draw attention particularly to the ways in which it influences and is affected by a surprising variety of human activities.

There are many types of population movements; some have persisted from time immemorial, while others which once flourished no longer take place and they have been replaced by new types. Those movements which have remained unchanged have customs and traditions associated with them which may inhibit progress at the present day, though movements which have developed more recently may also have features which are undesirable in the context of modern development. Both continuity and change are important in any study of population mobility. Changes in human circumstances have resulted in movements of people and also these circumstances have been changed radically as a result of movements.

Population movements in the past played an important part in the diffusion of ideas, techniques and material equipment. Their study requires an inter-disciplinary approach, for only this will permit adequate reconstructions to be made. Historians work not only with archaeologists, social anthropologists, geographers and linguists, but also with less usual collaborators like serologists and botanists (Gray *et al.*, 1962). The present-day distributions of blood groups give clues to population movements in the past, and botanical studies of the origins and dispersions of food crops inform on the capacity of Africans in the past to exploit various environments (Portères *et al.*, 1962).

At the present day mobility is one of the most important factors in African demography and influences the character of populations in many parts of the continent. It is of immediate practical concern to governments in the conduct of administration and in promoting economic and social developments. These may be either helped or hindered by movements; for instance, migrant labour may assist in the development of areas where a labour shortage would otherwise be a limiting factor, or, on the other hand, a mobile population may prevent the successful application of measures for the improvement of public health (Prothero, 1961). Mobility may lead to social disruption or to greater social cohesion.

Movements which existed in Africa before the era of colonial administration may be distinguished from those which developed subsequently. The colonial era, lasting for less than a century and drawing rapidly to a close during the last decade, contrasts in length with the previous period. With the coming of independence to many countries there have already been some changes in the nature of population mobility, and though these have been significant in the areas in which they have occurred, they have been of minor importance for the continent as a whole.

PAST MOVEMENTS

Population movements in Africa in the past often involved large numbers of people who could be distinguished on the basis of race, language or culture. Details of many of these migrations have still to be worked out and opinions on many of them are controversial, notably on the dispersion of Bantu-speaking peoples throughout central, eastern and southern Africa. This controversy is concerned with the nuclear area from which dispersions took place, the dates when they occurred and the routes which were followed (Guthrie, 1962).

Some tribal movements were accomplished by peaceful infiltration of new lands and were followed by the assimilation of their inhabitants with the incoming peoples. Such situations are likely to have been exceptional and it was much more common for inter-tribal warfare and the devastation which accompanied it to be both the cause and the effect of population movements. Warfare was frequently associated with slave raiding and in the general pattern of events weaker tribes were displaced or enslaved by stronger and more warlike neighbours. Tensions and pressures were thus built up which set in train population movements that involved successive groups of people. Conquered tribes were enslaved to meet the requirements of indigenous social and economic systems or to be sold through middlemen to Europeans on the west coast, or to Arabs in East Africa. In this way, the demands of economic and social systems of non-African peoples, far away from Africa itself, were indirectly responsible for population mobility within the continent. Large numbers of people were affected by slaving; nearly fourteen million are estimated to have been shipped from West Africa to the New World from the seventeenth to the nineteenth centuries (Oliver and Fage, 1962). Here, and later in East Africa, great areas were depleted of their inhabitants, if not wholly depopulated, and evidence of these conditions was recorded by European explorers in the nineteenth century and by the first colonial administrators (Barth, 1858; Livingstone, 1857; Northern Nigeria, 1900-11).

Many of the elements in the patterns of population distribution at the present day are the result of warfare and slavery and the mobility associated with them, with important implications for social and economic development in terms of the balance between people and resources. Even where people were not carried off into slavery warfare caused devastation and a fundamental disruption of life; this was inevitable in circumstances where food supplies were closely related to a seasonal pattern of production. If stocks of food were destroyed by raiders in the early months of the dry season they could not be replaced until cultivation was possible in the next wet season, by which time people were dead from starvation or too weak to cultivate or had eaten what should have been used as seed. In famine conditions so easily created many deaths occurred not only directly from lack of food but also from disease aggravated by malnutrition. It is therefore not surprising that migration and depopulation were common, and though there is no quantitative evidence of these conditions it is reasonable to infer that they helped to limit the size of populations in Africa before the present century. Recent population increases have come about as a result of the more stable conditions under colonial administrations and the establishment of medical services, even though these have been inevitably restricted in scope and have tended until recently to concentrate more on curative than on preventive medicine.

NOMADIC PASTORALISM

Some details of the movements of people in the past are known, particularly where a group has remained distinct and has continued its movements up to the present day. Fulani-speaking people, who still display some non-negroid physical features in spite of admixture with negro peoples, are one of the most important of these groups. Their ancestors are believed to have migrated to West Africa from somewhere to the north-east of the Sahara desert though their exact origin is unknown. Their first movements were in a south-westerly direction and brought them to the Fouta Toro in the middle section of the Senegal valley whence, from the fourteenth century onwards, they dispersed gradually southward and eastward until today they are an important element in the population of the northern parts of West Africa from Senegal to Cameroun (Figure 1). As nomadic pastoralists, with herds of zebu cattle as the mainstay of their economy, they were limited in their southward spread in West Africa by areas infested with the tsetse fly and the threat of trypanosomiasis. On the Fouta Djallon plateau, which they finally occupied in the eighteenth century, they adapted their economy to a tsetse-infested environment by exchanging their zebu cattle for a breed with a considerable tolerance of trypanosomiasis (Richard-Molard, 1958).

The factors which controlled their movements eastward are not known in detail but their gradual dispersion over many centuries was to influence significantly many of the areas into

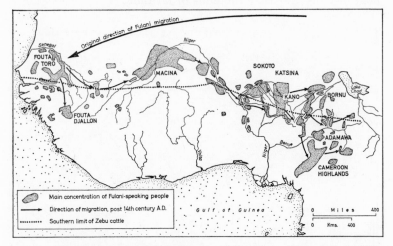

Figure 1. The movements and distribution of Fulani-speaking people in West Africa. (Based, in part, on a map in Stenning, 1959)

which they migrated. For the most part they infiltrated peacefully, coming to live alongside, yet remaining quite distinct from, sedentary cultivators whom they found already settled. But Fulani occupation did not always maintain this peaceful character and in the early decades of the nineteenth century, in those parts of West Africa which are now Northern Nigeria, they established themselves by force as overlords of almost all the Hausa kingdoms, some of which had been in existence since about the tenth century A.D. The empire which they established remained in existence until the British Protectorate over Northern Nigeria was declared in 1900, and the imperial system of administration based on emirates or chiefdoms was retained as the framework for colonial rule. Even within the modern political organization that has been developed in the Northern Region as a part of the independent

Federation of Nigeria the emirs are still powerful. Their Fulani kinsmen who have continued the traditional life of pastoral nomadism remain a reserved and distinct group in the population of Northern Nigeria, with their economy divorced from that of cultivation and thus proving a major hindrance to the development of more intensive methods of farming.

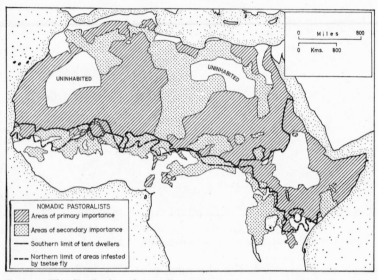

Figure 2. The distribution of nomadic pastoralists in northern Africa. (Based on information in Murdock, G. P., *Africa: its peoples and their culture history*, New York, 1959)

Nomadic pastoralism as practised by the Fulani represents the outstanding type of population movement which has persisted from the past, remains virtually unchanged in character, and involves large numbers of people at the present day. The lives of nomads are controlled by the availability of pasture and water for their flocks and herds in arid and semi-arid lands so that continual movements of men and animals are necessary (Berque, *et al.*, 1959). This constant mobility permits only a minimum of personal equipment to be transported from one camping place to another and necessitates dwellings which can be easily erected and dismantled. These are of two main types each with a different area of distribution; the tents of the Arab and Berber nomads of North Africa and the Sahara are replaced to the south and east of the desert by shelters constructed on a framework of poles covered with skins, mats or leaves, or with several of these (Figure 2). The nomadic life is strongly traditional and pastoralists are conservative not only in their dwellings and equipment; they are reserved by nature and tend to be suspicious of other peoples among whom they live and with whom they come into contact. Among the peoples of Africa they have been the least affected by political, social and economic changes during the present century and normally they resent any attempt to interfere with their way of life. The pastoralists' major concern is for their animals on which they depend for their livelihood. They maintain a traditional disdain for cultivation which complicates plans for bringing their nomadic life to an end and settling them. The abandoning of a nomadic for a sedentary life raises many problems of economic and social adjustment and Egypt is the only African country where official policy has been directed towards achieving the settlement of nomads (Abou-Zeid, 1959). In the majority of countries in the continent where there are nomads they form only a small minority of the total population, and it is easier for governments to ignore them than to devise policies which will inevitably create difficulties.

Somali nomads

Somali nomads represent a majority in the population of the Horn of Africa, 85 per cent of the total in Northern Somalia (formerly British Somaliland) and 65 per cent in Southern Somalia (formerly United Nations Trust Territory). These two regions together make the Republic of Somalia with a total population of two million, nearly all of whom are Somalis, members of an ethnic group whose complete distribution extends northward into French Somaliland (18,000 Somalis), westward into Ethiopia (500,000) and south-westward into Kenya (80,000) (Figure 3). All speak the same language and are further united by their adherence to Islam (Lewis, 1961). Like many ethnic groups else-where in Africa they were the victims of the delimitation of boundaries by the European powers at the end of the nineteenth century and in the early years of the present century (Barbour, 1961). The boundary between Ethiopia and what is now Northern Somalia was defined and was agreed to in an Anglo-Ethiopian treaty in 1897 (Hertslet, 1909). It not only divided the Somali people from one another but more seriously, from the point of

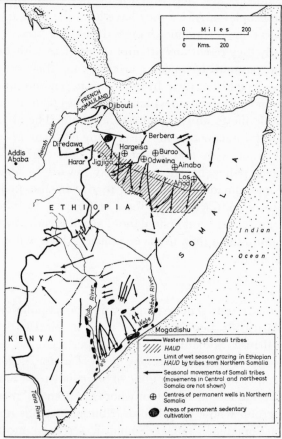

Figure 3. The distribution and movements of Somali tribes in the Horn of Africa. (Based, in part, on maps by I. M. Lewis and W. H. Zaphiropoulos)

view of their movements, it divided the region of the Haud. This is a plateau ranging between 2,000 and 4,000 feet above sea-level, which provides grazing for the animals of Somali nomads during the wet season but which is waterless in the dry season. Men and animals must then move northward to sources of permanent water at Hargeisa, Odweina, Burao, Ainabo and Los Anod (Figure 3). By the treaty of 1897 the greater part of the Haud became Ethiopian territory, but as the Somalis have no option but to use all of it for grazing there were provisions in the treaty which specifically safeguarded their traditional rights. These rights were reaffirmed in an agreement signed between Ethiopia and Britain in 1954 when the British Military Administration finally came to an end in north-east Africa (Brown, 1956 and 1961).

Even with these safeguards the boundary has always been unsatisfactory for the Somali pastoralists and yet no attempt was made by Britain to settle its problems before granting independence to the Somaliland Protectorate in 1960. Now with the Republic of Somalia as a focus for the aspirations of the Somali people, problems associated with grazing are of less importance than those associated with demands for frontier revision in order to realize the concept of Pan-Somalia which would unite all members of this homogenous ethnic group (Somali Information Services, 1962). The national prestige of Somalia is involved in these demands, though naturally the concept is unacceptable to adjacent countries with Somali minorities, for they have to safeguard their own prestige. Since 1960 there has been continual tension along the boundary between Ethiopia and Somalia with frequent outbreaks of violence occurring between nationals of the two countries.

The environmental conditions in Northern Somalia offer only very limited prospects for anything other than a nomadic way of life. The amount of cultivable land is limited by low and erratic rainfall, and prospecting for minerals up to the present time has shown that there are no major resources to be exploited (Odone, 1961). Poor economic prospects coupled with the nomadic way of life restrict the introduction of social improvements among the majority of the population. Little progress has yet been made in devising satisfactory means of raising the very low standards of education (Bonnani, 1961). In the fields of public health and preventive medicine it is equally difficult to improve the conditions of people who are mobile for most of the time and whose social organization is based upon small groups, each of a few families, whose composition is frequently changing. Furthermore, since the movements of these people involve the crossing of an international boundary and there is a lack of understanding between Somalia and Ethiopia, there is none of the co-ordination in preventive medicine that is essential if diseases of major importance, like malaria, are to be eradicated from the Horn of Africa. Pastoralism and politics together retard the progress of public health. Unfortunately this is by no means an isolated example of the way in which health problems in Africa may be aggravated by population movements and by the absence of inter-territorial co-operation (Prothero, 1961).

In the south of Somalia, beyond the Juba River, Somali pastoralists have migrated into the Northern Frontier District of Kenya, part of a long-term migratory drift which has taken them to the extent of their present distribution in north-east Africa (Lewis, 1960). This drift is quite distinct from their seasonal movements and has been accomplished over many years, for the most part almost imperceptibly (Hunt, 1951). The southern spread of the Somali is particularly distinctive because it has involved incursion into Kenya. Only by strict administrative measures was it prevented from continuing southward and it was halted along the line of the Tana River in the 1930s. The presence of a majority of Somalis in the sparse population in this part of northern Kenya has resulted in demands in recent years for the area to be included in the Republic of Somalia. The situation has been complicated by the approach of self-government and independence for Kenya, whose politicians understandably wish to maintain the country's present frontiers intact, for reasons of prestige if for nothing else. A commission appointed by the British Government to investigate the facts of this problem reported at the end of 1962 that the Somalis in northern Kenya wished to be independent of that country and contemplated joining the Republic of Somalia (H.M.S.O., 1962). However, the constitutional developments for Kenya announced by Britain in 1963 included the maintenance of the present Kenya frontiers but granted a degree of regional autonomy to the north. Dissatisfaction with these arrangements led to the Republic of Somalia severing diplomatic relations with Britain and to a situation among the Somalis in Kenya which is potentially of a highly explosive nature. The situation might be eased if the proposed federation of territories in East Africa was to include Somalia. Whatever the outcome the point that is emphasized here is that the factors which have brought about these problems are associated with the traditional mobility of a pastoral people in conflict with modern political concepts. This conflict illustrates the almost irreconcilable juxtaposition of the past and present such as may be found in so many parts of Africa today, and is one example of the anomalous position of nomadic pastoralists in the middle of the twentieth century.

PILGRIM MOVEMENTS

Pilgrim movements like those of nomadic pastoralists represent continuity of mobility from the past, though they have not produced comparable problems which endanger international relations. Pilgrimages from West Africa have taken place since the conversion of people in these parts to Islam from the twelfth century onwards; today they indicate the continuing and increasing strength of this religion in Africa. The motive and purpose of pilgrimage remain the same but the ways by which it is accomplished change with the times. The wealthier and more sophisticated pilgrims, who wish to complete their journeys in a short time, travel by air, and charter flights to Mecca are a feature of the business of travel agencies in West Africa today. But the majority of pilgrims still journey overland by way of the sahel/savanna lands, the grasslands with light woodland cover, which have provided easy routeways for movements in both directions for many centuries (Mather, 1956; Riad, 1960). Few pilgrims still travel on foot or by animal; now they make the journey by lorry or by car. But journeys are still made in stages, and though the distance between each stage is traversed with the speed of modern transport pilgrims may take years to reach and to return from Mecca. At each of several places *en route* they may work for several months to gain sufficient money to proceed on the next stage.

West African pilgrims on their way to Mecca and on their return journeys are attracted particularly to the Gezira in the Republic of Sudan, where the cultivation of cotton on a large scale creates heavy demands for labour. The 'Westerners', the name given to those who come from lands which lie westward of the White Nile, have a reputation in the Sudan for the excellence of their work and they are an important element in the economy of the Gezira and of the whole country (Hassoun, 1952; McLoughlin, 1962). Some 'Westerners' have settled permanently in the Sudan and form significant proportions of the population in some parts of the country. But while making a permanent home there they retain their identity and some, for example, live in villages in Blue Nile Province which are similar in appearance to, and with the same names as, villages in Northern Nigeria. It is with their kinsmen in these villages that West Africans stay when they are on their way to and from Mecca.

Two features of the mobility associated with pilgrimage are of particular significance. The first is of immediate concern, and relates to the health of pilgrims and to their role as actual and potential carriers of disease. Regulations require pilgrims in transit through the Sudan to possess valid certificates of vaccination against smallpox and inoculation against yellow fever, and to enter from the west by way of one of the frontier control posts, of which the most important is at Geneina. But there are many miles of open uncontrolled frontier which may be crossed by those who think these formalities involve unnecessary interference, or who may wish for other reasons to avoid them. At the present time the Sudan is embarking on a programme of country-wide malaria eradication, the success of which will depend ultimately on it being possible to prevent the introduction of fresh infections of the disease. Pilgrims will be a likely source of infection and will need to be taken into account in planning this programme, though there are many other forms of population mobility within the Sudan which are likely to present even greater problems.

Secondly, increasing conversion to Islam, which seems likely among people in Africa, will result in a corresponding increase in the volume of pilgrimage. This will bring about increased contacts between the peoples of different African nations who are united in their allegiance to the same religion. It may help to promote in a positive and practical way the development of genuine Pan-African feelings, beyond the stage at which these are discussed by statesmen and politicians. Already the religious bonds of Islam link the countries of North Africa with those of the Middle East though admittedly they are also linked by Arab ethnic ties. Likewise Islam may become a powerful link between peoples in countries south and east of the Sahara.

RECENT MOBILITY

While pastoral and pilgrim movements represent continuity of mobility from the past, other types of population movements have disappeared and their place has been taken by new forms. The European colonial administrations brought tribal warfare and slaving to an end and established peace and stability, thus changing the previously fluid situation to one that was relatively static. Until then the areas occupied by various tribes had been either expanding or contracting, depending on their relative strength or weakness. The Zande, a powerful tribe occupying parts of the Nile-Congo watershed, was one such group which found that it could no longer enlarge its territory at the expense of its weaker neighbours, as it had been doing for many years (de Schlippe, 1956). Not only did expansion come to an end but the Zande also found that internal tribal relationships were complicated by the demarcation of the boundaries of the Anglo-Egyptian Sudan, Uganda and the Congo Free State which divided the tribe.

The situations created by tribal expansion and contraction resulted in anomalies in population/land relationships which are still apparent. Areas that were depopulated subsequently became infested with tsetse-fly, and sleeping sickness has prevented the resettlement of some of them even up to the present day. They stand out as regions of low population density, often contrasting with adjacent regions of high density which may suffer from population pressure and land hunger.

Although administrative stability thus brought long-established forms of mobility to an end it also influenced the development of new types of population movements.

Downhill movements

The establishment of peaceful conditions saw the beginning of movements of people from mountainous areas, where in the past the difficult terrain had provided weaker groups with refuge and relative safety from their stronger neighbours. In West Africa these movements are still in progress, from the Fouta Djallon plateau in the west, from the hills in north Togo and Dahomey (Froelich, 1952; Mercier, 1952), from the Jos plateau in Nigeria and from the Adamawa and Cameroun highlands farther east. A distinctive feature of these movements has been the consequent changes that have taken place in farming practices. In remote mountain fastnesses conservative farming was necessary because of the restricted amounts of cultivable land available, and one of the characteristic features of the highland landscapes was the well-developed terracing, which permitted the maximum use of cultivable land on steep slopes and at the same time prevented soil erosion. With migration down to lowland areas in recent decades these conservative methods have been abandoned and clearance and cultivation have taken place indiscriminately on the much greater areas of land available, without thought for the preservation of soil cover or soil fertility. The Dimmuk, who descended from the southern periphery of the Jos plateau to settle and farm in the lowland of the Shendam valley, were described as farmers who are 'most destructive as well as the most productive' (Findlay, 1945).

Several resettlement schemes were established in the lower-lying lands around the Jos plateau, to prevent the deterioration of large areas through the indiscriminate use of wasteful farming methods and to teach efficient methods suited to the new environment (Buchanan, 1954). The schemes met with varying success but all were interesting experiments not only in controlled farming but also in new forms of administration and in the organization of the social welfare in each settlement (e.g. the provision of schools, dispensaries and other amenities). Most of the settlements were established with only limited capital investment and with the principles of self-help and community work strongly emphasized in their development.

Labour migration

The greater changes in the character of population mobility during the era of colonial rule were related to economic developments initiated and influenced both directly and indirectly by European finance and organization. Through the exploitation of her agricultural and mineral resources during the last sixty years Africa has been brought into the mainstream of world economy. The production of traditional crops has been increased, and new crops have been introduced into indigenous rural economies to satisfy export demands. In several parts of the continent Europeans acquired land for large-scale agricultural production on farms and plantations. There has also been widespread and in some instances large-scale exploitation of minerals and the establishment of various industries. These profound economic developments contrast with conditions in the past and they have all in varying ways influenced the development of labour migration as a form of population mobility.

On a conservative estimate at least five million people are involved each year in migrant labour movements in Africa south of the Sahara. Those who migrate are influenced primarily by a desire to enjoy the higher standards of living which they can achieve by contributing their labour to, and acquiring skills in, modern economic developments. Their labour is required in areas of cash crop production, on large farms and plantations, in mines and factories and at commercial centres and sea-ports. But migrants are also influenced by conditions in their home areas, where often there is pressure of population on resources and serious shortages of land for cultivation with resultant low standards of living. These may be so severe that people are left with little alternative but to migrate in order to supplement their incomes. A variety of other factors, social, psychological and political, may exercise an influence on labour migration, but it has been conclusively proved from studies in various parts of Africa that the economic factors are dominant (Mitchell, 1959).

Much research has been carried out on the motivation, nature and effects of migrant labour but little is known in detail of the numbers of migrant labourers, the patterns of movements and of the routes which are followed in journeys to and from work. The general directions of migrant labour movements are shown in Figure 4 and these may be grouped into those which take place in North Africa, in West Africa and in the eastern and southern parts of the continent. The three groups differ not only in their geographical location but also in the characteristics of the movements which take place in each.

The movements in Africa south of the Sahara with the most definite pattern are those in West Africa; they follow a north–south axis, with migrants originating particularly from Mali, Haute Volta and Niger, and from the northern parts of Ghana and Nigeria and seeking work in the economically advanced regions farther south. They find work in areas of groundnut cultivation in Senegal and Northern Nigeria, in the coffee and cocoa regions of Ivory Coast, Ghana and Western Nigeria, in the iron ore mines of Sierra Leone and Liberia and at the ports and major towns like Dakar, Abidjan, Accra, Kumasi, Lagos, Ibadan and Kano. To reach these, migrants have to travel long distances – 600 miles and more on their way to and from work – and though

journeys were and still are, in parts, made on foot, the development of communications has had an important influence on
movements. There is no detailed information on the different

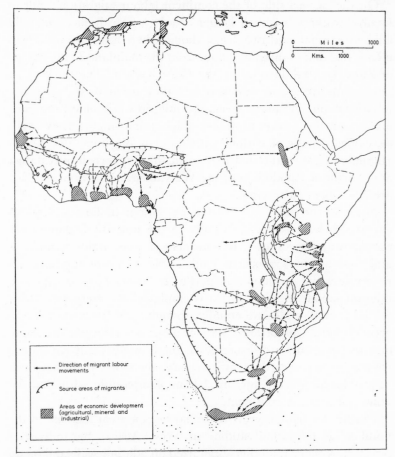

Figure 4. Movements of migrant labour in Africa

forms of transport and the times taken on various journeys but
these are relevant factors in the timing of migrations which generally in West Africa are annual events. Migrants leave home to seek
work between late September and November, when work on the
harvest has been finished, and they return home in the following

April and May to cultivate their farms at the onset of the wet season. Distinct seasonal changes in climate permit migration to be well integrated into the annual cycle of activity.

On the eastern side of the continent labour migration tends to involve workers in much longer absences from home, generally for between one and two years, though there are seasonal movements, like that of migrant labour from the mainland to the islands of Zanzibar and Pemba for the clove harvest. The patterns of movements are less well-defined than they are in West Africa, but in eastern and southern Africa also migrants originate from poor areas and seek work in those which are comparatively well-developed – areas of cotton cultivation in Buganda, the Kenya Highlands, sisal estates in Tanganyika, the Copperbelt of Katanga and Northern Rhodesia and the Witwatersrand in South Africa are main foci of attraction.

Many of the enterprises employing labour in East and South Africa are large-scale, and many of the migrant labourers are recruited under contract. Recruitment is quite highly organized, and there are thus recorded details of the origins of migrants and their routes and means of transport to and from work. Much of the migrant labour in West Africa is employed in enterprises which are on a small scale individually, though collectively they are of great economic importance. Labour migration is largely spontaneous and migrants are dispersed in these many small enterprises which keep no records. Until recently, therefore, there has been little information on migrant labour comparable with that for other parts of the continent.

During the last ten years there has been a great increase in the number of migration studies in West Africa, by individual research workers and others organized on a larger scale and on an inter-territorial basis (Prothero, 1962*a*). The individual studies have tended to throw light upon particular features of migrant labour in limited areas; as, for example, the marked variation in the amount of labour migration that takes place from different tribes in Portuguese Guinea (Carriera and de Meirles, 1960), a feature which has been noted in other parts of Africa (Southall,

1961). Intra-territorial movements may vary, as between the temporary migrations of the Toucouleur from the Senegal valley to Dakar (Diop, 1960), and the permanent migrations of cocoa farmers in Ghana who have migrated westward into Akim country from the Akwapim towns to the north of Accra (Hill, 1960*a* and *b*). The Toucouleur migrants are young men who work in Dakar usually for less than one year, while the Akwapim farmers, who migrated early in the present century to establish cocoa farms in Akim country, are settled there permanently with their families, though they keep their tribal individuality and maintain links with the towns from which they originate.

Most of the migrant labourers in West Africa are adult males who go to work without their families; frequently they are un-married and one of their motives for going away to work is to earn sufficient to make a marriage possible. The majority of men who migrate from north-western Nigeria during the dry season travel without wives or other dependants. On their long journeys to work in Ghana and the Western and Eastern Regions of Nigeria, they travel distances of up to 800 miles in each direction, with a minimum of personal equipment – a sleeping mat, a stick (some-times still a sword or bow and arrows) and a small bottle-shaped gourd for carrying drinking water; they are known as the *yan tuma da gora*, 'the young men who travel with a gourd' (Prothero, 1957 and 1958). Economic factors cause them to seek work away from home each year, for environmental conditions are difficult and there is some pressure of population on resources in the northern parts of Sokoto Province from which they come (Prothero, 1962*b*). Other factors undoubtedly influence them, for if they were concerned solely with economic gain they could achieve this by settling permanently in the southern parts of the province, where there is plenty of land and where the rainfall and soils are favourable for groundnut and cotton cultivation. But they are reluctant to make this permanent move, because of close attachment to their home areas in the north of the province and because of satisfaction, other than that of economic gain, which they experience by going far afield to work. Even in their home areas there are limited opportunities for extending cultivation in the dry season by irrigation, but these are not taken because men prefer to migrate annually. It is wrong to over-emphasize the influence that social and other amenities in more advanced areas have had upon the development of African labour migration, but they undoubtedly offer some attraction. Migrants may also be seeking some release from the restrictions which they feel are placed upon them by the customs and traditional obligations of the social group to which they belong. Unpopular arbitrary administration by a local chief or village headman can be responsible for people migrating either temporarily or permanently. Though the effects of social factors on labour migration may be of secondary importance to economic factors they are none the less significant.

There are important aspects of the lives of migrant labourers at the places where they work – the ways in which they organize themselves, their social status in strange communities and the influences to which they are subjected and which they may eventually transmit to their own communities when they return home. The most detailed information on these aspects of migration in West Africa has been collected by Jean Rouch, from personal investigations in Ghana a decade ago (Rouch, 1957) and from a research project on migration into Ivory Coast and Ghana which he organized and directed for the Commission for Technical Co-operation in Africa south of the Sahara in 1958 and 1959. The latter, the most comprehensive study of inter-territorial migration that has been undertaken in Africa, was of particular importance since it was organized on an inter-territorial basis. So many African migrants cross international frontiers, not once but several times, and an international approach in the study of their movements is the only one likely to obtain worth-while results. Few inter-territorial agreements on labour migration have been concluded and some of these are nowadays of little significance. This is a regrettable situation which may be remedied among independent African states.

Rouch's work has shown that since tribal affinity still transcends a sense of nationality, migrants from the same home area will tend to remain together for work, friendship and mutual protection even when they are working in another part of their own country. He and others have pointed out that while migration inevitably weakens peoples' traditional ties with their home areas it may promote new forms of association which still may be based on old allegiances (Rouch, 1961; Little, 1962). Length of stay away from home may be an important factor, and it is therefore important to distinguish between people who alternate between their home areas and places of work and are away from home for relatively short periods, and those who make a more permanent break. If the latter settle in a social and economic environment which is totally different from the one they have known they may respond markedly to the new influences to which they are subjected. This is happening in Morocco where the large exodus of rural population is directed towards a limited part of the country, and especially to the city of Casablanca. In an urban environment the Moroccan countryman loses many of his rural characteristics, by cutting himself off from traditional influences and values; exchanging, for example, the old ties of the patriarchal family for those of the conjugal family, with consequently a much more limited range of social contacts (Adam, 1959). Yet in contrast to Morocco, in Ibadan, the largest town in tropical Africa, there are distinct areas that are inhabited by people from the different parts of Nigeria and they maintain their tribal identities even though they are settled permanently (Mitchel, 1961).

Movements of people in the past have been responsible for the spread of political and religious ideas and similar diffusion takes place now. Political developments in the Gold Coast from 1951 onwards, culminating in independence in 1957, had a profound influence on surrounding territories which were still under French colonial rule and stimulated them to demand independence. The presence in Ghana of large numbers of migrants from these territories undoubtedly contributed to the diffusion of political ideas to French West Africa and helped to inspire the nationalist movements which existed there.

In the future it is probable that population mobility will

contribute to the development of a sense of national identity within countries since it brings people of different ethnic groups into inevitable contact with one another. This will in time lead to a better appreciation of the differences between one group and another and thus to better understanding. This has been shown to happen with the children of Kabre migrants from northern Togo who are very receptive to new influences, particularly if they receive any formal education when they are away from home (Pauvert, 1960). Though children do not usually accompany migrants in West Africa it is likely that young adults, who form a high proportion of migrants, are comparably receptive to the new social environments in which they find themselves. Where migrations involve the crossing of international boundaries they may in time contribute to the development of a sense of inter-national relationship and to the growth of Pan-Africanism among ordinary people.

FUTURE MOBILITY

All students of human society in Africa today are conscious of the existence, side by side, of rapid change and of the strength of tradition. Though all the types of population movement in Africa are not linked directly with the past, mobility in various forms is a continuing feature which is always being influenced by, and is itself influencing, social change. In the foreseeable future neither of the two major forms – nomadic pastoralism and migrant labour – are likely to come to an end and pilgrimage will increase with the further spread of Islam. Both nomadic pastoralism and migrant labour have features that inhibit social and economic advancement, but it would be neither socially nor economically feasible to bring them quickly to an end. Neither of them is static in character; each is changing in response to various factors, and they display features which suggest that greater stability is being attained. Eventually nomads will become sedentary and migrant labourers will become part of the permanent population of towns. The processes by which these conditions will be achieved are developing very slowly and independent African governments may feel that it is desirable for political, social and economic reasons to stimulate them, and perhaps even directly to accelerate them. They may be prepared to adopt measures which would have seemed repressive if they had been applied by colonial governments.

The future will bring changes in population mobility, just as in recent years refugee movements, a new form of mobility, have involved considerable numbers of people, particularly in the Congo. These movements are the result of instability consequent on newly won independence, but they have implications for the whole field of political, social and economic development. Their immediate effects are on the health and nutrition of those involved (Lowenstein, 1962). Some of these refugee movements have been created, and certainly have been exacerbated, by the reappearance of ancient tribal animosities which had been repressed or suppressed during the period of colonial rule. This may give rise to fears for a possible return to the disturbed conditions of the past, though it is probable that it is only a passing phase in African history. Population mobility in Africa in all its forms is likely to diminish progressively, but, while it continues, with all its disadvantages, it should exert more influence in bringing people together than in setting them apart.

NOTE

This essay is based on a paper, 'Migration and social change in Africa', read at a symposium of the Deutsche-Afrika-Gesellschaft in Cologne in November, 1962. I wish to thank Professor W. Fröhlich, the editor of the *Proceedings* of the Symposium, and the publishers, E. J. Brill of Leiden, for permission to reproduce much of the text and the illustrations in this essay.

REFERENCES

ADAM, A. (1959) 'Problèmes sociaux du Maroc: l'exode rural', *Collection d'études juridiques* (Faculté de Droit du Maroc), *4*, 67-87.

ABOU-ZEID, A.M. (1959) 'The sedentarization of nomads in the Western Desert of Egypt', *Int. Soc. Sci. J.*, *11*, 550-8.

BARBOUR, K.M. (1961) 'A geographical analysis of boundaries in tropical Africa', in BARBOUR, K.M. and PROTHERO, R.M. (eds.) *Essays on African Population*.

BARTH, H. (1858) *Travels and discoveries in northern and central Africa*.

BERQUE, J. *et al.* (1959) 'Nomads and nomadism in the arid zone', *Int. Soc. Sci. J.*, *11*, 481-585.

BONNANI, C. (1961) 'Literacy for nomads in Somalia', *Overseas Educ.*, *33*, 88-94.

BROWN, D.J.L. (1956) and (1961) 'The Ethiopia-Somaliland frontier dispute', *International and Comparative Law Quarterly*, *5*, 245-64; and 'Recent developments in the Ethiopia-Somaliland frontier dispute', *ibid.*, *10*, 167-78.

BUCHANAN, K.M. (1954) 'Recent developments in Nigerian peasant farming', *Malayan J. trop. Geogr.*, *2*, 17-34.

CARREIRA, A. and DE MEIRLES, A.M. (1960) 'Quelques notes sur les mouvements migratoires des populations de la province Portugaise de Guinée', *Bull. Inst. Franc. d'Afrique Noire*, *22*, 379-92.

DE SCHLIPPE, P. (1956) *Shifting cultivation in Africa: the Zande system of agriculture*.

DIOP, A. (1960) 'Enquête sur le migration Toucouleur à Dakar', *Bull. I.F.A.N.*, *22*, 393-418.

FINDLAY, R.L. (1945) 'The Dimmuk and their neighbours', *Farm and Forest*, *6*, 137-45.

FROELICH, J.C. (1952) 'Densité de la population et methodes de culture chez les Kabre du Nord Togo', *Comptes Rendus du Congrès International de Géographie*, *Lisbonne 1949*, Tome IV, Section 5, 168-80.

GRAY, R. *et al.* (1962) Third conference on African history and archaeology, *J. Afr. Hist.*, *3*, 175 ff.

GUTHRIE, M. (1962) 'Some developments in the prehistory of the Bantu languages', *J. Afr. Hist.*, *3*, 273-82.

HASSOUN, I.M. (1952) 'Western migration and settlement in the Gezira', *Sudan Notes and Records*, *33*.

HERTSLET, E. (1909) *The map of Africa by treaty*, Vol. 2.

HILL, P. (1960a) 'The migration of Southern Ghanaian cocoa farmers', *Bull. I.F.A.N.*, *22*, 3-4, 419-25.

— (1960b) 'The migrant cocoa farmers of Southern Ghana', *Africa*, *31*, 3, 209-30.

H.M.S.O. (1962) *Report of the Northern Frontier District Commission*. Cmnd. 1900.

HUNT, J.A. (1951) *A general survey of Somaliland Protectorate, 1944-50*. Hargeisa.

LEWIS, I.M. (1960) 'The Somali conquest of the Horn of Africa', *J. Afr. Hist.*, *1*, 213-30.

— (1961) *A pastoral democracy*.

LITTLE, K. (1962) 'Some traditionally based forms of mutual aid in West African urbanization', *Ethnology*, *1*, 197-211.

LIVINGSTONE, D. (1857) *Missionary travels and researches in South Africa*.

LOWENSTEIN, F.W. (1962) 'An epidemic of Kwashiorkor in the Southern Kasai, Congo', *Bull. Wld. Hlth. Org.*, *27*, 751-8.

MCLOUGHLIN, P.F.M. (1962) 'Population, output and expenditure in a Sudan flood irrigated region: the Gash-Tokar deltas', *Indian Econ. J.*, *10*, 49-59.

MATHER, D.B. (1956) 'Migrations in the Sudan', in STEEL, R.W. and FISHER, C.A. (eds.) *Geographical essays on British tropical lands*.

MERCIER, D. (1952) 'Densités de population dans le Moyen-Dahomey', *Comptes Rendus du Congrès International de Géographie, Lisbonne 1949*, Tome IV, Section 5, 181-91.

MITCHEL, N. (1961) 'Yoruba towns', in BARBOUR and PROTHERO, *op. cit.*

MITCHELL, J.C. (1959) 'The causes of labour migration', *Bull. Inter-African Labour Inst.*, *6* 12-46.

NORTHERN NIGERIA (1900-11) *Annual reports*.

ODONE, A. (1961) 'Somalia's economy: prospects and problems', *Civilisations*, *11*, 444-8.

OLIVER, R. and FAGE, J.D. (1962) *A short history of Africa*.

PAUVERT, J-CL. 'Migrations et éducation', *Bull. I.F.A.N.*, *22*, 467-75.

PORTÈRES, R. *et al.* (1962) 'History of food crops', *J. Afr. Hist.*, *3*, 195-267.

PROTHERO, R.M. (1957) 'Migratory labour from north-western Nigeria', *Africa*, *27*, 251-61.

— (1959) *Migrant labour from Sokoto Province, Northern Nigeria*. Kaduna.

— (1961) 'Population movements and problems of malaria eradication in Africa', *Bull. Wld. Hlth. Org.*, *24*, 405-25.

— (1962*a*) 'Migrant labour in West Africa', *J. Local Admin. Overseas*, *1*, 149-55.

— (1962*b*) 'Some observations on desiccation in north-western Nigeria', *Erdkunde*, *16*, 112-19.

RIAD, M. (1960) 'The Jukun: an example of African migrations in the sixteenth century', *Bull. I.F.A.N.*, *22*, 476-85.

RICHARD-MOLARD, J. (1958) 'Essai sur la vie paysanne au Fouta Dialon', in *Problèmes humaines en Afrique occidentale*. Paris.

ROUCH, J. (1957) 'Migrations au Ghana', *Journal de Société des Africanistes*, 33-196.

— (1962) 'Second generation migrants in Ghana and the Ivory Coast', in SOUTHALL, A.W. (ed.) *Social change in modern Africa*.

SILBERMAN, L. (1959) 'Somali nomads', *Int. Soc. Sci. J.*, *9*, 559-71.

SOMALI INFORMATION SERVICES (1962) *The Somali peninsula*. Mogadishu.

SOUTHALL, A.W. (1961) 'Population movements in East Africa', in BARBOUR and PROTHERO, *op. cit.*

STENNING, D.J. (1959) *Savannah nomads*.

Changing patterns of African employment in Southern Rhodesia

THE Second World War is important in the analysis of events in Southern Rhodesia because of the profound effects it has had on economic development and social change over the last twenty years. During the war isolation from the traditional sources of supply in Europe stimulated the expansion of manufacturing industry in a country previously dependent on its primary industries. Between 1945 and 1957 the value of manufacturing output rose steadily until it was challenging agriculture's place as the leading economic activity in the country (Mitchell, 1961). The war also caused a world-wide upheaval of population. Large numbers of people were encouraged to leave England and South Africa to settle in Southern Rhodesia. In consequence the number of Europeans in the population increased from 82,386 in 1946 to 135,596 in 1951. At the same time the indigenous African population began to move towards the towns in greater numbers than ever before. Whereas there were only 68,510 Africans registered in employment in the seven main urban areas at the 1941 census, in 1946 there were 99,388, and in 1951 a total of 163,314.

Expansion in the manufacturing industries and large-scale movements of population have had the effect of creating favourable conditions for rapid social change in Southern Rhodesia. The trend of events since the war has been much discussed from many different points of view. Taken collectively this work shows the impact of an accelerated rate of social change and points to its importance in the future development of the country. To appreciate the problems facing present-day Southern Rhodesia, it is necessary to consider carefully the nature of change and its implications for society.

One aspect of change is dealt with in this essay. The general trend of events relating to African employment illustrates the overall pattern and provides a stimulating field for the study of its implications. This essay is concerned particularly with the nature and extent of the changes that are taking place in the structure of the labour force, and their influence on the planning of future development. Although there has been great interest in some aspects of African employment, notably the circulation of population between rural areas and centres of employment, and penetrating studies have been made of its impact on the way of life in these areas (Orde Browne, 1933; Elkan, 1960; Mitchell, 1961), relatively little attention has been paid to changes in the character of the labour force. These changes are vital clues to the future for planners in Government service and industrial management who are concerned with the formulation of development policies, as a realistic appraisal of prospects can only be made by studying them in relation to the whole labour force.

PRE-WAR AND POST-WAR POLICIES

In the virtual absence of detailed statistical information on this topic the policies of the Southern Rhodesian Government provide a useful indication of changes in the pattern of African employment. At the start of the Second World War an attitude of *laissez-faire* characterized official policy on this matter, and, with few exceptions, legislative action was taken only to prevent the worst abuses of the system. It was apparently assumed that workers and employers had established a satisfactory relationship which necessitated no further intervention.

At that time the most important factor influencing the Government's attitude was the decision, taken entirely on political grounds, to allocate separate areas for European and African settlement. The main obstacle to the implementation of this policy lay in the growing demand for African labour in areas reserved exclusively for European occupation. The employment of Africans in European areas could be reconciled with the principles of racial separation only if the continuing existence of labour migration was accepted as one of the principal aims of Government policy (Gray, 1960). As long as African workers were forced to circulate periodically between centres of employment and the reserves, they could be allowed to stay in European areas while they were working. In this way it was possible for Africans to be temporary residents in European areas without affecting the permanent allocation of land.

Since the war conditions in the towns have dominated thinking about African employment. The publication, between 1943 and 1945, of the data from economic surveys of Salisbury and Bulawayo drew public attention to the plight of the African worker and compelled the Government to reconsider the relationship between employer and employee. In 1945 and in 1948 African workers went on strike to express their dissatisfaction with existing conditions. In 1947 the Government set up Native Labour Boards to look into these matters and, on their recommendation, legislation was enacted which specified the minimum permissible standards for the employment of African workers in urban areas. Under the scrutiny of the Boards working conditions improved steadily until legislation enabling African workers to join trades unions was passed in 1959 (Barber, 1961).

Sustained increases in the level of real wages are dependent on a parallel rise in productivity. The use of official powers to improve working conditions forced employers to make better use of their labour, but in every field attempts to increase efficiency were hampered by the basic instability of the migrant worker. As early as 1945 the Howman Committee drew attention to the precarious nature of African life in the towns and concluded that:

until we cater for family and community life in an urban environment we cannot expect industrial standards to emerge, except the superficial and unpleasant standards which we now impose by force of law and punishment, and we throw a burden of patience and forbearance upon employers that only the best of them can carry (Southern Rhodesian Government, 1945).

During the next fifteen years many employers began to question the desirability of a system based entirely on the use of migrant labour, in spite of the vital part it was playing in the implementation of the policy of racial separation. In response to pressures from social reformers as well as employers the Government accepted the need to encourage a stable labour force in the towns. In 1958 a special division was set up in the Department of Labour, Social Welfare and Housing 'to stabilize labour forces; [and] to provide opportunities for increased permanent employment in the towns for indigenous Africans in order that they may acquire skills' (Southern Rhodesian Government, 1960). In addition to projects for the development of permanent communities there was a change in attitude towards the migrant worker. Since 1958 African workers from outside the Federation have been prevented from taking jobs in urban areas, and the Act providing special facilities for migrants from Northern Rhodesia and Nyasaland was repealed in 1960.

During the last twenty years the Southern Rhodesian Government has begun to appreciate the economic and social significance of African employment. Official intervention, by the imposition of minimum standards subject to constant scrutiny, has led to a noticeable improvement in working conditions. Although this change is more pronounced in the urban areas, its impact has been felt throughout the country with the result that the African worker's prospects have increased and he has been given a new incentive to gain experience and knowledge. Rising standards of living have made it necessary to increase the productivity of the labour force, and to introduce policies aimed at the stabilization of population, even though permanent settlement in the towns conflicts with the principles of racial separation expressed in the Land Apportionment Act and strengthens the argument for its repeal. The trend of events, apparently, is leading towards a revolution in policy which will have far-reaching implications throughout the whole country.

In spite of the changes in official thought, Southern Rhodesian employers have kept most of their special powers over their African workers. These extend far beyond the immediate work relationship. Employers are directly responsible for housing their workers, and, because of the rudimentary state of Government social services, they are also expected to look after their general welfare. Consequently the extent to which changes in official policy have affected the daily life of each worker depends largely on the attitude of his employer. Within limits imposed by the state of the labour market at any point in time, a bad employer has it in his power to slow down the rate of change, whereas an enlightened one can take steps to improve the standards of life for all his workers.

As a place for the exercise of the employer's powers the factory has come to occupy an important position in the study of social conditions in Southern Rhodesia.[1] It provides an opportunity to examine, in miniature, the nature of changes that are taking place throughout the whole country. This approach also makes it possible to assess, under carefully controlled conditions, the implications of change on future policy, a task which can be undertaken on a national scale only with the greatest difficulty in view of the many factors needing consideration. The remainder of this essay is devoted to some of the results of an intensive study of conditions in a tobacco factory based on fieldwork carried out between September 1960 and August 1961. Its principal aim was to produce a case history of change which could be measured quantitatively.

FACTORY SURVEY

Background

The Salisbury branch of a British tobacco company was selected for study largely because its management had taken steps to stabilize the labour force. As a result it was possible to consider some of the implications arising from a policy whose aims were

[1] There are studies of Salisbury factories made by E. M. Bell (1961) and S. J. T. and T. M. Samkange (1960). Similar investigations have been undertaken in South Africa, notably by E. Hellman (1953) and the Department of Economics at the University of Natal (1950), and in Uganda by W. Elkan (1956). Elkan's study is of particular interest as it is also concerned with the tobacco industry.

similar to those of the Government. This branch was set up in Salisbury in 1948 to undertake the purchasing of tobacco at the auctions and its preparation for shipping to Great Britain. At the end of 1960 these activities, together with several basic processes, occupied 1,100 African men and 300 African women, and 80 Europeans in executive or specialist posts. Although most of the Africans were engaged in unskilled work, some occupied technical, clerical and supervisory positions in the factory.

Work in the factory is essentially seasonal in nature. In Salisbury the auction sales usually run from March to September. Work begins soon after the start of the sales and usually continues until November in order to deal with stocks accumulated during the auctions. Between November and the following March there is no work in the factory apart from routine maintenance, and it is the custom of the firm to give most of its workers unpaid leave during this period. A large number return to their homes at this time and cultivate land to supplement their cash wages. This regular break plays an important part in the life of each worker and has influenced the policy of the management.

The management's attitude towards African employment has changed since the war in a way similar to that of the Government. Because of their special powers they have been able to take direct action to improve the standards of living of their workers. When they took over the factory in 1948 nearly all the labour force lived in mud huts and corrugated iron quarters adjacent to the factory buildings. The compound was classed as temporary accommodation and the Municipality undertook to re-house them in single quarters in the nearby township of Harare. As there was a chronic housing shortage after the war the re-housing process was a tedious one. Fifty places in a municipal hostel were allocated to the firm in 1953 and three years later only half the workers were housed in this way. It was not until ten years after the firm took over that the last of the temporary huts was demolished. By 1960 an increasing number of workers were being found married accommodation in Harare, Highfields or Mufakose, while the bulk of the remainder lived in a hostel built for the firm in Harare.

As the temporary housing on the factory site was being demolished an ambitious programme was begun to increase the facilities available to African workers. A modern hospital was built on the cleared land between 1959 and 1960 to replace the two brick huts that had previously served as a clinic, and a crèche was erected in 1960 to provide facilities for the care of children whose mothers worked in the factory. Qualified European staff were appointed to run them, and an African welfare clerk was appointed to look after the recreational needs of the worker. Apart from its novel features the programme also involved the extension and replacement of existing facilities such as the showers and the canteens, with the result that in 1960 the firm was able to offer its workers a range of welfare services equalled by very few other employers in Southern Rhodesia.

At the same time working conditions in the factory were kept consistently above the minimum standards laid down by the Government.[1] The cash wage paid monthly to each worker was supplemented, often to a considerable extent, by bonuses derived from incentive schemes designed to encourage stability and increase productivity. As early as 1952 every worker completing the season was paid a cash sum equivalent to a month's pay, and in 1958 the system was revised so that workers received part of this sum when they returned for the start of the next season. The whole system of piece-work bonuses was reorganized in 1959 to take account of the quality of the work as well as its volume; it was also decided that workers performing tasks involving sustained physical effort or special responsibility should be paid an extra daily rate. To increase the effectiveness of these schemes a works committee was set up in 1960, thereby making possible an exchange of opinions between management and worker. This committee was made up of members elected democratically in each department. At a time when only a handful of Africans in

[1] In November 1960 working conditions were controlled by the Tobacco (Miscellaneous) Industries (Native Employment) Regulations, published as Government Notice No. 109 of 1959, and amended by Government Notice No. 466 of 1959 and No. 492 of 1960.

the country had the right to vote, every worker was given a say in the organization of the factory.

Events since 1948 therefore show that the factory management has undertaken a wide variety of schemes in an effort to raise the standards of life for its workers. Up to 1956 the tempo of change was relatively slow in comparison with the marked increase that has taken place since this time. The economic justification for these schemes is based on the belief that personal productivity will increase as the workers gain in stability. In the eyes of the management their success or failure must be measured by the extent to which each worker's length of stay in employment has increased since 1948.

Labour turnover

Turnover rates provide a useful indication of changing stability. They measure the gross movement of workers into and out of employment over a given period of time, and relate it to the total volume of employment in the factory. A certain amount of this movement is clearly unavoidable. As workers reach the age of retirement their places must be taken by new recruits, and it is to the firm's advantage to replace workers who have proved themselves unsuitable by those better fitted for the jobs. On the other hand turnover rates that remain persistently high will be symptomatic of an unstable labour force.

Fortunate circumstances made it possible to examine the changes that have taken place in the turnover rate of African male employees between the end of the 1950 season and June 1961. The wage cards of every worker employed by the firm during this period have been preserved for record purposes. Collectively they provide the information about dates of engagement and discharge necessary for the construction of turnover rates relating to the African male staff.

Table I shows the rate of turnover during the period 1951-60. Special account has been taken of the seasonal nature of employment in the tobacco industry, which gives rise to two particular problems. In this type of work there are marked variations in the monthly totals of engagements and discharges. Between 60 and 80 per cent of all engagements during the period have been in the first three months of the season, and, apart from 1951, between 50 and 70 per cent of all discharges have been in its final month. The cyclical nature of movement makes it necessary to calculate turnover rates on a seasonal, rather than an annual or a monthly, basis. This, in turn, raises difficulties. The seasons vary in length. Although they usually start in March or April, their length depends on the size of the tobacco crop and the progress of the sales. In some years all the stocks have been dealt with by the end of October, whereas in others the work carries on well into January. There is also some slight movement of labour during the off-season. In the analysis the relatively small number of engagements and discharges that occur during the off-season have been incorporated in the seasonal totals, and the period covered by each season extended to run for twelve months from February in each year.

TABLE I

The seasonal turnover of African male staff, 1951-60

Season	Engagements during the season	Discharges during the season	Total movement during the season	Total in employment at 30th September	Seasonal turnover rate* %
1951	466	508	974	428	113·9
1952	300	413	713	399	89·3
1953	411	342	753	433	87·0
1954	697	685	1,382	603	114·6
1955	595	590	1,185	569	104·1
1956	733	626	1,359	667	101·9
1957	596	597	1,193	812	73·5
1958	876	557	1,433	1,050	68·2
1959	528	419	947	1,094	43·3
1960	438	276	714	1,122	31·8

* The turnover rate is calculated by

$$\frac{\text{Engagements} + \text{discharges}}{2 \times \text{total volume in employment at 30th September}} \times 100$$

The second problem concerns the volume of employment, which is much greater in season than out of season. As turnover rates are calculated as a percentage of the volume of employment, they will vary considerably according to the method used to measure the total strength. Both of the most frequently used measurements, the average daily strength for the whole period, and half the sum of the start of period and end of period strengths, tend to give low estimates of volume which produce inflated rates of turnover. A more sensitive measure, in seasonal terms, requires that the total flow is related to the strength in the middle, rather than the end, of the season. After a careful examination of changing volumes of employment, the 30th September was selected as a date which is characteristic of the middle of the season strength.

The table shows that between 1951 and 1960 the male labour force in the factory at mid-season grew from 400 to 1,100. Most of this expansion took place in two periods of very rapid growth, one during the 1954 season, and the other during the period from the start of 1956 to the end of the 1958 season. Prior to 1958 the seasonal fluctuations between these periods are a reflection of the quantity of tobacco coming into the factory. At this date female labour was introduced and the trend of rapid growth begun in 1956 has been continued in this section of the labour force up to 1960 while there has been only a very slight increase in the volume of male employment.

The trend of turnover rates shows a marked change at the end of the 1956 season. Between 1951 and 1956 they fluctuated between 87 and 115 per cent but they have fallen since then to only 31·8 per cent for the 1960 season. In effect the change is more pronounced than it appears, as the first part of the fall occurs during 1957 and 1958 when it would be expected that rates would be higher than in most seasons because of the rapid expansion of the labour force at that time.

The seasonal trend in the rate of turnover suggests that the labour force is increasing in stability. To find out how this increase has taken place the variations in the length of time each worker stays with the firm must be taken into account. Table II shows, on a seasonal basis, the survival of African male staff during the period. The upper part of it shows how many of the workers engaged in each season stayed with the firm to complete one, two, three or four consecutive seasons in employment. The lower part presents this material in a way that makes direct comparison between each intake of workers possible.

TABLE II

Survival of African male staff, 1951-60

Intake of workers during	Total	*1 season*	*2 seasons*	*3 seasons*	*4 seasons*
			Number completing		
1951 season	466	299	86	31	19
1952 ,,	300	156	49	14	7
1953 ,,	411	255	77	33	22
1954 ,,	697	462	124	51	28
1955 ,,	595	371	122	62	36
1956 ,,	733	581	191	77	41
1957 ,,	596	465	159	91	66
1958 ,,	876	694	439	293	*
1959 ,,	528	422	285	*	*
1960 ,,	438	365	*	*	*

Intake of workers during	Total	*1 season*	*2 seasons*	*3 seasons*	*4 seasons*
			Proportion completing		
1951 season	1,000	642	185	67	41
1952 ,,	1,000	520	163	47	23
1953 ,,	1,000	620	187	80	54
1954 ,,	1,000	663	178	73	40
1955 ,,	1,000	624	205	104	61
1956 ,,	1,000	793	261	105	56
1957 ,,	1,000	780	267	153	111
1958 ,,	1,000	793	501	334	*
1959 ,,	1,000	799	540	*	*
1960 ,,	1,000	833	*	*	*

* Not available at the time of the survey in mid-1961

The table illustrates the most serious problem that faces the management of a factory requiring seasonal labour. Throughout the whole period at least half the workers stayed to complete their first season's work, but only a fraction of these completed a second season with the firm. The lay-off between the seasons is disastrous in its effects on stability. Many of the workers who went back to their homes in the country do not wish to return for another season even though jobs are waiting for them, and some of those who looked for temporary employment in the city may have found themselves better jobs in the meantime.

Between the start of the 1951 season and 1960 there has been a considerable increase in the length of time that workers stay with the firm. The most marked changes have occurred in the proportion of staff completing two and three seasons in employment. Whereas only 185 out of every 1,000 workers engaged in 1951 stayed to the end of the second season, 540 out of every 1,000 did so in 1959. Similarly the number completing three consecutive seasons has risen from 67 in 1951 to 334 out of every 1,000 workers engaged in 1958. These increases suggest that, at the end of the period, fewer workers were encouraged to leave their jobs as a result of the lay-off than at its start. Particularly since 1958 more and more have returned for the start of each new season and this trend has continued since 1960: nearly 94 per cent of the labour laid off at the end of the 1961 season returned at the beginning of 1962, and this rose to 97 per cent between 1962 and 1963.

The cumulative effect of these changes on stability is tremendous. The rise in the proportion of workers from each intake who start each season acts with the increase in the proportion of those completing any season to multiply the chances of survival. Consequently more workers are staying for longer periods in employment, and the average length of service rose from 13·56 months at the end of the 1950 season to 16·50 months at the end of 1956, and reached 26·08 months in November 1960. This represents an increase of 22 per cent between 1950 and 1956, and 58 per cent between 1956 and 1960. There is a positive relationship between the increase in the length of stay and the improvements to the working conditions stimulated by the policy of the factory management. For both the tempo of change was slow up to 1956, and in both cases it increased considerably between 1956 and 1960.

It is difficult to assess the extent to which the management's policy is responsible for these changes. A large part of the increase in the length of stay must be attributed to certain factors which have affected the market for African labour throughout Southern

Rhodesia (Barber, 1961). It is due, in the first place, to the growing number of Southern Rhodesian workers coming into the labour market. This is a reflection of the deterioration of conditions in the rural areas brought about by increasing population pressures. It is also one of the results of Government measures to improve the economy of these areas. The Native Land Husbandry Act of 1951 proposed to replace the traditional system of communal land tenure by agricultural holdings allocated to individuals. Its implementation has meant that most of the men in wage employment, and even some of those resident in the reserves, have lost their right to cultivate land. It is assumed that most of these people will remain permanently in wage employment (Floyd, 1959). At the end of the period, then, the total number of work seekers had risen, and, because of the situation in Southern Rhodesia, there had been a marked increase in the proportion of those who were looking for permanent employment in the money economy.

In addition, the pace of economic development in Southern Rhodesia slowed down after 1957 and there was a relative decline in the demand for African labour. Stability tended to increase as jobs became hard to find, and those workers who were already in employment became reluctant to leave their positions of relative security. At the same time the Government took steps to restrict the inflow of migrant workers from outside Southern Rhodesia. These measures have particularly affected urban workers from Moçambique who, if employed, cannot leave their jobs without the possibility of having to leave the town as well.

The degree of stabilization in the factory is probably the result of the interaction of three main factors. Management policy has operated in conjunction with Government policy to increase the length of stay in employment by improving working conditions. The effect of these policies has been accentuated by rising unemployment produced by a growth in the numbers of workers seeking jobs at a time when the demand for labour is declining. A great deal of careful study will be required before it is possible to measure the pressures exerted by each of these factors.

Labour organization

Whatever their cause, longer periods in employment have significant effects on the organization of labour in any factory. One of the most important, in terms of its social implications, is the rise in the number of skilled workers in relation to the total strength. This is largely due to two factors. In the first place, as more workers stay longer in employment they are given greater opportunities to acquire skills as part of their experience. Secondly, better working conditions in themselves make necessary a more complex form of organization than before, and there is a corresponding increase in the number of skilled staff required for administration and maintenance.

Table III shows the occupations of African male staff in the factory at the end of the 1960 season. Although the number of skilled workers had risen since 1956 they accounted for under a quarter of the strength in November 1960. More than three-quarters of the workers were engaged in unskilled jobs, or tasks that required a simple routine skill. The skilled workers fell into two main groups: skilled process workers and supervisors in the productive part of the factory accounting for two-thirds of the total number, and the trades and the administrative staff in the organizational part making up the other third. Apart from a few gardeners and cleaners involved in the maintenance of the fabric, most of the unskilled workers were engaged in the production lines. Yet it is likely that the number in this group will decline if the length of stay of each worker continues to increase and the chances of acquiring skills multiply. If this happens, there will be a proportional rise in the number of skilled workers.

There were two types of employment at the factory in November 1960: 885 out of the 1,109 workers were paid off at the end of the season and given unpaid leave until the start of the next one, but the other 224 were retained by the firm to work during the lay-off period. Although over half of these were staff concerned with administration or routine maintenance, a relatively large number of skilled production workers were retained even though

TABLE III

Occupations of African male staff, November 1960

	Workers given unpaid leave in November 1960	Workers retained by the firm	Total strength on 5th November 1960
Productive Processes:			
Unskilled workers	758	28	786
Skilled workers	70	59	129
Supervisors	14	13	27
Maintenance:			
Unskilled workers	33	47	80
Trades	7	24	31
Administration	3	53	56
Total	885	224	1,109
%	79·8	20·2	100

there was no production over this period. This is mainly because good supervisors are hard to come by and they are looked upon as valuable assets to the firm. If, for any particular reason, they do not wish to leave Salisbury during the off-season the firm has begun to employ them for this period rather than risk losing them. This is becoming the case, to a lesser degree, with some of the other productive workers who have considerable experience in specialized jobs.

If the increase in the number of skilled workers continues at its present rate the management of the factory will be faced with the need to make important decisions about the future. The difference between seasonal work in the factory and off-seasonal work on a rural plot or in temporary employment will become more marked as the standards of living of skilled workers rise. Off-seasonal work is increasingly less attractive to workers who require permanent employment if they are to maintain the higher standards of living dependent on their skill, and they will tend to seek this type of post rather than seasonal jobs. In this event the long-term success of the firm's policy is endangered by the nature of employment in the factory, and the management is now considering an alternative to the present system. It has to decide whether it is more desirable to pay workers throughout a lay-off of up to five months, or whether the flow of tobacco can be regulated to extend the productive period. In either case the long term success of their policy involves important alterations in the organization of the factory.

Sources of labour

In addition to the problems posed by the increasing number of skilled workers on the staff, the success of the attempts to encourage workers to stay longer in employment has forced the management to make important decisions about the future composition of the labour force. In 1960 the firm was dependent on labour coming from areas outside Southern Rhodesia. Table IV shows that more than 70 per cent of the labour force came from Nyasaland. Most of these workers belonged to the Eastern Matrilineal group of tribes which include the Yao, the Lomwe and the Nyanja who live in the densely populated Shire valley, but there was also a small concentration of Ngoni in the neighbourhood of the Northern Rhodesian boundary. About 9 per cent of the workers came from Moçambique and belonged to the Lower Zambezi group of tribes which include the Sena and the Cikunda. Only 17 per cent of the total staff belonged to the Shona group who live in the northern part of Southern Rhodesia.

Most of the workers coming from outside Southern Rhodesia were still labour migrants. With few exceptions they had left their wives and families in their home districts and come to Salisbury as single men to seek work. Most of them had not been able, or had not wanted to bring their families to live with them once they found a job, and kept this close contact with their home area. On the other hand the proportion of Southern Rhodesian workers falling into this category was relatively low, and the majority lived in the townships around Salisbury with their families. Table IV shows that the migrants tended to concentrate in the unskilled jobs in the productive processes whereas Southern Rhodesian workers occupied a large proportion of the skilled maintenance and administrative posts. As a result it is possible to make a distinction between them on the basis of job type and wage differentials, as well as in terms of cultural background and the attitude towards the urban way of life.

TABLE IV
Origins of African male staff, November 1960

	Southern Rhodesia	Northern Rhodesia	Nyasaland	Moçambique	Total
Productive processes:					
Unskilled workers	103	16	614	53	786
Skilled workers	17	7	73	32	129
Supervisors	3	4	17	3	27
Maintenance:					
Unskilled workers	17	0	52	11	80
Trades	15	1	12	3	31
Administration	36	2	17	1	56
Total	191	30	785	103	1,109
%	17·2	2·7	70·8	9·3	100

This distinction has important implications for the future stability of the labour force. The ultimate success of a stabilization policy may well depend on the extent to which it has provided conditions that enable workers to live with their families in Salisbury. In spite of the way in which migrant workers have been incorporated into a work programme which allows them to spend part of the year with their families, their stabilization will depend, in the long term, on the number who are persuaded to bring those families to Salisbury. The management is faced with two choices. It has to decide whether it is more desirable to provide incentives for workers from Nyasaland and Moçambique to bring their families to live with them, or whether care should be taken to recruit only those workers who are likely to become permanent town dwellers. In either event the decision marks an important departure from management policy prior to this time.

In accordance with Government policy the management has tended to select more Southern Rhodesian workers rather than to provide facilities for migrants to bring their families to Salisbury. An examination of the intake between 1956 and 1960 shows the start of this trend. During the 1956 season 414 Nyasas were engaged, as against 246 from Moçambique and 54 from Southern Rhodesia. After 1958 the supply of Moçambique workers was restricted by the Foreign Migratory Labour Act and the totals for that season were 612, 154 and 91 respectively. During the 1960 season 288 Nyasas were engaged, 17 from Moçambique, and 142 from Southern Rhodesia. In 1961, for the first time in the factory's history, more Southern Rhodesian workers were engaged than any other group.

Events in the tobacco factory show that the increase in the stability of African labour between 1951 and 1960 has set in motion long-term changes in the structure of the labour force which make it necessary to re-examine the conditions of employment. The factory management is having to reorganize its policy to gain the benefits arising from a relatively stable labour force. The experience from this point of view is of interest when examining the trend of Southern Rhodesian Government policy towards African employment. Since the war official policy has increasingly emphasized the need for a settled labour force and definite steps have been taken towards stabilization. The evidence of the tobacco factory suggests that there is an urgent need for studies of the implications of these decisions so that Government policy can be formulated on the basis of a realistic appraisal of the prospects for the future development of the country.

ACKNOWLEDGEMENTS

The fieldwork for this study was undertaken in 1960-1 when the author held a Leverhulme scholarship for research at the University College of Rhodesia and Nyasaland. The author thanks the Leverhulme Trust and the University College for their technical and financial assistance, and expresses his gratitude to the management of the Salisbury factory for their co-operation and advice.

REFERENCES

BARBER, W.J. (1961) *The economy of British Central Africa: a case study of economic development in a dualistic society.*

BELL, E.M. (1961) *Polygons: a survey of the African personnel of a Rhodesian factory.* Dept. of African Studies: Occasional Paper no. 2. University College of Rhodesia and Nyasaland, Salisbury.

BROWNE, G.ST.J. ORDE (1933) *The African labourer.*

ELKAN, W. (1956) *An African labour force.* East African Studies: no. 7. East African Institute of Social Research, Kampala.

ELKAN, W. (1960) *Migrants and proletarians: urban labour in the economic development of Uganda.*

FLOYD, B. (1959) 'Changing patterns of African land use in Southern Rhodesia', *Rhodes-Livingstone J., 25,* 20-39.

GRAY, R. (1960) *The Two Nations: aspects of the development of race relations in the Rhodesias and Nyasaland.*

HELLMAN, E. (1953) *Sellgoods: A sociological survey of an African commercial labour force.* South African Institute of Race Relations.

MITCHELL, J.C. (1961) 'Wage labour and African population movements in Central Africa', in BARBOUR, K.M. and PROTHERO, R.M. (eds.), *Essays on African Population.*

SAMKANGE, S.J.T. and SAMKANGE, T.M. (1960) 'A survey of personal, employment, expenditure, and accommodation data of African employees of the Rhodesian Milling Company, Salisbury'. Unpublished.

SOUTHERN RHODESIA GOVERNMENT (1945) 'Report on urban conditions in Southern Rhodesia', *Afr. Stud., 4,* 9-22 (The Howman Report).

— (1960) *Report of the Secretary for Labour, Social Welfare and Housing for the year ended 31st December 1959.* Salisbury.

UNIVERSITY OF NATAL, DEPT. OF ECONOMICS (1950) *The African factory worker.*

BIBLIOGRAPHY

GUSSMAN, B.W. (1953) 'Industrial efficiency and the urban African', *Africa, 23,* 135-44.

INTERNATIONAL LABOUR OFFICE (1960) 'Labour turnover: meaning and measurement', *Int. Lab. Rev., 81,* 513-26.

MITCHELL, J.C. (1956) 'Urbanisation, detribalisation and stabilisation in Africa south of the Sahara: a problem of measurement,' in FORDE, D. (ed.) *Social implications of industrialisation and urbanisation in Africa south of the Sahara.* U.N.E.S.C.O. Tensions and Technology Series.

NORTHCOTT, C.N. (1949) *An African labour efficiency survey.* Colonial Research Pub. no. 3, H.M.S.O.

SOUTHERN RHODESIA GOVERNMENT (1946) *Report of the commission to investigate the grievances which gave rise to the strike amongst the African employees of Rhodesia Railways.* Salisbury (The Tredgold Report.)

— (1948) *Report of the National Native Labour Board on its inquiry into the conditions of employment in industry in Bulawayo, Gwelo, Que Que, Salisbury, Umtali, Gatooma and environs.* Salisbury.

— (1958) *Report of the Urban African Affairs Commission.* Salisbury (The Plewman Report.)

— (1959) *First Report of the select committee on resettlement of natives.* Salisbury.

STENT, G.E. (n.d.) 'An analysis of the supply and demand for African labour in Southern Rhodesia'. Unpublished.

THOMPSON, C.H. and WOODRUFF, H.W. (1955) *Economic development in Rhodesia and Nyasaland.*

UNITED KINGDOM GOVERNMENT (1951) *Central African Territories: comparative survey of native policy.* Cmd. 8235. H.M.S.O.

UNIVERSITY OF WITWATERSRAND, DEPT. OF COMMERCE (1948) *Native urban employment.* Unpublished.

VAN DER HORST, S.T. (1957) 'Native labour turnover and the structure of the labour force in the Cape peninsula', *South Afr. J. Econ., 25,* 275-89.

Aspects of Ushi settlement history:
Fort Rosebery District,
Northern Rhodesia

INTRODUCTION

POPULATION patterns are influenced by a wide variety of
factors and, as G. H. T. Kimble (1960) states, 'it is arguable that
over large sections [of Africa] man's presence, or absence, is more
readily accounted for in cultural and historical terms than in
physical ones'. Present situations can be fully understood only in
the light of past events but, particularly in local studies, geographers often have stressed the significance of environmental
factors and have given little attention to historical factors though
usually aware of their importance. The reasons for this bias no
doubt are the dearth of data readily available on even the recent
past and the peculiar difficulties that face the student of African
history, and, because historical factors cannot be analysed in
detail, their role is unwittingly minimized.

This essay is largely an exercise in historical geography. It outlines the settlement history of the Ushi since their occupation of
the Fort Rosebery District which is now their tribal area, and it
seeks to illustrate the importance of this history in the analysis of
some current situations. Full use is made of verbal accounts
provided by the Ushi themselves and of the ample records of the
British South Africa Company's administrators and the officers of
the colonial service. Much history prior to 1900 has to be constructed by projecting back from existing and recorded situations
and it is fortunate that the early European government officials
learned a great deal about the people they had come to rule and

235

recorded so much of this data in District Notebooks and in various reports.

A brief description of the Fort Rosebery District precedes a tentative account of the Ushi migration and settlement prior to 1900, and the history of the period since the advent of *Pax Britannica*, which culminates in the present settlement patterns, is given in more detail.

THE FORT ROSEBERY DISTRICT

The Fort Rosebery District (Figure 1) is essentially a plateau region. The level or gently undulating surfaces at about 4,000 feet are clothed with a very variable savanna woodland which is nowhere dense, and the undergrowth – much affected by fire – is light. It is easily penetrated and readily cleared to reveal infertile, sandy, lateritic 'plateau soils'. It once held numerous game animals but except for the ubiquitous wild pig and the small duiker they are now rare; even the Senior Chief's game reserve is only lightly stocked.

The plateau is bounded on the west and south by the Luapula valley which, downstream of Johnston Falls, has been recognized as a rift valley. Above Johnston Falls the river is deeply incised, and at its confluence with the River Mansa it is about 700 feet below the general level of the plateau. Above the Mumbatuta Falls, however, the river rapidly obtains plateau level and loses its identity in the swamps of the Bangweulu depression. This enormous shallow depression in the plateau surface, with its lakes, flood plains and swamps, provides the Fort Rosebery plateau with a marked eastern boundary.

The plateau is well watered. Three large perennial rivers – the Lwela, the Mansa and the Luongo-Lufubu – flow to the Luapula, and one, the Litandashi, flows east into the Bangweulu depression. The Luongo-Lufubu and the Litandashi mark the northern boundary of the Fort Rosebery District. Numerous tributary streams and *dambos* form a close network over the plateau surface, and while many of the smaller streams dry up during the dry season all but the smallest *dambos* hold a suspended, sub-surface reservoir of water throughout the year. *Dambos* thus have a vital role in the plateau habitat. Within the shallow valleys of the plateau the margins of the *dambos* are sharply defined by a steep drop of several feet and an abrupt end to the woodland. The *dambos* are treeless, grassy and often swampy plains; some are over a mile wide. Drainage within them is poor, and most of them are seasonally flooded. At their margins the earth is a stiff clay, usually grey in colour; but the beds of watercourses within them are often sandy. F. E. Kanthack (1945) argued that these 'great sponge areas which hold great quantities of water are the key to the understanding of the hydrographic characteristics of Northern Rhodesia catchment areas'. Their reservoirs feed the main streams and maintain their flow throughout the dry season and the *dambo* waters can be tapped, even in October and November, by shallow wells. As Livingstone (1874), noted 'these sponges are a serious matter in travelling', and they are today for road building. Embankments, culverts and bridges have to be built to carry a road across them and constant attention and repairs are necessary to maintain it. *Dambos* are avoided by most modern roads which are along the watersheds, while African villages and local routes are usually by *dambo* and stream.

USHI MIGRATION AND EARLY SETTLEMENT

The Ushi are one of the matrilineal, Bemba-speaking tribes which migrated from the Luba-Lunda empire in the Congo basin, though neither the date nor the cause of their migration are known precisely. They probably left *Kola* in the seventeenth century and tribal myths suggest civil disputes and unrest within the empire as likely causes of their exodus. Probably very early in the eighteenth century they crossed the Luapula, an event which marked the end of their wanderings. The Ushi declare that they found the Fort Rosebery plateau uninhabited, and this may be so, though such claims are commonly made to justify land rights. The plateau environment was eminently suitable for their way of life for they were, and are, essentially bush cultivators. Their traditional agriculture was based on the cultivation of finger millet by 'slash and burn' techniques and land rotation. This *chitemene* system was infused with cassava culture based on semi-permanent gardens before any Europeans visited the Ushi, and in densely peopled areas cassava is now more important than millet. The Ushi have never kept cattle and in the past they depended largely on hunting for their meat. They have a wide knowledge of animal, insect and plant life, and they fully exploit these resources of the woodland and *dambo*. They have always fished the small plateau streams and the *dambos*, but when they crossed the Luapula the larger rivers and the lakes do not appear to have attracted them. Muwe, who is believed to be the founder of the tribe, considered the plateau to be an ideal homeland and chose to settle in the Mansa basin to the south of the river. The traditional burial ground of the senior chiefs at the head of the Chansunsu *dambo* is in this locality.

Shortly after the first settlement was established political factors divided the tribe, and splinter groups under independent chiefs hived off to settle in other parts of the country. All the chiefs on the plateau but one are of the *ngulube* clan which is recognized as the royal clan. The exception is Kalasa Lukangaba, a member of the *shimba* clan and a son of a senior chief, who was made a chief because of his military prowess and exploits in the protection of the tribe. The chiefs in the Luapula valley downstream of the Lwela confluence, however, belong to the *mumba* clan, and their people are known as *bena mukulo*, waterside people. This *mukulo* sub-group generally claim that they preferred to stay by the big river where water and fish are always plentiful, where game are more numerous, and where crops grow particularly well. Several Ushi on the plateau deny these ecological reasons for the separation of the *mukulo*. They claim that members of the *mumba* clan were left by the Luapula or, according to other versions, were sent back to the river, in charge of forces protecting the ford which was essential should the tribe be forced to retreat. Whatever the reasons for living in the valley the *mukulo* have adapted themselves to conditions there, and are now skilled river fishermen. They, more than any other section of the tribe, have maintained contacts with related peoples in the Congo. Another group of Ushi settled the distinctive environment south of Lake Bangweulu (Figure 1). The flood plains there were soon noted amongst the Ushi for their large herds of game, particularly during the dry season, and they became a favourite venue of Ushi hunting parties. Temporary shelters grew into permanent settlements, and the area was colonized and divided into chiefdoms. In a different habitat the people developed different interests, and increasingly looked towards the peculiar resources of the flood plains and swamps for their living. Economic and cultural differentiation was accompanied by political separation, and despite all the efforts of the plateau Ushi, the Kabende were, and are, recognized as a separate tribe.

The history of Ushi expansion on the plateau cannot be fully and accurately reconstructed, for no one person knows the full story and each chief is concerned primarily with his own history. Their accounts contain much conflicting data and, though their arguments are usually at cross-purposes rather than contradictory, they do not provide a detailed factual history. They do, however, furnish a general picture of how the tribe became a loose association of relatively independent groups because of sub-divisions under an increasing number of chiefs and the political weakness of the senior chiefs, who were spiritual leaders and the keepers of the tribal god rather than effective overlords (Philpot, 1936). Only once, from about 1847 to 1877, was the tribe united by a strong senior chief, and it was then an important military and political power. When this chief died, he had no suitable heir, and his successor, who moved his village from the Mansa to the Lwela, was not recognized by many of the Ushi chiefs who reasserted their independence. P. Weatherly (1898) noted the independence of the local chiefs during his travels to Lake Bangweulu in 1896. 'The country', he wrote, 'is divided up under different subordinate chiefs who all acknowledge Miere-miere (Milambo) as supreme head. If they were united they would form

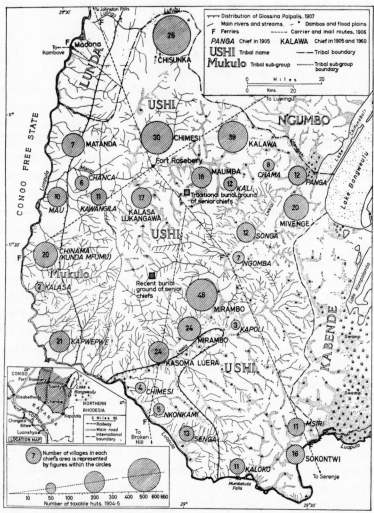

Figure 1. The Fort Rosebery Plateau, *c.* 1905. The distribution of the 27 Ushi chiefs, and the number of villages and taxable huts in each chief's area, are shown. The chiefs' names are spelt as in the District Notebook; these spellings reflect the phonetics of the 'Nyasa mission boys' employed by the administration. (*Based on maps and notes in the Fort Rosebery District Notebooks*)

a powerful nation, but this is far from the case'. By 1900 the Senior Chief had 'sunk so low that he was living as a mere headman . . . he died in 1904 . . . and hardly any of the Ushi chiefs attended his funeral'.

H. T. Harrington, the first administrative official of the Fort Rosebery District, mapped the distribution of the chiefs in 1904-5, and recorded the number of villages and taxable huts in each chief's area (Figure 1). These data provide an incomparable picture of the fragmentation of the Ushi tribe at a critical period. No less than twenty-seven chiefs were enumerated. Some had a very small following; four had less than fifty taxable huts in their areas, which suggests populations of less than 250 persons. Only eight chiefs had more than 200 taxable huts, but two, Milambo and Chisunka, each had well over 600 which suggests they had followings of about 3,000 persons each. The broad distribution of the population showed a marked correlation with the major valleys. The Mansa basin, cradle of the Ushi tribe, was well settled, the Luapula and Lwela valleys were occupied, and Chisunka's chiefdom was centred on the Lufubu. Vast areas of plateau were uninhabited, though the physical environment provided no obstacle to the spread of the Ushi and there remained ample room for further expansion.

It would, however, be a mistake simply to correlate territorial occupation with the multiplication of chiefs. The chief's role is primarily a political one and, though he bears the title of *mwine mpanga* – owner of the land – his concern is with people rather than land. His area (*icalo*) is that occupied by his people and his reputation is reckoned in terms of his following. Some of the first chiefs did, in fact, move into unoccupied areas but the greater part of Ushi territorial expansion was pioneered by men of lower political ranks, perhaps under the patronage of the chiefs. Any person of any clan who could raise a following and wished to break away from his own group could settle a new area, and the first settler in each locality was recognized as *mwine mpanga*. Each of these *mwine mpanga* and their successors have ritual powers and responsibilities for the well-being of their neighbourhood. These neighbourhoods, however, have not been clearly defined, and appear to be spheres of influence rather than precise territorial units. The Ushi have no classificatory name for them; they are variously referred to as *cipande*, *cipataulwa*, *citente*, or *mutala* – pieces, parts, sections or divisions of the chief's country. There are now seven such neighbourhoods in Chief Kalaba's Area, and each is referred to by a regional name, most of which are also stream names. There are six in Chief Kalasa Lukangaba's Area, and they are identified by reference to the owners. All of these neighbourhoods were established before the period of European rule.

In the first place there was probably a single settlement in each neighbourhood, but the processes of fission and dispersion continued within these areas and subsidiary settlements sprang up. These were probably small, and were based on an extended matrilineal family. It was, and is, every man's ambition to become the elder of a family group and to establish his independence as such. This independence was reflected in a new settlement in which the elder was recognized as *mwine mushi* – owner of the village, or village headman. Within each neighbourhood the village headmen recognized the ritual powers of the local *mwine mpanga*, and referred to him as *mwine mushi mukalamba* – the senior village headman – when it was necessary to differentiate between him and the chief. All the residents within a chief's area acknowledged the ritual and political position of their chief, and so in each neighbourhood two owners of the land were recognized, one by right of land occupation and one by right of political position; their titles were, and are, similar, but their roles are complementary. All the tribe accepted the supreme ritual position of the senior chief, the keeper of their god.

The pattern of settlement therefore reflected the Ushi's inherent social and political tendencies towards fragmentation and dispersion, and the inability of established authorities, both chiefs and headmen, to prevent these processes which weakened both their individual powers and prestige and the collective strength of the tribe. It is equally apparent that relatively small family units were economically viable as well as socially desirable, and the environment allowed these tendencies to be developed freely. The role of economic factors in the processes of dispersion was probably insignificant. The Ushi were, and are, prepared to make gardens as much as ten miles away from their villages, and there is no history of land hunger. Indeed, subsidiary settlements were often moved only a little way from their parent village and their members continued to cultivate in the same lands as previously and to some extent they kept the same social connections within the larger community.

Into this situation came the administrative officers of the British South Africa Company – a new and powerful outside force which manipulated tribal institutions into a pattern suited to the particular needs of the new Government. One of the first notes in the Fort Rosebery District Notebook provides a neat summary of the administrator's view of Ushi settlement patterns, and portends of changes to come.

Taken as a whole the Independent Chiefs are a decent lot; there are, of course the good, the indifferent and at least three bad. . . . They have but one grievance, that is the *insakwi* grievance viz: Heads of families who have no standing leaving their proper villages against the order of their chiefs and hiding themselves away in the bush in wretched grass shelters which they gradually make into villages and call themselves headmen and independent of their chiefs. (This causes endless trouble, especially in collecting the Hut Tax. . . .) The men who do this are usually old men with several daughters, and with these they are able to get some young fellows to follow them.

USHI SETTLEMENT UNDER COLONIAL RULE

The early administrators were energetic, courageous men with such a belief and confidence in the benefits of colonial rule that they were almost ruthless in establishing their powers. Their first concern was to obtain peace, and slave trading and tribal wars were stopped by the use or threat of armed intervention. Such action was generally welcome, though Harrington (1954) recalls that the Ushi Senior Chief asked him: 'Now you have turned out all the Arabs, what am I going to do with bad characters in my

243

country? . . . When any of my people got troublesome I sold them for calico'. At that time (1899) Harrington 'had no answer', but *Pax Britannica* was quickly followed by law and order – justice, according to the European pattern – and by taxes. At first huts were taxed, because huts could not disappear at short notice; later, tax was laid upon adult male heads and the poll tax is still employed. The task of pacifying Ushi country was quickly completed, but effective administration and tax collection depended upon a working knowledge of the land and people. Census-taking and map-making were completed in 1905, and gave the Native Commissioner a clear picture of the problems he faced. There was little in the pattern and form of Ushi settlements that recommended itself to him for he required: (i) a friendly, strong central authority; (ii) a manageable number of influential, co-operative chiefs; (iii) the people collected in relatively few, large and accessible villages. To obtain such a pattern the administration, as far as possible, intervened in normal social and political situations and rationalized, according to European views, certain tribal institutions rather than dictated entirely alien policies. With a local force of only ten Messengers and fifteen police in 1905 the administration could not continually bully the local peoples. In 1904 the Senior Chief died; his succession was disputed until 1907 and it was then apparent that none of the contenders could dominate all the Ushi chiefs. The Administrator followed the normal, but in this case unpopular, procedure and appointed the deceased's maternal nephew. However his 'was an empty title . . . the Ushi chiefs would have none of him', and it was clear that the Native Commissioner himself was to be the strong, central authority.

The Native Commissioner accepted the chiefs' areas and the villages as the basis of local government, and the neighbourhoods were either unknown or ignored. In 1905 both chiefs and villages were considered to be too numerous for administrative convenience; there were twenty-seven chiefs and 436 villages exclusive of embryonic settlements (*insakwi*). To prevent further sub-division of the tribal land each chief's area was demarcated and the whole country allocated to one chief or another. Inevitably border disputes were common and have continued, more or less peacefully, to the present day. To prevent further fragmentation of settlements *insakwi*, the necessary initial stage of village formation and building, were declared illegal in June 1906. The Native Commissioner thus sided firmly with the established tribal authorities, with the chiefs who wished to lose neither land nor people and with the headmen who wished to maintain or increase their following. It is also evident that these tribal authorities exploited the powers of the new Government for their own interests. This alignment of old and new authorities is apparent in the Native Commissioner's general comment on the situation and in his notes on an incident in Chief Kalaba's Area:

Chief Kalaba is a very good chief. Since his people have been collected into fewer villages he has done his best to get them to pay tax. In December (1906) he complained some of his people had again built *insakwi* away in the bush. Lent him Messengers to burn them, which he did, and brought the people before me.

This halting of the processes of fission was accompanied by more austere measures to reduce the numbers of both chiefs and villages. The application of these required much tact, particularly when negotiating for the abolition of a chieftainship, but it was facilitated by the fact that all the chiefs were not equal and the losses of one were the gains of another. By diplomacy and intrigue it was possible to get rid of less important chiefs and to amalgamate their Areas with those of neighbouring chiefs and to gain support for such actions from many Ushi chiefs who were anxious to ingratiate themselves with the all-powerful administration. Some of these cases were not simple and the fortunes of a chief could vary according to changes in prevailing arguments and interpretations by the Commissioners. For instance, Mibenge at first was recognized as a chief; later he was deposed but after strong protests was reinstated as a 'district headman' and in 1914 was again recognized as a chief; he is now one of the ten Native Authorities of the Ushi tribe. Before the introduction of Indirect Rule only two chiefs were removed simply by diplomatic means; Kapoli was merged with Milambo and Panga with Chama (Table I). The amalgamation of villages was carried out more ruthlessly. Small villages were abolished and burnt and their inhabitants required to move into other settlements, usually back into their parent village where the headman welcomed their return to his following. The rate of amalgamation varied considerably and was most thorough in the Senior Chief's Area where between 1905 and 1914 two out of every three villages were abolished. In Chief Chisunka's Area amalgamation was resisted and in the same period three new villages were formed there and officially recognized (Table I).

However, in many chiefs' Areas drastic measures taken under the Sleeping Sickness Regulations mask those of more normal reorganization. Sleeping sickness was first noted in the Luapula valley in Lunda country in 1906. In 1907 the Provincial Medical Officer investigated the situation in Fort Rosebery District and subsequently a ten-mile strip along the Luapula was put under his direct administration and all routes across the river were closed. By 1910 the outbreak was considered to be out of control, medical administration of the riverine strip was withdrawn, and plans were laid to evacuate the entire valley region during the following year. This operation inevitably caused a tremendous disruption, and provided an incomparable opportunity for the reorganization of settlement on lines approved by the administration. Every house in the valley was cleared of its inhabitants and burnt, and all canoes found on the river were destroyed. The people were moved *en masse* on to the plateau and were settled in large villages (Table I). Fourteen chiefs were involved in the evacuation, and six of them lost their positions during this disturbed period. Nkonkami, Senga and Kaloko were amalgamated with Kasoma Lwela into whose Area they were moved, and Kawangila was similarly merged with Kalasa Lukangaba. Kalasa and Chimese chose to flee with most of their people into the Congo Free State, and thus forfeited their positions as chiefs. Others also preferred to move across the border rather than leave the valley and as late as 1914 the Native Commissioner had to report that he was 'afraid the exodus of our natives is still going on, and will continue so long as

TABLE I

Chiefs and villages, 1905-60

Number of villages

Chief	1904-05*	1914	1917	1929-31*	1948	1956	1960
Matanda†	7	2	2	12	85	93	87
Chansa†	6	2	3	5	Matanda	–	–
Mabo†	10	1	1	4	Matanda	–	¬
Kapwepwe†	21	1	1	6	Matanda	–	–
Kalasa†	2	C.F.S.	–	–	–	–	–
Kundamfumu†	20	5	5	5	Kal. Luk.	–	–
Kalasa Lukangaba	17	15	16	15	65	76	77
Kawangila†	11	Kal. Luk.	–	–	–	–	–
Kasoma Lwela†	24	2	7	10	43	48	48
Nkonkami†	5	K. Lwela	–	–	–	–	–
Senga†	13	K. Lwela	–	–	–	–	–
Kaloko†	11	K. Lwela	–	–	–	–	–
Chimese†	4	C.F.S.	–	–	–	–	–
Sokontwe†	16	15	15	19	54	57	58
Msiri†	11	5	Sokontwe	–	–	–	–
Milambo	72	25	25	34	100	86	85
Kapoli	3	Milambo	–	–	–	–	–
Ngomba	7	4	5	8	Milambo	–	–
Mabumba	18	15	21	25	85	89	90
Nsonga	12	6	8	11	Mabumba	–	–
Mibenge	20	12	12	18	50	62	67
Kali	12	6	9	12	Mibenge	–	–
Kalaba	39	20	23	27	90	87	93
Chama	8	7	7	11	Kalaba	–	–
Panga	12	Chama	–	–	–	–	–
Chimese	30	19	22	30	80	92	92
Chisunka	25	28	36	40	48	52	53
Totals	436	190	218	292	700	742	750
Average size:							
Huts	24	ND	42	ND	ND	ND	22
Population	60	ND	105	ND	55‡	ND	79‡

* Counts for all chiefs' Areas are not available in a single year.

† Chiefs affected by the evacuation under Sleeping Sickness Regulations.

‡ Registered population, i.e. including absent members.

ND. No data.

the Sleeping Sickness Regulations remain in force'. Clearly the riverside people liked neither large villages nor plateau life, and with their connections across the Luapula they were able to escape the measures planned for them with good intentions by the administration. W. Lammond (1955), a resident in the Luapula valley at Johnston Falls during the evacuation, has written,

I trust I shall not witness such misery again. More people died of hunger and hardship than died of the sleeping sickness. . . . The Government tried to help a little but what they did was altogether inadequate, and crowds of the weaker and older people succumbed. Here arises a very curious problem. The Belgian villagers still used the river and lived on its banks, crossing over and hunting game in our territory. . . . In spite of this the sleeping sickness died out and when [the people] were allowed to return twelve years afterwards there was no trace of sleeping sickness.

Sleeping sickness and the events associated with it were not the only set-back that the Ushi population received in the early years of colonial rule. In 1901 an outbreak of smallpox 'lasted a whole year and hundreds of natives died', and in 1912-13 there was famine throughout the Fort Rosebery District largely because the absence of many men at work in the Congo had temporarily upset food production. In 1917 there was another famine largely as a result of war demands on foodstuffs and labour, and yet another in 1918 which was more serious and during which many deaths were reported. In the same year an influenza epidemic proved fatal to many; Messengers counted 455 deaths in one area. The rapid growth of population, so often assumed as a concomitant of *Pax Britannica*, did not begin in the Fort Rosebery District for at least twenty years after slave trading and tribal wars were stopped. In 1905 the official estimate of the Ushi population based on a ratio of three persons per hut was 31,000. Later calculations suggested 2·5 persons per hut as being more accurate and this estimate might, therefore, be reduced to 26,000. In 1917, when there was half the number of villages and when administrative machinery was more efficient and therefore fewer huts were likely to escape being counted, the population estimate was 22,000 persons, a decrease of over 4,000 since 1905.

After the disturbances of the outbreak of sleeping sickness and of the First World War the Ushi enjoyed a relatively quiet phase. The Luapula valley was reopened for settlement and was reoccupied over a decade or so. After twelve years of plateau life only one chief, Kundamfumu, elected to remain away from the river, and this choice may have been for political rather than for ecological reasons. The administration kept strict control over the spread of settlements, but did allow some dispersion more or less commensurate with population growth. By 1931 there were 292 Ushi villages, an increase of 34 per cent since 1917 but still only 66 per cent of the number in 1905 (Table I). Regulations concerning local movements of population were codified. No person could move from one village to another without the permission of both headmen concerned and their chief. No person could move from one chief's Area to another without the permission of both chiefs; and all movements had to be reported to the administrative officials. Such regulations were no doubt frequently broken, but generally they were effective and more or less stabilized the population. Each chief's people and their increase were contained within their particular Area, and therefore in considering population distributions the boundaries of chiefs' Areas are lines of importance.

In 1953, during investigations following disturbances caused by the allocation of a large area on the east bank of the River Lwela as a Game Reserve, some evidence emerged which illuminates the official attitude to settlements in the period of direct colonial rule and helps to elucidate some peculiarities in the distribution of villages:

It was claimed that in 1930 and 1931 many villages were moved for administrative convenience to form a line along the right bank of the Lwela. . . . In this way what appeared to be an empty area had been created by order some twenty years ago.

No reference to such a movement has come to light in contemporary records, but this is not to deny the claims made in 1953. The concentration of settlement on the west bank persists today

(Figure 4) and is very convenient because the Lwela is a difficult river to cross. Similar asymmetrical distributions appear along other streams and this is a feature which has not been adequately explained.

USHI SETTLEMENT UNDER INDIRECT RULE

The decade preceding the outbreak of the Second World War saw sweeping changes in the form of local government and the era of direct colonial rule came to an end. Unfortunately detailed local records do not exist for much of this decade because essential economies during the war not only prevented the preparation of many reports but also consumed quantities of those from earlier years.

By 1930 administrative machinery was operating smoothly and communications were relatively adequate. It was, therefore, possible to implement slowly the principles of Indirect Rule, and in 1930 'the delegation of real powers to the chiefs, and the substantial increases in their subsidies, gave them a much greater interest in their work'. The Native Authority and Native Courts Ordinances of 1936 and 1937 handed more administrative and judicial power to the Ushi chiefs than they had ever had. They also led to the final reduction in the number of chiefs. Ten Native Authorities and Courts were considered to be sufficient for the tribe and so eight chiefs were required to retire from their positions, at least so far as local government was concerned. The largest reorganization took place amongst the Mukulo sub-group where four chiefs' Areas, those of Matanda, Mabo, Chansa and Kapwepwe, were merged into one and Matanda was elected as chief. Because his home village was not centrally placed Matanda was required to establish his official headquarters in Mabo's former Area, but he still maintains his home village north of the Mansa. On the plateau Ngomba was merged with Milambo, Nsonga with Mabumba, Kali with Mibenge, Chama with Kalaba, and Kundamfumu with Kalasa Lukangaba (Table I). The deposed chiefs were compensated with paid posts in the new Native

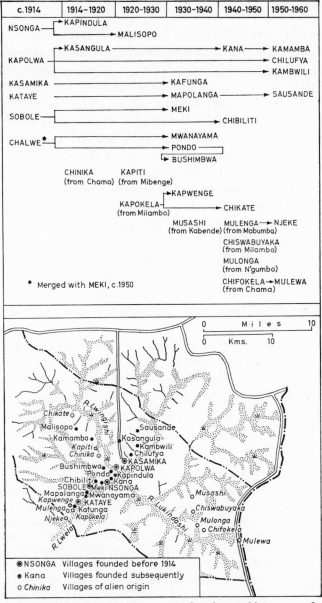

Figure 2. Nsonga's Area: a summary of settlement history, 1914-60. The villages have not dispersed widely, though the environment would permit this. The main axis of settlement has remained on the north bank of the Lwela, along an important route between Mufulira (via Chembe) and the western shores of Lake Bangweulu (Figure 4). Most villages of alien origin cluster together and remain outside the heart of Nsonga's country. Such nuclei, particularly that on the Lukindashi, could formerly have formed new neighbourhoods, or even chiefdoms. (Based on field enquiries)

Courts, and several of them, in fact, still retain some of their traditional dignity in their own localities. This reorganization of chiefs and the amalgamation of their Areas is responsible for peculiarities in the shapes of several chiefs' Areas. The enlarged Areas permitted greater freedom of movement to the villages within them but generally the villages of the former chiefs have remained in their traditional localities and are still reflected in settlement clusters within the larger Areas (Figure 4).

Matters of local importance, including the control of settlements and local population movements, were delegated to the chiefs about 1930. To forestall the sub-division of villages and the dispersion of settlements that might ensue the District Commissioner informed the chiefs in 1928 'that the formation of new villages will only be allowed if a person suitable to be a headman collects 15 able-bodied males whose removal from other villages will not deplete such villages unduly'. Also to keep the villages compact attempts were made to restrict the area a village might occupy and the most practical of these was to forbid building beyond hailing distance of the headman's hut. But not all administrators were anxious to retain the large compact villages for some believed that these placed unbearably heavy pressure on the resources of their immediate locality, were overcrowded and unavoidably dirty and unhygienic, engendered disrespect for elders and tribal traditions, and promoted social, religious and political unrest. In a report made at this time (Phillips, 1931) it was noted:

From the native point of view there are neither social nor economic advantages in (large villages). A single native family is, in food production and domestic management, a self-supporting whole. . . . There is at present a gradual process towards decentralization which plainly shows that the village unit is to a great extent an artificial and not a natural division. . . . Without doubt the government regulation is the only force which restrains the whole community from breaking up into single groups living by themselves under an elder.

In spite of regulations once the control of settlement passed to the chiefs the large villages began to disintegrate. The District Commissioner decided in 1932 that:

provided the limitations imposed by His Excellency were not disregarded he would not advocate active measures being taken against the forming of smaller villages in certain areas. All chiefs, however, would be warned of the administrative difficulties ahead of them. . . .

By 1948, when the minimum number of taxpayers which might comprise a village had been reduced from fifteen to ten, there were 700 Ushi villages with an average population of fifty-five persons, roughly the same size as prevailed in 1905. Faced with the problems of administering the ambitious post-war development programmes, the inadequacies of the village unit were again realized, and a system of parishes was invoked by the Government as an alternative:

The essence of the parish system was that individuals were to be registered as belonging to an area instead of a village, and that subject to the permission of the parish authority they might build and cultivate anywhere inside the area to which they belong (*Native Land Tenure Committee*, 1945).

This scheme involved fundamental changes in local government and in the attitude to settlements. The officers of the Provincial Administration generally were neither enthusiastic nor optimistic about the scheme, but by 1950 the Fort Rosebery District was demarcated into parishes and the scheme had been outlined to the people. There appears to have been no use made of the traditional neighbourhoods as a basis for the parishes, and those which were created did not function as hoped. The scheme was ultimately shelved and the village continues as the basic unit of local administration.

But the number of villages has not continued to increase rapidly. From 1948-56 there was an increase of only forty-two villages, and from 1956-60 a further increase of only eight (Table I). But these figures refer to *registered villages*, and during the past decade, while the processes of disintegration have ceased to cause a proliferation of villages, they have increasingly affected their form. This change is partly due to the ill-fated parish system which permitted the dispersion of families within a limited area, and partly to the realization by the Native Authorities that every family group cannot be registered as a village nor every elder as a headman.

Most Ushi villages are now divided into a number of sections which are generally referred to as *fikongwani*.[1] No official data exist on these and little is known about them. They are mostly composed of small family groups each of which recognizes an elder as *mwine mushi* (village headman), though in talking to Europeans this term is usually reserved for the *registered* headman of the administrative village. The typical form of three large villages is shown in Figure 3. Kasamika's village dispersed from its former site near a large fig tree which has an important role in the village's history. There are now eight sections in the village. Some of them are not easily distinguished until one becomes acquainted with the village, and then hitherto insignificant features such as a path, a line of cassava mounds, the chapel, and a few trees are seen to have the role of domestic boundaries. On one side of a path you are a guest of Malaya and his family; take a few steps across the path and you are in Posta's company and the pattern of social behaviour should change accordingly. Kasamika, the headman, lives at one end of the village, some distance from his nearest neighbours. He, naturally, did not wish to leave the traditional site by the fig tree, nor to break up the compact village. Ironically he has been fined for living away from his village. The structure of Weta Musebo's and Mpita's villages are similar. Mpita's village split into four sections, and once again it was the headman who refused to move from the site of the original compact village. There are seven sections within Musebo's village, five upstream of Mpita's village and two, one of which is Musebo's, downstream of Mpita. There has been a major dissension in the village with complicated arguments on both sides. The case revolves around an alleged attempt by Chisheta to seize the

1. *Fikongwani* (sing. Chi . . .) is the word used to describe a section of a road marked out as a day's work for a labourer engaged on piece work in the construction or repair of roads. In other parts of the Northern and Luapula Provinces the sub-divisions of a village are variously referred to as *amapalashi*, derived from 'parish'; *amafam*, derived from 'farm'; *mitanda*, a traditional Bemba word for a temporary gardening camp; and *fitente*, a traditional Bemba word for a section of a village.

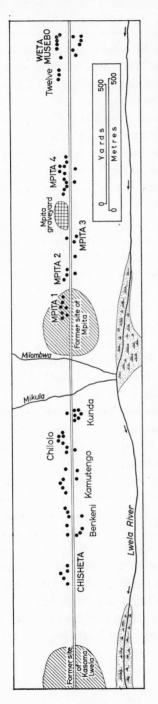

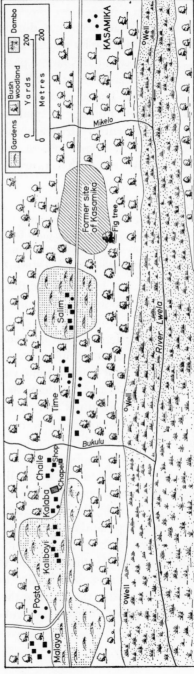

Figure 3. The characteristic form of Ushi villages, 1960. (Based on field survey)

position of village headman during Musebo's absence, and of trying to kill Musebo by witchcraft on his return. Musebo, in fear of Chisheta, has left the larger part of the village, and Chisheta hopes to be registered as a village headman by the Provincial Administration. The form of the village reflects this dissension.

An increasing number of small settlements is characteristic of many parts of Central Africa and there have been several attempts to account for their development. It has often been thought of as a feature of the twentieth century and due to changes brought about by European rule:

It is partly due to Government policy . . . to the *Pax Britannica* . . . and to the rapid extermination of lions. Everywhere the need to rely on one's kin and neighbours is being reduced by these factors. Quite as importantly perhaps, labour migration . . . is positively emancipating the individual from his obligations to his kinship group (Turner, 1957).

It has been attributed also to the break-up of traditional social and economic life so often assumed to have been based on village communities (Culwick, 1944), and to the possibilities nowadays for economic differentiation between individuals which is incompatible with community life. Clearly in the case of the Ushi such reasons, though not without some validity, can only partly explain the proliferation of small settlements because these are not so much a feature of modern times as a resurgence of the traditional territorial unit that prevailed prior to colonial rule, though modern *fikongwani* may be smaller than the nineteenth-century *mushi*.

Many Ushi are unable to provide spontaneous replies when asked why they like to live in small settlements and many of the answers they give eventually are superficial. They try to justify rather than explain the preference for small residential units – livestock are kept and they are a nuisance in a large village; living amongst one's gardens permits more attention to the crops; hunting provides insufficient meat to share among a large community; or more space was needed to build new brick houses. An ex-chief came nearer the heart of the matter, and his explanation of the break-up of villages, particularly chiefs' villages, is worth quoting:

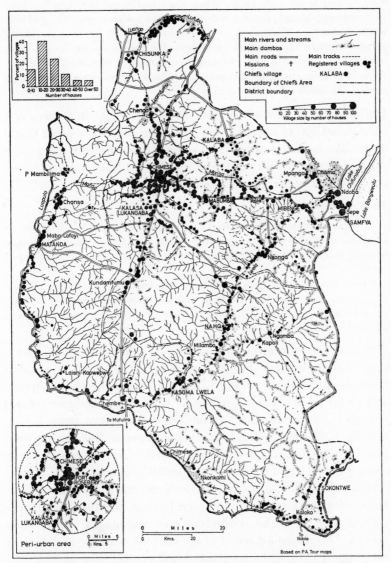

Figure 4. The settlement pattern of the Fort Rosebery District, 1960. (Based on tour maps and house counts made for the author by officers of the Provincial Administration during 1960)

257

Well, sorcery is the main cause. When chiefs had power they kept powerful witchdoctors (*n'ganga*); these would smell out the sorcerers (*muloshi*), and they would be beaten, driven away, or killed. So people felt secure in the chiefs' villages with the chiefs to look after them. But the Europeans do not allow witch hunts – sorcery is rife; sorcerers go unpunished, they are found everywhere. In a large village there is too much jealousy and envy – and these beget sorcery. No one is safe unless he lives alone.

During 1961 at least three Ushi chiefs confirmed that there is a widespread fear of sorcery by conceding to popular requests that a powerful witchdoctor from the Congo should be employed to ease the situation. One of them, mindful of his official position, issued the following written announcement:

To whom it may concern.

In accordance with the African custom and tradition I allow Chisala Chisanda to smell out the witches in my area, and to find those bad people who kill others by bewitching them, and to collect all their witchcraft implements.

I allow him on the strength that I do not rule animals at all. If there were no people only ruins would remain here, and without people there would be no chief. Hence from today I allow this man to smell out the witches in my area in accordance with our custom.

Needless to say the administration intervened. It can prevent such large-scale operations but it cannot eradicate the innumerable cases of witchcraft or alleged witchcraft that occur daily. Sorcery and social dissatisfaction are closely related and the one reflects the other. Large settlements facilitate social unrest on many fronts, and the Ushi have a deeply ingrained desire to live among only those of their family group, relatives and friends whom they can trust, particularly if their personal mobility is reduced by capital investment in the form of a relatively expensive and permanent Kimberley brick house – and recently there has been a remarkable change from the traditional pole and dagga hut to such houses. This desire for social peace coupled with the ambition of every adult male to be recognized and respected as an elder – a *mwine mushi* of his own people and not necessarily of the administration – inevitably leads to small settlements. Each elder might seek to enlarge his following and thereby enhance his prestige, but he will succeed only if he can maintain a happy atmosphere in his settlement and can prevent potential elders canvassing for a following amongst his people. But the Ushi are also a gregarious people, and though they desire independence they do not seek isolation. They are not scattered widely over the plateau, and many habitable areas are devoid of people (Figure 4). Villages and their sections are usually quite close to one another (Figure 3). The Ushi share the sentiments of many Englishmen; their home is their castle, and, while they would be suspicious of hotel life or multi-storey flats, they would prefer a suburbia of semi-detached houses to the loneliness of a cottage on the moors.

Limitations of space do not permit a full analysis here of the complex of man/land relationships in the Fort Rosebery District. Inevitably this essay has dealt lightly with the role of environmental factors in the study of settlement pattern and form, and in particular the important recent effects of Fort Rosebery township and of certain main routes on the distribution of population have not been mentioned (cf. Kay, 1960). The influences of environmental and historical factors are inextricably bound together, and without a detailed study of both a full interpretation of the settlement pattern shown in Figure 4 is not possible. But from the above account of Ushi settlement history the significant role of such historical studies in the analysis of present situations, both local and regional, is evident, and this essay supports Kimble's statement. Clearly it is important for geographers to remember that Africa no less than other parts of the world has a past, and that they should seek to analyse present problems in their historical context so far as is possible.

ACKNOWLEDGEMENTS

This essay is based on material collected whilst the author was a Research Officer of the Rhodes-Livingstone Institute. Many Government officials assisted the author, particularly in collecting data on which Figure 4 is based and in making past records available for study. The valuable contribution of the Ushi people and their chiefs is also evident in this essay. To these and all others who assisted in the production of the essay the author extends his sincere thanks.

REFERENCES

CULWICK, A.T. (1944) 'A new beginning', *Rhodes-Livingstone J.*, *1*.

CUNNISON, I.G. (1962) *Historical traditions of the Eastern Lunda*. Rhodes-Livingstone Communication no. 23. Lusaka.

GUERNSEY, T.D. (1951) *A summary of the provisional geological features of Northern Rhodesia*. H.M.S.O.

HARRINGTON, H.T. (1954) 'The taming of north-eastern Rhodesia', *Northern Rhodesia J.*, *2*, *3*, 3-20.

KANTHACK, F.E. (1945) 'The relationship between rainfall and run-off in Central Southern Africa', *Proc. S. Af. Soc. Civil Engineers*, *43*, 29.

KAY, G. (1960) *A social and economic study of Fort Rosebery*. Rhodes-Livingstone Communication no. 21. Lusaka.

— (1961) 'Population surveys as prerequisites of Community Development', in APTHORPE, R.J. (ed.) *Social Research and Community Development*. Lusaka.

KIMBLE, G.H.T. (1960) *Tropical Africa: Land and livelihood*, Vol. 1.

LAMMOND, W. (1955) 'The Luapula Valley', *Northern Rhodesia J. 2*, *5*.

LIVINGSTONE, D. (1874) *Last Journals* (ed. H. Waller).

PHILLIPS, F.R.G. (1931) 'The human geography of the Fort Rosebery District', MSS. SEC/NAT/398. National Archives, Lusaka.

PHILPOT, R. (1936) 'Makumba, the Baushi tribal god', *J. Roy. Anthrop. Soc.*, *66*.

RICHARDS, A.I. (1951) 'The Bemba of north-eastern Rhodesia', in COLSON, E. and GLUCKMAN, M. (eds.) *Seven Tribes of British Central Africa*.

TRAPNELL, C.G. (1953) *The soils, vegetation and agriculture of north-eastern Rhodesia*. Lusaka.

TURNER, V.W. (1957) *Schism and continuity in an African Society*.

WEATHERLEY, P. (1898) 'The circumnavigation of Lake Bangweulu', *Geogr. J.*, *12*.

Report of the Native Land Tenure Committee (1945). Lusaka.

MSS. SOURCES. *District Notebooks*.

— *Annual Reports* and *Tour Reports* of the Native (District) Commissioners of Fort Rosebery District in the National Archives of Rhodesia and Nyasaland, Lusaka.

All quotations except those indicated otherwise are taken from these MSS. sources.

Land use in the Maracas –
St Joseph Basin, Trinidad

THE Maracas River, which is called the St Joseph south of the town of that name, flows from the Cerro de las Cuevas y Maracas, the main water-parting of the Northern Range of Trinidad, almost due southward to join the Caroni, the island's longest river (Figure 1). From its source at about 3,000 feet above sea-level the river falls in approximately ten miles almost to sea-level at the edge of the Caroni swamp. The headwaters of the Maracas and of the Acona, its main left-bank tributary, flow in narrow, ungraded V-shaped valleys which widen in places to form basin-like depressions bounded by steep slopes. One of these depressions between Loango and the Caribbean Training College is over a mile wide. Upstream of the town of St Joseph the river meanders in a deeply incised valley on the sides of which there are eight clearly recognizable levels; these are erosional features at the highest altitudes and terraces excavated in sand and gravel at the lower levels. South of St Joseph town the river follows a relatively straight course at less than 50 feet above sea-level until it joins the River Caroni, and in places the land is waterlogged and there are lagoons.

Las Cuevas, including El Tucuche (3,072 feet), Trinidad's second highest peak, and the country southward to St Joseph are formed mainly of resistant quartzites and phyllite schists, with some softer marble and crystalline limestone which have been eroded to form the depressions in the river valleys (Suter, 1960). The lowland south of St Joseph is covered with recent alluvium and to the west it merges into the Laventille and Caroni reed and mangrove swamps.

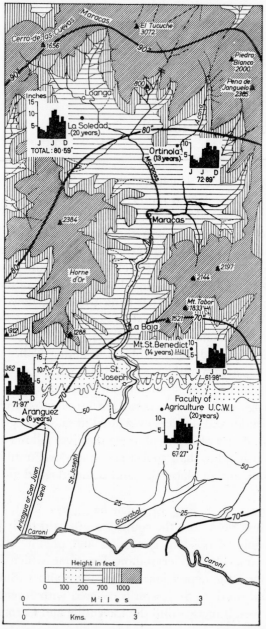

Figure 1. Maracas – St. Joseph basin: relief, drainage and rainfall

The higher parts of the Maracas–St Joseph basin receive an average of over 80 inches of rainfall per annum and this is one of the wettest regions in Trinidad, compared with the St Joseph lowland where the rainfall is between 60 and 70 inches (Figure 1). Temperatures are high throughout the year with highest mean maxima in January (84° F) and in May (88° F) and on nearly every day there are more than six hours of brilliant sunshine. It is the seasonal changes in rainfall distribution which affect both the natural vegetation and the farm practices. A pronounced dry season in all parts of the basin coincides with the highest daily mean temperatures with consequent high evaporation rates, and the average rainfall in February, March and April is inadequate for agriculture without irrigation (F.A.O., 1957). In contrast, during the wet season flash-flood damage results from rainfall of high intensity (Smith and Wehekind, 1955). For instance, in 1955 floods in the lagoons on the St Joseph lowland caused severe losses in the rice crop and during one flood in the Maracas basin more than half an acre of land situated on the inside of a meander was washed downstream.

EARLY ECONOMIC DEVELOPMENT

When Trinidad was discovered by Columbus in 1498 much of the island was probably covered with three- or four-tier tropical forest, with swamp forests in Caroni, Nariva and Oropuche. To-day the swamps are much less extensive and only 45 per cent of the island is forested and much of this is secondary growth (*lastro*). When the Spaniards first arrived they found the indigenous inhabitants living in forest clearings on the terraces above the swamps at the foot of the Northern Range and they raided them to obtain slaves to work on the Spanish Main and on the island of Santa Marguerita. Trinidad provided no precious minerals and disappointment at their absence undoubtedly influenced the Spanish attitude to the island's economic development. It was not until 1592 that the first Spanish settlement and capital was founded at San José del Oruna (St Joseph) and little effort was made to establish commercial agriculture. Cocoa cultivation was begun in 1686 by Capuchin Fathers who founded mission stations where they employed Indians to cultivate this crop which was interplanted with corn, plantains and cassava (Ottley, 1955). Not until later was cocoa grown by Spanish planters in the Maracas–St. Joseph basin, and in spite of a serious crop failure in 1727, and the consequent emigration of Spaniards and Indians from most of the island, cocoa cultivation continued there though on a reduced scale.

African slaves were introduced in 1701 to increase the supply of labour and in 1783 the Spaniards, in another attempt to cure a desperate labour shortage, invited French planters and their slaves to settle in Trinidad. It was the French who introduced the cultivation of sugar cane, mainly near Port of Spain and later in Caroni county, and when Spanish rule came to an end in 1797 Spaniards controlled most of the cocoa-growing and the French most of the cultivation of sugar and coffee. Sugar cane required a much larger labour force than cocoa and so, after emancipation in 1834 when many slaves left the plantations, it suffered more than cocoa, and East Indian indentured labourers were brought in at various times between 1845 and 1917 to make good this deficiency in the western cane-growing areas. The East Indian element in the present-day population of the Maracas–St Joseph basin is thus of relatively recent origin and very few have yet penetrated into the upper part of the basin which is still a stronghold of Spanish-Negro and French-Negro elements.

PEASANT FARMING

Peasants practise land rotation which is known locally as 'recent cultivation', involving forest and bush clearing by cutlassing in the dry season (March to May) followed by burning, and then when the wet season begins the land is planted with peas, cassava, tannias (*xanthosoma*), tomatoes, maize, hill rice and salad vegetables as main crops, with beans, cucumber and sweet potatoes less important. These crops have replaced cocoa on much of the

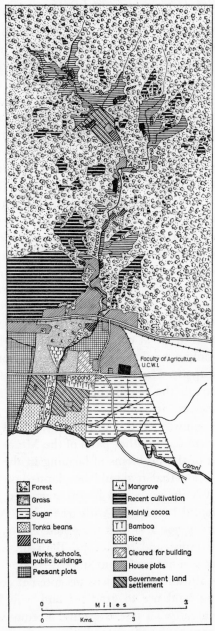

Figure 2. Maracas – St. Joseph basin: land use

Forest		Mangrove	
Grass		Recent cultivation	
Sugar		Mainly cocoa	
Tonka beans		Bamboo	
Citrus		Rice	
Works, schools, public buildings		Cleared for building	
Peasant plots		House plots	
		Government land settlement	

0   M i l e s   3

0   Kms.   3

land which was cleared after the cocoa depression of the 1930s. The amount of 'recent cultivation' varies throughout the basin. In the forested area north of the Eastern Main Road it occupies an average of 17·5 per cent of the total area and there are many plots which are too small to be mapped (Figure 2). In the southern parts of the basin 46 per cent has been denuded of forest compared with only 11·5 per cent in the northern parts; the former are within easy reach of St Joseph and are accessible by the main roads and by side roads, whereas the latter are accessible only by track from the roadhead at Loango and much is in the El Tucuche forest reserve. These figures are based on calculations from air photographs, but since these were taken in 1957 there has been an extension of areas of 'recent cultivation'. A map prepared in 1953 (Goodlet) shows only nine clearings above Loango compared with twenty-two recorded during fieldwork in 1960, and what were scattered clearings for cultivation in the Naranjo valley in 1953 had been enlarged to an area of about 80 acres in 1960.

A survey carried out in Floradale in 1948 showed that no attempts had been made at contour-ploughing and ditching and that there was only a haphazard distribution of cultivated plots (Collings-Wells, 1948). There was ample evidence of erosion of the top soil and though the remaining soil retained a 'remarkable degree of cohesiveness' it had deteriorated and the peasants complained that the soil was too thin and that 'the land grows stones'. Conditions were similar in other parts of the Maracas basin.

Consideration of the problems of farming in the hill areas has led to the suggestion that it should be planned on an altitudinal basis and over twenty years ago it was suggested that the land over 500 feet should be planted with tree crops. After a United States aerial survey 700 feet was suggested in 1953 as the limit between ground crops and tree crops. Both these heights were arbitrary choices and are irrelevant since it is slope which is more important than altitude. If this was accepted it could lead to a policy of relating land use to gradient and would result in an extension of the area under tree crops and a reduction in the area under ground crops in the Maracas–St Joseph basin.

LAND SETTLEMENTS

Peasant farms of under 15 acres usually support a family in food, and in theory should provide an income from the sale of small surpluses, and house gardens ('spots') in all the settlements in the Maracas–St Joseph basin are useful sources of subsistence food. Farms may be privately owned, rented or on loan from an estate and in addition there are the land settlements which were begun in the 1930s, during the period of general economic depression and at a time when cocoa-growing in Trinidad had been severely hit by the high incidence of witches' broom disease. Holdings on the land settlements were never intended to make a family self-supporting, but were designed to supplement income derived from other sources and to increase the supply of home-grown food in order that Trinidad should be less dependent on imported food.

By 1960 the pattern of peasant cultivation in the Maracas–St Joseph basin had been considerably modified by the development of four land settlements (Figure 2). The Maracas settlements were established on the former Cadbury experimental cocoa estate (Williams, 1931), and the Bamboo Grove settlements on land formerly belonging to a paper pulp firm which had planned to use bamboo for paper production but had found that it could not compete successfully with Canadian pulp. Holdings at Bamboo Grove vary from 1 to 2·6 acres with an additional acre of lagoon land for rice. Root crops and vegetables are most generally grown where the rainfall in the wet season is adequate, and the soils are light and freely-drained sandy loams, and where the proximity of Port of Spain provides a ready market. Soils with impeded drainage are unsuitable for either root crops, vegetables or settlement and are used for rice cultivation. In the dry season cultivation without irrigation is unreliable but the flat land flanking the St Joseph River is too low for water to be fed by gravity and to install pumps would add too much to the cost of production.

Compared with Bamboo Grove the Maracas holdings are usually larger;[1] there is more variety in land use and tree crops are

[1] e.g. one settler farms 17 acres of steeply-sloping land in addition to 5 acres on the valley floor between Loango and the Caribbean Training College.

general. Many cocoa trees from the former Cadbury estates remain and there are stands of citrus and *tonka*. On the flat or undulating land of the depressions, where there are deep lacustrine soils and the water-table remains high but with little danger from waterlogging, tree crops, root crops and vegetables are grown and poultry are reared. On the steep valley sides where slopes range from 10° to over 45°, the soils are shallow and bare rock sometimes outcrops, but a similar range of crops is grown. The Government has tried to encourage sound hill-farming methods to minimize the effects of rapid run-off and consequent soil erosion; these include experimental terracing, contour ditching and the planting of tree crops on plots limited to 3 acres until the trees are established. In 1960 these methods had been applied only in a few parts of the Maracas settlements.

TREE CROPS

In spite of the reduction in the number of cocoa trees in the 1930s, as a result of economic depression and witches' broom disease, the crop remained important and in 1946 there were over 400,000 trees and thirty-five farms with cocoa as the main crop in the Maracas basin. In 1960 it occupied approximately 60 per cent of the farmland. Cocoa is grown on the floors of both the Maracas and Acona valleys and on the slopes which border them up to 700 feet above sea-level, and to 1,000 feet north-west of Loango and on Mount Tabor. The first varieties were probably introduced from Mexico and were prized for their quality, but after the failures of 1727 Venezuelan trees were imported and 60 per cent were concentrated in three of the valleys of the Northern Range including the Maracas valley. The strength of tradition in the cultivation of cocoa may be seen from the fact that some Spanish families in Maracas can trace their ancestry from the cocoa planters of the eighteenth century through to the depression of the 1930s when many were forced to sell their holdings.

Today there is a wide variety in quality and the hot, humid conditions favour fungus growths and disease. To combat these the Cocoa Board and the Government have experimented in propagating trees which are resistant to disease, especially witches' broom, and have begun a programme of cocoa rehabilitation based on clonal propagation (Moll and Verteuil, 1954). Where land is considered to be suitable for cocoa cultivation to continue, a subsidy is given towards the cost of replanting with free clones provided by the Cocoa Board. But rehabilitation is making very slow progress, and often the demand for clones exceeds supply. There is also an understandable reluctance on the part of some people to concentrate on this one crop when memories of the cocoa depression remain very clear.

As an alternative, and in addition to cocoa, citrus fruits have the advantage of easy marketing, without the expense of fermenting and drying which the cocoa beans require. With the exception of limes the cultivation of all citrus fruits has expanded and the largest concentration is south-east of Maracas Roman Catholic church where the deep lacustrine soils provide the necessary root-run of 900 cubic feet (Cooper, 1955). There are few orchards which are sited on steep slopes and most lie between 250 feet and 400 feet. Many soil deficiencies have been remedied to improve quality and yields but in these sheltered valleys there is a high incidence of scale insects, rust mites and parasol ants. About 60 per cent of Trinidad's grapefruit suffers from skin damage though generally Trinidad citrus has a relatively high proportion of pulp and juice and a very high sugar ratio compared with fruit grown in Texas, Florida and Puerto Rico. The canning of juice and fruit is carried out under the control of the Co-operative Citrus Growers' Association.

Where land is considered unsuitable for continued cocoa cultivation, financial help is given for the establishment of other crops and for the keeping of livestock. There is, however, a dearth of pasture throughout the basin, with the exception of that on the Government experimental stock farm south of St Joseph and three playing-fields which are sometimes used for pasturing animals. The preservation of pasture in the dry season is virtually impossible without irrigation, and the usual practice is to lead tethered cattle, goats and donkeys along roads for them to eat on the verges and in the ditches. Under these conditions the yield and quality of milk are understandably low.

FORESTRY

The Cerro de las Cuevas, the main ridges which extend southward from it, and some of the ridges between small tributary streams are forested, with types ranging from Lower Montane rain-forest to young secondary bush. Three-tier forest, with *crappo* (*Carapa Guianensis*) and *guatacare* (*Eschweilera Subglandulosa*) as dominant trees, still covers some of the highland on the periphery of the basin and the slopes of El Tucuche. The latter form a forest reserve established by the Forestry Department to maintain a protective covering of trees for the control of run-off and soil erosion. There has been progressive destruction of forest in the northern parts of the Maracas basin since the sixteenth century but, because of its situation at the head of the Maracas valley, this reserve is inaccessible and commercial timber extraction would be virtually impossible.

Elsewhere secondary forest (*lastro*) is the main cover with kiskidee (*Visniia falcata Rusby*), trumpet (*Campsis radicans*), balsa (*Ochroma lagopus*), sandbox (*Hura crepitans*), and cocorite (*Maximiliana elegans Karst*) trees and trash palms (*Scheelea osmantha*) and varieties of epiphytes where the forest is well established. Young secondary bush colonizes the land after clearings for cultivation have been abandoned for several years and this contains mainly cannah grass (*Cannaceae*) and dense bamboo thickets with very few trees.

PRESENT-DAY ECONOMY

In a plan for land allocation in Trinidad (Council Paper, 1944), most of the Maracas basin was scheduled for acquisition by the Government for controlled farming. Some small areas, such as that south-west of la Baja, have been acquired and terraced, contour-ditched and planted with tree crops. Some cocoa estates in the mountains, the Government stock farm and sugar cane estates on the plain are as fully productive as modern science and technology can make them. But the greater part of the Maracas–St Joseph basin, including the land settlements, is not as productive as it might be.

The limitations of the physical environment are understood and accepted by only a few people, and there are also social and economic factors which hinder the making of improvements. The renting of land from private owners on a one-year lease is all too frequent and makes long-term development impossible even if the peasants have the necessary skill, knowledge and initiative. Tenants without any security tend to take all they can from the land and when yields fall they abandon their plots and move on to others (Caribbean, 1947). Too often crops are grown for which there is a quick financial return without regard to requirements in terms of soil, slope and aspect and the balance between subsistence and cash crops. Enforcement of legislation aimed at punishment for allowing land to deteriorate and reward for land improvement is necessary to change these conditions. Short-term leases might then become unprofitable to landlords whose concern hitherto has been only with the collection of rents.

Though official control over development in the land settlements should be effective, in fact the results have been poor. A survey in 1957 showed that many settlers had not paid rents, many had not developed their land on the right lines and some had not developed it at all (Guyadeen, 1957). Crops were in poor condition and yields were low. The picture of agriculture was a disappointing one, but balancing this to some extent were the improvements effected in living standards by the installation of domestic water supplies, the drainage of land and the construction of roads. When the plots were established they were not intended to support families fully; this would be possible only at bare subsistence level. The original purpose, to provide only part-time employment, may be legitimately questioned. A man with divided loyalties is not likely to be a good farmer, and numbers of settlers have regarded their plots only as an insurance against hard times and have given their main attention to other jobs. In 1956, in the St Joseph section of the basin, 55 per cent of the working population was engaged in agriculture compared with 39 per cent in the Maracas section and 25 per cent in St Joseph town. Although there is almost no mining or manufacturing industry and very little commerce immediately in the area, many travel to work in the industrial units aligned along the Eastern Main Road between St Joseph and Port of Spain. The nearness of a large European community at St Augustine results in over 40 per cent of the adult working population being engaged in 'services'. The numbers of agricultural workers are small in the Maracas basin north of St Joseph, since even in the nucleated rural settlements farming is often a part-time occupation. Some of their inhabitants keep shops, others teach or drive taxis or are in domestic service, and all of these occupations confer a status higher than that of farming. Few can envisage a peasant farmer ever rising above the subsistence level.

The former Imperial College of Tropical Agriculture, now the Faculty of Agriculture in the University College of the West Indies, conducted a series of experiments on the economics of peasant farming (Jolly, 1954). Five farms were established, concerned with dairying, market gardening, livestock with draught animals, arable with livestock and arable with manual labour respectively. They ranged in size from 1·5 acres (market gardening) to 5 acres (dairying) and each was worked for a maximum of seven years by a peasant and his family with no hired labour. Detailed records were kept and from them it was concluded that it was possible to organize peasant farming to yield a respectable standard of living. Each farmer worked a 48-hour week and earnings averaged 2,000 dollars a year, a figure far above peasant subsistence level. But this was possible only because of the influence of the Imperial College, especially the scientific and technological skill of the staff and their drive and perseverance. None of the peasants concerned in the experiment would have achieved these results through their own efforts.

Sir Alan Pim (1946) considered that, in spite of their lack of self-reliance and their tendency to rely on Government help rather than their own efforts, more peasants should be settled on the land. An F.A.O. survey (1957) of the possible reclamation of the Caroni, Nariva and Oropuche areas strongly supported this view, and recommended the development of existing under-developed land rather than the reclamation of swampland, even though such a major project might be attractive. But improvements in agriculture and increases in production depend less on adding more acres of land to the total under cultivation and more on raising the standard of efficiency of existing small farmers. The possibility of attaining a level higher than that of subsistence should make farming an attractive occupation and not a last resort to which to turn in desperation when nothing else offers itself. But such levels can be achieved only with efforts such as the majority of people are not prepared to make.

SETTLEMENT (Figure 3)

Settlements cover 8 per cent of the Maracas–St Joseph basin. There are nucleated settlements where numerous tracks converge on the roadhead at Loango and at Maracas village, which is grouped round the Roman Catholic church and at the confluence of the Maracas and Acona streams. Small ribbon settlements, like la Baja, are sited above the St Joseph gorge north of St Joseph town. In the northern parts of the basin the people are descendants of Spanish planters and their negro slaves, together with the French planters and their slaves who infiltrated into the valley in the late eighteenth century across Las Cuevas. There is still a Spanish-speaking minority but French patois is the language of the rural population. Two alien elements have been introduced recently into this traditional situation. The Seventh Day Adventists have established the Caribbean Training College and a well-equipped school which has attracted children from the less modern Roman Catholic school, and ex-servicemen from other parts of Trinidad were given holdings in the Maracas land settlements.

Curepe and the Bamboo Grove settlements are sited respectively on upper and lower terraces of the Caroni River where there are no physical obstacles to growth and they have developed a rectangular pattern. Below the terraces the heavy soils are unsuitable for settlement and the symmetry of Bamboo Grove 2 is broken where these soils extend northward. Most of the inhabitants of these settlements are the descendants of former indentured East Indian labourers, some of whom were dispossessed of their former holdings of land by the Bejucal–Caroni irrigation project and the construction of the Princess Margaret highway and were provided with plots on the land settlement in compensation. Others have come from the Caroni canelands in search of non-agricultural employment.

The main urban centre is St Joseph, a town which has been influenced and restricted in its growth by a ravine to the west and the St Joseph gorge to the north and east. It is built on steeply sloping land rising from the Eastern Main Road. From the time that it was founded by the Spaniards in 1592 until 1757 it was the official capital of Trinidad and it remained the chief port until the mid-nineteenth century. It now functions as a shopping centre with some public works, but its only extractive industry is gypsum quarrying on a small scale and many of its working population are employed either in the industrial units between St Joseph and Port of Spain or as domestic labour in St Augustine. Culturally and racially it is an epitome of Trinidad. It has the longest history of Spanish settlement and tradition, and for thirty-three years after 1797 when British rule began, the administrative body of the town continued to be known as the Cabildo and its discussions were held in Spanish. French influence was such that as late as 1839 it was still considered essential for the British magistrate in St Joseph to have a knowledge of French. Spanish and French influences remain in St Joseph today, especially in religion and in education. British influence in the nineteenth and twentieth centuries is reflected in administration, in the use of English as the official language at the present day and also in the landscape, for example, by the building of Anglican and Nonconformist churches

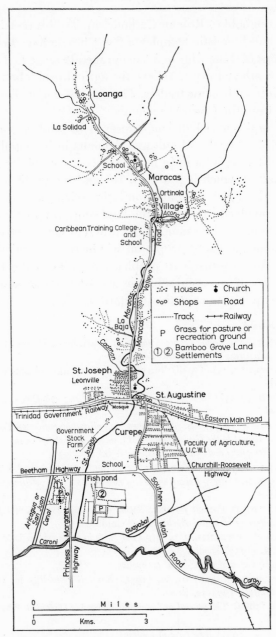

Figure 3. Maracas – St. Joseph basin: **settlement**

in this stronghold of Roman Catholicism. To this racial, cultural, religious and linguistic complex a few Chinese have been added, descendants of those who were encouraged to settle in Trinidad in the nineteenth century to relieve the agricultural labour shortage but who instead became traders. There are also some East Indians, migrants from the Caroni canelands.

In its rural and urban landscapes, in its land use, and in the variety of the racial and cultural elements in its population, the Maracas–St Joseph basin in many respects exemplifies the island of Trinidad of which it is a part. Its land-use problems indicate not only the need to understand the scientific and technical problems involved in making the land more productive, but also the need to appreciate some of the different characteristics of the heterogenous groups of people on whom economic development depends. Any approach to problems must be made from both points of view if successful solutions are to be found, and these are urgently required to raise the standard of living.

REFERENCES

CARIBBEAN (1947) *Land Tenure Symposium.* Caribbean Committee on Agriculture, Nutrition, Fisheries and Forestry.

COLLINGS-WELLS, L.J. (1948) 'Survey of peasant agriculture, Part. 2.' Unpublished.

COOPER, ST G. (1955) *Citrus production in the Santa Cruz and Diego Martin Valleys of Trinidad.*

COUNCIL PAPER (1944) NO. 56 *Proposed land allocation policy for Trinidad.*

F.A.O. (1957) *Report to the Governments of Trinidad and Tobago on the reclamation of the Caroni, Oropuche and Nariva areas,* no. 636.

GOODLET, J.A. (1953) 'Shifting cultivation in the Maracas valley'. Unpublished.

GUYADEEN, K.D. (1957) *Report on twelve maintenance land settlements in northern Trinidad.*

JOLLY, A.L. (1954) *Peasant farming. Report on peasant experimental farms at the Imperial College of Tropical Agriculture.* Trinidad.

MOLL, E.R. and VERTEUIL, L.L. (1954) *A guide to cocoa rehabilitation.*

OTTLEY, C.H. (1955) *Spanish Trinidad.*

PIM, A. (1946) *Colonial agricultural production.*

SMITH, G.W. and WEHEKIND, W. (1955) *Rainfall reliability in Trinidad and Trinidad rainfall, 1933-52,* Pt. 2.

SUTER, H.H. (1960) *The general and economic geology of Trinidad.* Second revised edition.

WILLIAMS, I.A. (1931) *The firm of Cadbury.*

Chinese settlement in the Kulai
Sub-District of Johore, Malaysia

SETTLEMENTS UNDER THE *KANG CHUE* SYSTEM (1830-1917)

BEFORE the nineteenth century, the interior of Johore was undeveloped, for thick jungle and swamp repelled any efforts at settlement made by the people of the small towns on the coast. Moreover, their interests lay towards the sea rather than in the undeveloped and unhealthy hinterland. In the 1830s, however, a policy was adopted which was to lead to the opening up of great areas of the interior previously only occupied by a few aboriginal tribes. Taking advantage of the demand for *gambir*[1] and for pepper the Johore Government decided to grant land in the hinterland to anyone who showed himself capable of clearing the jungle and planting these two crops for export.

The best means of access to the interior lay along the numerous small rivers such as the Scudai, the Tebrau, the Sayong and the Johore, which run southward to the coastal settlements on the Straits of Johore, and it was up these rivers that pioneer settlers first penetrated. The importance of the rivers is reflected in the name and substance of the document of title which was granted to the early settlers; the *surat sungei* (river document) generally defined the watershed between two rivers as the area in which the holder was to clear the jungle to plant *gambir* and pepper and to make his settlement. To the west of the Johore Bahru district in Pontian, the Malay inhabitants of the coastal strip were prevented from penetrating quickly into the interior by a belt of swamp land; but the Chinese settlers who came from the Straits of Johore or

---

[1] A woody vine (*uncaria gambir*) producing a yellow catechu used for chewing with betel nut and for tanning and dyeing.

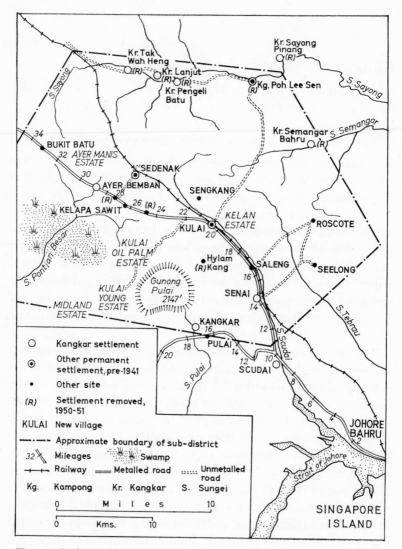

Figure 1. Settlements in Kulai Sub-District

from Singapore were eager to clear the land of jungle and to plant *gambir* and pepper and they penetrated far inland by means of small boats on the winding rivers.

The earliest recorded *surat sungei* is for an area near to the Scudai, and it would seem that the first settlement in the Kulai Sub-District was made at Senai which was reached by settlers coming up the river. On earlier maps the full name of Senai is given as Kangkar Senai, a reminder of the interesting and highly practical system which was adopted by the Government to promote the colonization of the country and to ensure subsequent control of the population. It worked excellently in a territory where previously there had been hardly any people, let alone any administration, and it was also ideally suited to the structure of the Chinese communities who settled there.

The holder of the river title was known as *Kang Chue* ('river master'), invariably a person with a fair amount of capital and no small amount of enterprise. The *Kang Chue* would select his own followers to help in the development of the settlement, and, as such followers were of the same dialect group and very often clansmen, he was able to keep firm control over his settlement, and was the natural and only link between the Government and the colonizing population. Settlements were always made on the banks of a river and were prefixed *Kangkar* or 'river-foot' settlements: thus the distribution of *Kangkar* place-names shows the position of the earliest settlements in the interior (Figure 1). It is probable that there were more place-names prefixed by the word *Kangkar*, but settlements which previously existed have now disappeared, or are no longer inhabited, or have changed their names completely. Such is the case with Ayer Bemban which was formerly called Kangkar Batu, while in the Batu Pahat District a few miles from Chahar, the great house and courtroom of the Kang Chue, now overgrown and decayed, still stands on the banks of a deserted river.

The *Kangkar* place-names show that the Johore Bahru District was first penetrated by way of the Scudai, the Pulai and the Tebrau rivers from the south, but farther north in the

Sub-District of Kulai settlers also appear to have come from the east up the Semangar and Sayong besides coming from the south. In the upper reaches of the Sayong there are the now deserted settlements of Kangkar Tak Wah Heng, Kangkar Lanjut and Kangkar Pengheli Batu, and in the upper reaches of the Sungei Semangar stood Kangkar Semangar Bahru, all of which are near to the north-eastern border of the Kulai Sub-District. The place-name Kangkar Batu, already mentioned, suggests an additional penetration into the Ayer Bemban area from the west coast up the Sungei Pontian Besar. Unfortunately much of the historical detail of this early settlement has disappeared for ever and there are questions relating to it which may never be answered. Recent settlers at Senai came across a Chinese cemetery whose existence had been forgotten and presumably Senai was colonized and then abandoned, only to be reoccupied at a much later date. The details will never be known, but it is clear that the forgotten pioneers in this unhealthy jungle and swamp land performed an heroic labour in making the first permanent settlements in this part of Johore.

Some time in the middle of the nineteenth century specific powers were delegated to the *Kang Chue* in the form of a *tauliah* ('letter of authority') which conferred on him a legal position both as head of his community and as representative of the authority of the Sultan. It was made clear in the *tauliah* that the power of the *Kang Chue* derived exclusively from the State and could not be mortgaged or sold. He was enjoined to enforce the Sultan's authority and to carry out such orders as might be issued by Government. Although each *Kang Chue* had to bear the expense of maintaining one Malay policeman, the real force of his authority lay in his economic leadership which enabled him to command the obedience of the inhabitants of the settlement, for he was the one in whom the title to the land was vested. He had the right of granting permission to smallholders to fell and to clear, and it was he who provided the capital to employ labourers to clear the jungle and grow crops. Quite often the *Kang Chue* had a shop in Singapore and owned the boats which brought foodstuffs and equipment up the river to stock the settlement. Some writers have suggested that the *Kang Chue* was in a form of feudal relationship to the Sultan and to his people, but this was not so. The feudal leader of medieval times in Europe depended on military force to maintain his position and took by right from the villein, in the form of labour, produce or money that which he required. The *Kang Chue* was not in such a position: he was a small capitalist and the recognition of his authority by the State, by granting him legal rights, was no more than a recognition of the fact that in the Chinese society of those times such people were accepted as natural leaders by those who were their employees. The State Government was realistic enough to recognize that the *Kang Chue* was the real administrator, and that to superimpose any other form of administration was undesirable, even had it been possible, in a sparsely populated area which was in course of colonization.

The *Kanun Kang Chue* (Kang Chue Laws) which was issued in 1873, gives a picture of the system which by then had developed. It is clear that the *Kang Chue*'s position was lucrative for he had a monopoly for the organization of gambling and pawnbroking and for selling spirits, pork and opium; he also took a certain commission on the sale of *gambir*, pepper and rice. Some who had become wealthy lived in Singapore and their legal authority had been given to their representatives on the new settlements. These were estate managers, responsible, as far as the *Kanun Kang Chue* was concerned, to the Sultan, but economically to the *Tuan Sungei* ('head of the river settlement') in Singapore.

The *Kanun Kang Chue* carefully enjoins the *Kang Chue* to rule the settlers with justice and firmness, but although it makes provision for serious offenders against the law to be handed over to the police at Johore Bahru for judgment, it is clear that for the most part the *Kang Chue* was a fairly free agent and the merit of his rule depended to a large extent on his character. Nevertheless the evident advantage of the system was that the local administrator was a person of the same race and probably dialect as the settlers. He would therefore understand them, the more so since he was also their leader in the development and expansion of the settlement.

The success of the system is attested by the fact that in the whole of Johore the number of river settlements in 1880 was more than double the twenty-nine which had existed in 1870. The degree of satisfaction felt by the Chinese with the system is shown by the award in 1893 of the First Class Order of the Double Dragon by the Emperor of China to the Sultan Abu Baker for his justice to the Chinese settlers in Johore.

In the Kulai Sub-District this system would seem to have existed at Senai and at the small *Kangkar* settlements in the upper Sayong–Semangar area and at the present Ayer Bemban village. Senai was the largest of these settlements and it was there that a fundamental weakness in the working of the *Kang Chue* system was revealed. The settlement of the area was initially undertaken by Khek people but from an unknown date there was a division of this community into two groups, the Hoh Poh Khek and the Wai Chau Khek. The oldest inhabitants of today remember a tradition of rivalry between the two groups which the rule of the *Kang Chue* of the area had never stopped. *Kang Chue* rule would seem to be at its best when a settlement was homogeneous and fairly small. When two or more communities existed (and this tended to occur as the settlements expanded), the leaders of the community to which the *Kang Chue* did not belong would naturally try to assert themselves. In Yong Peng in the Batu Pahat District old inhabitants tell a similar story of conflict which occurred at the beginning of the twentieth century when Hockchew settlers began to intrude into an area previously ruled by a Hainanese *Kang Chue*.

Other defects developed in the system, for as the pioneering aspect declined, the opium, gambling and pawnbroking interests seem to have expanded and government was not carried out in the ideal manner laid down in the *Kanun Kang Chue*. By 1917 it was clear that some new form of administration was overdue and the system was abolished, but before considering what happened after that date the results of the system must be outlined: Chinese colonies had been established in an area where previously only a few aborigines had lived. They were completely Chinese in nature, the culture of the inhabitants being modified only to suit the needs of colonization and of a tropical climate. Hardly any of the settlers learned to speak Malay and the sole contact with the Malay Government of Johore was through the *Kang Chue*. Communications were first effected by means of the rivers alone but later bullock-cart tracks linked the settlements on different rivers. The line of the present trunk road was first traced out by bullock carts pressing north to Scudai, and then to Senai and on to Kulai and farther north: later tracks linked the earliest settlement at Kulai with the Sayong–Semangar area which had earlier been approached only by river. Considerable areas of forest had been cleared for the cultivation of *gambir* and pepper, though by the end of the nineteenth century these had lost much of their earlier importance, and for the provision of fuel for the boiling of *gambir* to prepare it for use in tanning. It must be emphasized, however, that the extent of the individual settlements was very small, being little more than the first clearings in the forest, and in size they numbered a few hundred persons.

DEVELOPMENTS FROM 1917 TO 1945

After 1917 the *Kang Chue* system was replaced by an administration based on the Districts which still exist today. Of the *Kangkar* settlements only Senai and Ayer Bemban remain as inhabited places; all the others decayed progressively until they came to an end finally with the resettlement of population that took place during the early years of the Emergency (see page 289).

Kulai, the chief town in the sub-district, was not a *Kang Chue* settlement; in the first years of the twentieth century the Kulai area was a good hunting place often visited by the Sultan of Johore. Initially some Malays had built four or five huts there but later a Hainanese protégé of the Sultan was granted land and built the first stone shop-houses. Other Hainanese arrived and obtained grants of land which they cleared to plant tapioca and pineapple. Soon the Hainanese Association, representing the landowners of the area, became the most influential body in the town and undertook the administrative functions which in other places had been performed by the *Kang Chue*. The Khek community, which now outnumbers the Hainanese, was initially very small and was composed mainly of labourers.

The clearing of the forest about Senai and the new settlement of Kulai increased greatly with the development of the rubber industry. The usual pattern of development was to plant a newly-cleared area for a number of years with pineapple and then to replace this with rubber. Thus the present areas of cleared land came into existence during the First World War and during the 1920s. From Senai the jungle was pushed back to and beyond the site of the present Seelong New Village, where a small shopping centre was established. On the west side of Senai rubber planting was extended to the village of Hylam Kang, and from Kulai development pushed north-east along the bullock track to Kampong Poh Lee Sen, where extensive tapioca and pineapple cultivation also gave way in time to rubber.

An important factor in development was the construction of the railway which reached Johore Bahru in 1909, and about the same time the bullock cart track which ran northward through Senai and Kulai was metalled and became the main trunk road. The rivers began to lose their significance as means of communication, and the bicycle attained an unusual degree of economic importance. European capital was brought into the Kulai Sub-District: the older Chinese estates were bought up by European concerns, as in the case of Kelan Estate near to Kulai, or new estates were carved out of the jungle as at Sedenak further north. Small shopping centres at Saleng, Sengkang and Sedenak were located by the railway, while along the trunk road at the twenty-fourth and twenty-eighth milestones from Johore Bahru small groups of shop-houses sprang up to serve the needs of the population in the surrounding areas as these were being cleared and developed as rubber estates. This concentration of settlement along the new main lines of communication was nevertheless unfortunate, for it contrasted with the more widespread colonization of the *Kangkar* settlements, whose continued development would have done a great deal to open up great areas which are now abandoned and virtually denuded of population.

The pattern of settlement did not for the most part consist of large villages; Senai and Kulai were the only ones which exceeded 1,000 persons and these, together with the villages at Sedenak and Ayer Bemban, became Town Board areas controlled by the Johore Bahru Town Board.[1] Most of the settlers were scattered in small groups on the large and small rubber estates which now occupied the area. The inhabitants were in some cases small-holders themselves, but mostly they were labourers employed as tappers, and permitted by the owner to live on his land in huts which they themselves erected, and around which they cultivated plots of vegetables mainly for their own use. They were not squatters, for they had obtained the landowners' consent to live on the land. At this time, too, numbers of Malays entered the area from Pontian, sometimes coming by boat up the Sungei Pontian Besar to settle near to Ayer Manis, or else settling in small groups near to the Chinese settlements in the area.

It is probable that the majority of the scattered population was not affected by the abolition of the *Kang Chue* system in 1917 since it had not experienced it in its early and best form. Neither were they greatly affected by the establishment of a District Administration. The middle-aged and older inhabitants of today who remember the inter-war years invariably say that they had little contact with the administration in Johore Bahru. Even those with land who had to pay rents, often did this through a middleman, who might be a self-appointed petition-writer with a knowledge of English and contacts with the Land Office, or perhaps, as in Senai, through a Christian priest who was able to help them in their relations with the Government. Nevertheless there was no breakdown in land administration at this period and the illegal squatting which later became such a problem dated from the period of the Japanese occupation in 1942–5. The police force

---

[1] A local authority set up under a Town Board Enactment and empowered with administrative functions in urban areas. The members of Town Boards were appointed by the State Government.

was small and this is a tribute not so much to the peaceful nature of those years as to the fact that the Chinese were left to themselves to settle most of their quarrels without Government interference.

At that time the object of most Chinese settlers was not to remain in Malaya, but to amass enough money to retire to their home districts in China. They had therefore no desire to take part in politics in a country in which they had no intention of remaining. Currents of thought in the Malayan Chinese community ran parallel to those in China, where practically all the settlers had their families. The Chinese community belonged very much to the larger Chinese world, rather than to Malayan society. The clan associations of China had branches in Malaya and the Chinese secret societies established lodges when their members were in sufficient numbers in Malayan towns. The books that contained the new currents of Chinese thought were read as a matter of course in Malayan Chinese Schools, and Chinese political parties had their branches among the overseas Chinese communities, who were often wealthy enough to supply the money which was not so easily forthcoming from poorer communities in China itself.

But though the ties with China were close, as the 1930s progressed and greater control of immigration was established, the ratio of Chinese women to men approached equality and the number of Chinese whose children were Malayan-born increased significantly. The Chinese were becoming a permanently resident population and the ties with their homeland were weakening.

The barrier of language effectively helped to keep the administration and the Chinese population apart in Malaya. Few senior British or Malay administrative officers, with the exception of the Protector of Chinese, knew or intended to learn the Chinese language, and only a few Chinese saw in English a means of acquiring greater knowledge, generally for making money. As the Malay population was small, few Chinese children had the opportunity of learning Malay naturally in childhood.

Up to the outbreak of the Second World War the Chinese population was, therefore, to a large extent left alone by the administration, but by the same time new ways of thought and new attitudes were profoundly influencing the community internally. The older successful business people remained the formal leaders of the community somewhat in the same way as the *Kang Chue* previously, and, organized into District Associations, they had considerable power and often represented the interests of Association members when contact with Government was necessary. It is clear, however, that in the Kulai Sub-District the lack of homogeneity prevented any one group from establishing its undisputed leadership in any settlement. At Senai the rift between the two Khek groups, the Hoh Poh and the Wai Chau, continued. Often their dissensions would reach such a violent state that battles occurred in which offensive weapons, including granite from the railway track, were freely used, while the few police in the area wisely kept out of the way. In Kulai the power of the former dominant group, the Hainanese, was threatened by the great increase in the number of Khek, who outnumbered all other communities by 1940.

As rubber planting had increased, population had been drawn into the area from many different parts of Malaya as well as from China. Estates might often draw a whole group of workers from as far afield as Kuala Lumpur. Among the Chinese, Khek people became the most numerous, followed by the Hainanese, with smaller groups of Cantonese, Teochew, Hokkien, and Kwongsais. The numerical dominance of Khek and Hainanese was significant, for these two groups, both in China and beyond its borders, had shown themselves receptive to the new social and political ideas that were becoming current. Both Chinese Nationalist and other revolutionary political and social concepts found a receptive audience among these two communities. From the period of the First World War onwards the Kuomintang established itself and made nationalist influence felt through constant propaganda carried on in schools, reading rooms and discussion groups. The younger generation no longer accepted the outlook of the older people who had wished only to acquire enough money to return to China. From this period there was a breakdown of the control of the family by the elders and children began to look to political parties rather than to their parents for guidance. The ideas in every textbook read by Chinese children concerned nationalism, the past greatness of China and the need to right her present humiliations.

In the Kulai Sub-District, Communist influence seems first to have been felt in Senai, possibly about 1924 or 1925. The Communist Party gradually built up some support in the town, exerting much more power over the Khek population there than in Kulai where a large section of the Hainanese and Khek business community supported the Kuomintang. Thus during the pre-war years the influence of both the Kuomintang and the Communist Party developed in the Sub-District. After the outbreak of the Sino-Japanese War in 1937 organizations exhorting people to aid China in her struggle sprang up in Senai and Kulai as elsewhere in Malaya. The Communist influence was initially weak, for the majority of the Chinese were enjoying a fairly reasonable standard of living and there was no exploited landless peasantry. However, the anti-Japanese movements enabled the Communists to extend their power, for these were often organized by them. Even the respected figures of the Towkay class, the small capitalists, would for patriotic reasons willingly give their support to the movements which were, from the Communists' point of view, primarily a means of expanding their influence. By December 1941 Communist influence had become quite strong among the Chinese throughout Kulai Sub-District and especially in the Senai area.

It was during the Japanese occupation, 1942-5, that Communist domination over the working people in the Kulai Sub-District was firmly established. Initially many of the people left for the jungle when the Japanese arrived, but later, on receiving assurances from the new rulers, shop-owners and business people returned to carry on their trade. Opposition to the Japanese rule came mainly from the Communist-dominated Malayan People's Anti-Japanese Army (M.P.A.J.A.) which easily extended its domination over the scattered rural population from which the greater part of its support came. The shop-owning class of Kulai, probably because it had more to lose, was not so actively anti-Japanese and was rewarded for its better behaviour by gentler treatment than other sections of the population in the Sub-District received. The Japanese policy of encouraging the people to grow more food also helped the Communists for it led to a further dispersal of population which 'squatted' without legal right in the jungle fringe areas where their domination by the M.P.A.J.A. was an easy matter. From this scattered population the Communists derived adequate supplies of food and money. The Communists' policy was not one of active military confrontation with the Japanese but an extension of their influence over all sections of the Chinese population against the day when, with the defeat of the Japanese by the allies, they would be able to gain control. It was probably a wise policy since the Japanese forces were better equipped and ruthless in their methods. The Japanese were largely content if military requirements were met and so a tacit *modus vivendi* was established between the two sides.

THE EMERGENCY AND RESETTLEMENT

When the Japanese were defeated the withdrawal of their troops was followed in name by the British Military Administration, but in fact for some time the M.P.A.J.A. was in complete control of both town and country. Government control of the main lines of communication and the principal settlements was only gradually established and even then Communist domination of the rural areas, and indeed their intimidation of the Chinese population living in the settlements themselves, remained almost unimpaired. Thus when the Emergency resulting from Communist subversion was declared in June, 1948, the Government exercised a certain amount of control in the towns but very little in the countryside.

Initially it was not known how Government control of the rural areas could be gained and the methods at first employed did not produce any lasting effect, except to accentuate the pro-Communist feeling of the masses. For example, in 1949 two small villages on the Johore Bahru–Ayer Hitam road and at Hylam Kang were raided by Government forces; their populations were either interned or deported to China. In the area of Hylam Kang the operation was far from being a complete success for many of the population escaped to the jungle, either to join the Communists or to await the end of the operation. There is no doubt that the population as a whole was willing to collaborate with the Communists, either because they were active supporters or because they feared to do otherwise. The Communists were, moreover, quite often their own relatives and friends and it was natural to support them rather than the representatives of a colonial government which did not always appear to understand the local people and local conditions.

The domination of the rural population by the Communists was the main reason for the policy of resettlement which was adopted by Government from 1950 onwards. It was based on the principle of regrouping the multitude of scattered homesteads, where intimidation by the Communists was an easy matter, into a small number of planned villages, each with its own administration and served with schools, basic health services, markets, shopping centres and other amenities. The villages were protected by perimeter fences and in course of time defence was, at least in part, undertaken by the people themselves organized into home-guards. The establishment of the villages for the first time brought the Government and the Chinese population into close contact with one another, and initially this contact was not always pleasant. A directive issued in 1950 had insisted on the completion of resettlement by May 1951 and the hurried methods which had to be adopted to meet this target date were naturally resented because of the hardships they involved.

The population during the physical process of resettlement was, however, to a large extent cowed by the military activities of both sides. The Communists quickly realized that resettlement would weaken their control of the masses and cut off their major source of supplies of food and money, and so they urged the people to refuse to move into the new villages which were portrayed as prison camps. It was, however, apparent that the Government meant business and people were not sufficiently in support of the Communist Party to resist the resettlement orders *en masse*. The truth was that the Chinese population was not in an economically impoverished or exploited condition such as might have given rise to a genuinely revolutionary fervour. Few people were out of work, and wages on the rubber estates were quite good. Once Government had made it clear that everyone must move into the new villages, resettlement took place, reluctantly but without any great difficulty. Naturally there was irritation at having to dismantle and re-erect houses, but once in the new villages there was a feeling of security and peace which did not exist on the outside of the perimeter.

Previously in the development of Chinese settlement, Senai and Kulai were the only large centres of population, but with resettlement eight additional villages were established, while Senai and Kulai increased in size (Figure 1). During resettlement the principle was adopted that farmers should not be moved too far from the lands they cultivated and that rubber tappers should be resettled not more than two or three miles from their work. The new villages in the Sub-District turned out to be either primarily agricultural or ones in which the largest single working group consists of rubber-tappers.

The first area to be resettled was about Kulai itself and north of the town towards the thirtieth milestone. Many outlying areas were completely denuded of population including the old *Kangkar* settlements in the Poh Lee Sen area. The population moved was heavily dominated by the Communists and it was concentrated in a new village named Kelapa Sawit, after the neighbouring Oil Palm Estate.

The population which was moved into Kulai itself consisted mainly of tappers and a few smallholders from areas round about. The new village was built adjacent to the existing town whose population was primarily engaged in commerce and which had been politically inclined to the Kuomintang. Between the townsmen of Kulai and the new villagers, who were drawn from

TABLE I

The ethnic composition of new villages on 31 December, 1954

Ethnic group	Kulai	Senai	Saleng	Seelong	Sedenak	Ayer Bemban	Sengkang	Bukit Batu	Kelapa Sawit	Roscote	Total
Hakka	4,003	2,571	798	432	575	448	386	597	2,437	14	12,261
Cantonese	740	127	138	17	208	64	72	19	29	36	1,450
Hokkien	339	37	51	3	1	–	11	6	36	–	484
Teochew	201	262	74	4	40	19	15	–	116	–	731
Kwongsai	98	–	16	1	204	29	8	11	34	–	401
Hainanese	1,075	152	110	41	104	61	220	–	83	104	1,950
Other Chinese	21	–	–	3	–	–	–	–	–	–	24
Total Chinese	6,477	3,149	1,187	501	1,132	621	712	633	2,735	154	17,301
Malays	210	85	23	41	70	54	68	–	120	–	671
Indians	94	28	–	–	32	7	2	–	–	27	190
Others	3	–	–	–	–	–	11	–	1	–	15
Total non-Chinese	307	113	23	41	102	61	81	–	121	27	876
Total population	6,784	3,262	1,210	542	1,234	682	793	633	2,856	181	18,177

Communist-dominated areas, there was thus an economic, social and political rift.

Whilst these resettlements were going forward, a survey was made in June 1950 of the area between Kulai and Senai on either side of the main road, and four resettlement areas were proposed at Saleng, Roscote Estate, Seelong and Senai. It was also recommended that an all-weather road should be constructed to run from the main road at Saleng to Roscote, thence southward to Seelong and on to Senai, in order to link up what were remote and Communist-dominated areas. The new villages were constructed but the road linking them remained a track. The population of the surrounding area and the remnants of the population of the Hylam Kang area were moved into Senai and as at Kulai there was something of a rift between the commercial element of the old town and the rubber-tappers of the new village, although Senai in the past had been less influenced than Kulai by the Kuomintang.

In the middle of 1951 three more new villages were made; these were at Ayer Bemban, adjacent to the existing village and in close proximity to a Malay settlement, at Sedenak near to the railway, and at Sengkang. Ayer Bemban does not seem to have been so dominated by Communist influence, possibly because of its proximity to a Malay population, but the more isolated Sedenak and Sengkang new villages contained populations mainly engaged in rubber-tapping and hence they were still easy to intimidate.

Table I shows the ethnic composition of the villages at the end of 1954, three and a half years after they had been established. The figures indicate their preponderantly Chinese character, with the relative size of the various dialect groups within the Chinese communities. The total population of the villages was not the total population of the sub-district as the various rubber and oil-palm estates each had accommodation for their own labour forces which were not so predominantly Chinese in composition. Table II gives the occupations of the inhabitants of the villages in 1955 and the importance of the rubber industry is clearly evident. In only two villages, Bukit Batu and Kelapa Sawit, was rubber tapping less important than farming. The large number of people in the 'miscellaneous' group reflects a degree of concealed unemployment which is common in Chinese society. People with little work to do are maintained by their families and they contribute what they can by doing odd jobs. There is always a reluctance to admit unemployment and when asked their occupation, the unemployed often reply *chaap kung* ('miscellaneous work'). As the group which does such work includes women, the figure includes a considerable number of people who might more correctly be returned as housewives.

In December, 1951, the Resettlement Department of Johore was abolished as the work of resettling the Chinese population of the state had been completed. In the Sub-District of Kulai the Department had transformed an area of dispersed settlement with only two small towns into one of ten nucleated villages. The basic reasons for undertaking resettlement were military and political. It was necessary that a population which had developed independently since the days of earliest settlement, with an outlook alien to the country in which it was living, should be brought under administrative control, in order to end the Communist influence and to integrate it, if possible, into a Malayan society. To a large extent these objectives were achieved. Isolated from the material support of the population and unable to carry on their propaganda with any facility, the Communist influence slowly began to decrease. Gradually the Government and the people were brought into closer contact and Local Councils, democratically elected and financially autonomous, were set up in each village. The participation of the inhabitants in these new processes of local government, and later, through the state and national elections, in the political life of Malaya as a whole, had a profound effect in winning over the greater part of the population from their former Communist leanings. After the independence of Malaya was achieved in 1957 the sense of belonging to the country rather than to distant China became even stronger.

There were, of course, economic disadvantages in the process of

TABLE II

The occupations of the inhabitants of new villages on 30 June 1955

Occupations	Kulai	Senai	Saleng	Seelong	Sedenak	Ayer Bemban	Sengkang	Bukit Batu	Kelapa Sawit	Roscote	Total
Rubber tappers	1,114	802	417	230	231	140	273	19	48	106	3,380
Hawkers and vendors	171	41	2	–	11	3	1	2	13	–	244
Shopkeepers	204	87	22	8	32	16	9	10	38	–	426
Shop assistants	200	53	10	2	12	5	–	6	10	–	298
Labourers	376	118	39	21	197	51	48	67	337	–	1,254
Farmers	90	85	3	–	12	63	23	102	379	–	757
Rubber smallholders	14	9	–	–	1	6	2	4	6	–	42
Mechanics and engineers	53	6	2	2	2	–	1	2	–	–	72
Govt. servants and police	115	36	17	22	14	19	25	17	41	–	306
Miscellaneous	1,639	578	92	18	125	209	170	159	806	5	3,801
Total working population	3,976	1,815	604	303	637	512	552	388	1,682	111	10,580
Total population	6,784	3,374	1,209	544	1,215	682	786	633	2,824	181	18,232

resettlement. Workers had to travel farther to the estates and farmers were prevented from cultivating areas too far from the village boundaries; thus once-settled areas well away from the main trunk road and the railway were virtually abandoned. But these disadvantages could not outweigh the political and social benefits which the new villages conferred by beginning the integration of the Chinese population into the framework of Malayan society. The process was far from quick or easy and it was not until 1960 that the military power of the Communists was finally broken: indeed there are still undoubtedly some people in the Sub-District who are potential Communist supporters. But to gain the political support of a sizeable part of the Chinese population in an area with such a history of settlement was a formidable achievement on the part of the Government.

It is now probable that the rural development policies of the Government of Malaysia will again lead to the establishment of settlements in areas away from the trunk road and the railway, and the abandoned sites of *Kangkar* settlements may again be reoccupied. Henceforth, however, new settlement is likely to be planned, with the establishment of less exclusively Chinese nucleated villages which will be economically viable. Their nature and organization will owe not a little to the new villages which were created during the period of resettlement in the early years of the Emergency.

ACKNOWLEDGEMENTS

The material on which this essay is based was collected when the writer was a member of the Malayan Civil Service. Much of the information came from interviews with Chinese inhabitants of the Kulai Sub-District in 1956. For the early history of settlement, reference was made to Winstedt, R. (1932) 'History of Johore', *J. Roy. Asiatic Soc.* (Malayan Branch).

L. S. BHAT

Aspects of regional planning in India

THE term 'region', used in the context of planning in India, denotes an area with unified characteristics in respect of natural environment or resources and problems of development. Regions for resource planning should have distinctiveness of their own and stand in contrast to neighbouring areas. They should possess distinct regional structure, in respect of agricultural land use, industrial and urban patterns, communications and the overall pattern of economic development. Contrasts in the distribution of resources and levels of economic development in India necessitate planning on a regional basis (Planning Commission, 1961). This approach is emphasized particularly in the Third Five-Year Plan which states that regional planning is as important as national planning and that the development of each region should be concerned with the resources with which the region is best endowed. A suitable regional framework for resource planning is also considered essential particularly because of the arbitrary nature of the administrative boundaries, but the boundaries of regions should be adapted to those of administrative units.

A systematic academic approach to regional definition was first proposed in a scheme of three major natural regions and twenty-two sub-regions (Stamp, 1929), where the criteria used were 'physiography and structure at the primary level and climate for sub-divisions'. J. N. L. Baker (1928) outlined a scheme of natural regions which was closely similar. Major natural regions like the extra-peninsular mountain wall, the Indo-Gangetic plain and the peninsular block stand out vividly in contrast to one another and such contrasts are illustrated in the more comprehensive regional treatment suggested by O.H.K. Spate (1954).

Regionalism in the broader sense is not new in India. The historical and the cultural differences between the southern

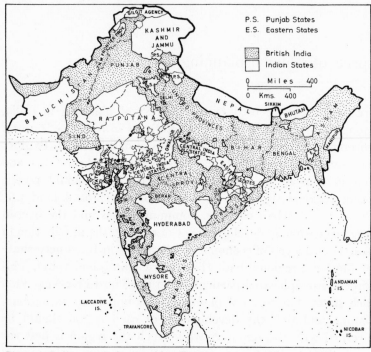

Figure 1. India 1947, before partition (Based on a map in Menon, 1956)

(Dravidian) and the northern parts of India are well known. Distinct cultural traits have also been identified as an expression of regional differences (Bose, 1961). The idea of a regional approach as a counter to narrow linguistic, communal and political outlooks was put forward when the Coupland scheme, following a suggestion made in the census of India 1941, proposed 'a broad division of the country into four regions demarcated according to economic or geographic principle' (Coupland, 1944). These regions were the Indus basin, the Ganges basin as far as the Bengal–Bihar border, the Brahmaputra basin together with the Ganges delta, and the Deccan. The boundaries of these regions claimed to follow those of natural divisions and also to correspond to the concentration of population according to the major religious communities. There have been numerous other instances of regional division of the country worked out in isolation by different Government Ministries and organizations – census regions in 1951, agricultural, livestock and meteorological regions, regions for the transportation of coal and a scheme of forty regions delimited for the National Sample Survey in 1960.

ADMINISTRATIVE REORGANIZATION AND PLANNING

After the partition of the sub-continent in 1947 there were two events which were of importance for regional studies. First, more than 550 princely States were consolidated with the other parts of India to bring about political unity, and a hierarchy in administration was established linking the nation with the States (Figures 1 and 2). The administrative States contained within their boundaries mixtures of various linguistic and cultural groups and they lacked homogeneity in respect of resources and regional character. The old Mysore State, for example, had a better network of roads, electricity supply, irrigation and town development which stands in sharp contrast within the enlarged Mysore State which includes the peripheral areas of the old Bombay Province and the Hyderabad State. The city of Hyderabad with a population of more than a million had grown rapidly in a surrounding area of low density of population and low land productivity, because of its position as capital of the former Hyderabad State. On the other hand, States like Uttar Pradesh, Bihar and West Bengal have undergone very little change and they correspond broadly with the major natural region of the Ganges plain. Where anomalies occur they need to be corrected by the reorganization of economic activities through planned development.

The second event was the reorganization of States in 1956 and the subsequent division of the Bombay State (1960), providing an administrative framework of fifteen linguistic States and Union territories, the States in turn being grouped into five zones for purposes of inter-State co-ordination of administrative functions (Figure 3). Linguistic and cultural homogeneity, financial, economic and administrative convenience and the successful working of the national plan towards the economic development of the

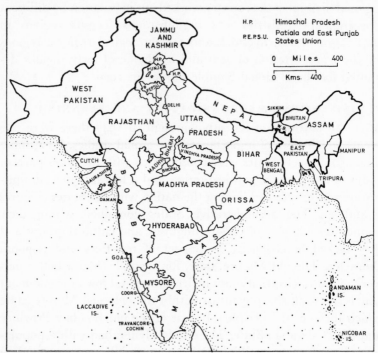

Figure 2. India after partition (1947) and integration of the States (1950). (Based on a map in Menon, 1956)

country were stated as the main objectives of reorganization (Reorganization Commission, 1955). Regional disparities in physical and economic resources and levels of economic development are inevitable in a country the size of India. The present administrative structure with linguistic and cultural unity is more efficient for economic development than the former one in which a variety of fragmented linguistic groups within a State would have impeded development. In South India, for example, more efficient development of natural resources of the Western Ghats region can be expected since much of it now lies within Mysore and Kerala, whereas formerly it was divided among five States (Bombay Province, old Mysore State, Coorg, Madras Province and Travancore-Cochin) of different sizes, administration and powers of development.

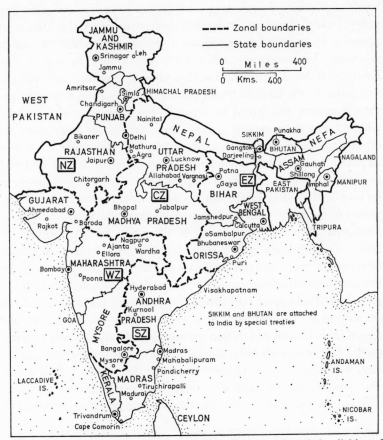

Figure 3. India after the reorganization of the States (1956) and the division of Bombay State into Maharashtra and Gujarat (1960). (Based in part on maps in *Agricultural Atlas of India*, Ministry of Food and Agriculture, 1958)

Almost all the States are divided for administrative convenience into Divisions, Districts, Development Blocks or former *talukas*[1] (roughly a group of 100 villages with a total population of about 150,000), and villages. These play important roles in the implementation of the State planning programmes which in turn are a part of the overall national plan. The idea of hierarchy in different

[1] In the majority of the cases a Development Block is equivalent to a *taluka*; otherwise the *taluka* is split up into two or three Development Blocks.

levels of planning in this approach differs from regional planning proper which involves integrated development of the sectors of economy in terms of areas/regions and their functional and space relations. Various approaches were considered by the States Reorganization Commission with a view to grouping administrative units on the basis of broad principles of regional delimitation. Consideration was given to river valley regions, nodal regions where areas are grouped around important cities and towns, or other centres of economic activity, and regions with minimum disparity in *per capita* income in comparison with the national average. However, the data required for delimiting these were lacking and so they could not be used. Zonal councils were suggested to facilitate inter-State co-ordination of administration and economic planning,[1] since this is necessary for such things as transport, irrigation and power development. Strong economic interdependence between regions was also considered essential for the economic development of the country as a whole. Though the Five-Year Plans have laid special emphasis on regional aspects of development, the plan-frame is essentially a multi-sectoral one which takes into consideration mainly the overall national requirements and the available financial resources. It is necessary, therefore, to study the present pattern of the distribution of resources and production and then to prepare regional estimates which in turn can be reconciled with the national targets and estimates.

PLANNING REGIONS IN INDIA: SOME GEOGRAPHICAL CONSIDERATIONS

The concept of a planning region, like the regional concept itself, implies hierarchy and this is important in resource planning for a country the size of India. For example, the problem of industrial-

---

[1] *i.* Western zone: Gujarat, Maharashtra and Mysore.
    ii. Southern zone: Andhra, Madras and Kerala.
    iii. Eastern zone: Bihar, Orissa, West Bengal and Assam.
    iv. Northern zone: Punjab, Rajasthan, Jammu and Kashmir, Delhi and Himachal Pradesh.
    v. Central zone: Uttar Pradesh and Madhya Pradesh.

ization, particularly basic and heavy industries, has different dimensions – local, regional and national – since these industries tend to be highly localized in areas most favourable for them. The North-eastern Plateau as a whole (including Chota Nagpur Plateau, Bastar Hills, Orissa Hills, and so on) is basically a region of forestry and mineral resources (coal, iron, manganese) and is tending to develop a major industrial complex which contributes a large share to the national industrial production and to income from basic and heavy industries. This area, though split up among the States of Bihar, Orissa, Madhya Pradesh, Maharashtra and West Bengal, needs to be considered as a single major region for purposes of resource development.

Agricultural development, which is considered in national planning to be of equal importance to industrial development, requires a regional approach because of the contrasts in cropping patterns arising from regional variations in physical conditions. Economic and social factors also exercise their influence on land-use patterns and in some cases they may dominate, but through long-term planning the patterns should be adapted to physical conditions (Land Use Planning, 1958). Land use may undergo rapid changes in and around the large cities and major development projects (e.g. irrigation projects and areas of large-scale reclamation of forest lands and mineral exploitation); but these cover only a small part of the agricultural land in the country as a whole. It is estimated that even after the exploitation of all the potential irrigation resources only 50 per cent of the cropped area is likely to be irrigated.[1] In a major part of this potential irrigated area the existing land-use patterns are likely to be intensified rather than changed since the cropping patterns are mostly adapted to local conditions. For example, the perhumid west coastal plains of India have near-optimal conditions for the cultivation of paddy and coco-nut; the former is cultivated either in rotation, with

[1] Of the 318 million acres of net area sown, only 70 million acres (22 per cent) were irrigated during 1960-1. In terms of the areal spread of irrigation benefits it is necessary to distinguish between areas covered by major irrigation projects (31 million acres) and those from minor irrigation schemes (39 million acres).

TABLE I

Inter-State disparities in selected sectors of the economy

States	Population density per sq. mile (1961)	Growth rate (% increase 1951–61)	% of rural non-agricultural popn. to total rural popn. (1951)	% of urban popn. to total popn. (1961)	% of urban popn. in each State to total urban popn. in India (1961)	% of net total area area sown to total area (1955–6)	% of area under forest to total area
INDIA	370	21·50	18·46	17·84	100·00	44·11	23·86
1. Andhra Pradesh	339	15·65	22·57	17·40	8·04	41·10	22·72
2. Kerala	1,127	24·76	41·10	15·03	3·26	46·63	31·90
3. Madras	669	11·85	22·01	26·72	11·55	44·17	16·49
4. Mysore	318	21·57	13·88	22·03	6·66	51·38	18·31
5. Assam	252	34·45	23·44	7·50	1·14	16·98	36·78
6. Bihar	691	19·78	9·54	8·43	5·03	43·27	19·77
7. Maharashtra	333	23·60	19·29*	27·92	14·17	54·87*	16·81*
8. Gujarat	286	26·88		25·61	6·78		
9. Jammu & Kashmir	N.A.	9·73	N.A.	16·80	0·77	N.A.	N.A.
10. Madhya Pradesh	189	24·17	12·92	14·29	5·95	35·21	38·83
11. Orissa	292	19·82	17·95	6·33	1·43	35·98	40·86
12. Punjab	430	25·80	20·96	20·96	5·24	59·05	12·42
13. Rajasthan	153	26·20	17·85	16·05	4·15	21·04	12·85
14. Uttar Pradesh	649	16·66	16·05	12·85	12·17	57·37	13·51
15. West Bengal	1,032	32·79	23·98	23·15	10·40	60·43	13·04

* Maharashtra and Gujarat combined. N.A. – Not available.

	Based on Agriculture		Industries Textiles		Basic and heavy industries		Power	Communications
	% of factories in each State (1957)	% of workers in each State (1957)	% of factories in each State (1957)	% of workers in each State (1957)	% of factories in each State (1957)	% of workers in each State (1957)	% of electricity consumption in industries (1959–60)	Road density per 100 square miles (1958)
INDIA	100·00	100·00	100·00	100·00	100·00	100·00	100·00	100·00
1.	13·48	12·98	1·76	1·62	5·89	2·88	3·65	14·4
2.	3·46	9·41	7·30	2·68	2·76	2·79	4·05	32·7
3.	12·54	7·40	16·76	10·29	13·01	11·63	9·14	32·3
4.	5·28	4·56	7·21	2·65	3·99	2·75	7·75	20·4
5.	4·94	7·16	0·09	0·02	0·62	0·58	0·03	1·9
6.	18·20	5·81	0·83	0·72	5·13	7·52	7·74	8·4
7–8.	22·77	23·95	41·50	44·15	31·45	27·10	28·35	10·3
9.	N.A.	N.A.	N.A.	N.A.	N.A.	N.A.	0·26	1·0
10.	5·43	7·21	1·27	4·13	3·36	2·81	2·46	6·7
11.	0·89	0·79	0·38	0·44	0·49	1·50	5·06	6·5
12.	2·55	2·54	13·77	2·45	6·59	4·08	3·42	10·7
13.	1·35	1·14	0·71	1·01	0·86	2·15	0·30	5·3
14.	3·34	9·26	2·48	5·80	8·03	8·25	5·82	10·3
15.	5·76	7·76	5·94	24·04	17·81	25·96	20·20	18·2

TABLE II

Regional framework for resource development – some selected components

Region	Cultivated area			Forests		Density per sq. mile (1961)	Population	
	% of total area of India	% of total area of the Region	% of total cultivated area of India	% of total area of the Region	% of total forest area of India		% of total popn. of India (1961)	% of rural non-agric. popn. to total rural popn. (1961)
All India		46·70		17·00		370		18·44
I. West Coast	2·63	40·97	2·31	23·59	3·66	822	6·37	36·19
II. Western Ghats	3·23	44·30	3·07	19·21	3·65	388	3·03	15·12
III. Central Plateau	15·21	59·08	19·24	12·98	11·62	256	10·19	14·43
IV. Eastern Ghats*	–	–	–	–	–	–	–	–
V. East Coast	6·05	50·28	6·51	13·92	4·95	571	9·38	20·52
VI. North-eastern Plateau	15·20	35·24	11·47	39·61	35·41	213	8·75	13·15
VII. Ganges Plain	16·86	79·47	28·68	4·70	4·66	783	36·88	16·11
VIII. Assam	8·78	12·54	2·37	27·35	14·12	286	3·67	24·67
IX. Gujarat	6·10	50·78	6·63	4·40	1·58	286	4·73	25·36
X. Rajasthan	10·72	32·60	7·48	3·85	2·42	150	4·40	17·83
XI. Kashmir & Northern Hills	N.A.	N.A.	N.A.	N.A.	N.A.	N.A.	N.A.	N.A.
1. Godavari Trough	1·72	36·30	1·33	23·56	2·38	257	1·20	29·82
2. Telangana	1·82	42·28	1·65	11·59	1·24	339	1·71	24·23
3. Rayalaseema	2·42	44·33	2·30	21·14	3·01	243	1·59	22·23
4. Mysore Plateau	1·24	41·66	1·10	7·71	0·56	430	1·43	13·47
5. Coimbatore Plateau	2·39	53·32	2·73	21·26	2·99	599	3·87	22·29
6. Chambal Ravines	1·61	39·37	1·36	14·92	1·42	244	1·13	13·04

* Data are included in the adjoining regions. Detailed studies at *taluka* level are necessary. N.A. – Not available.

pulses during the dry season in unirrigable areas in coastal Mysore, or with double- or even treble-cropping as in the Kerala coastal plains with tank irrigation supplementing the south-west monsoon and the winter rains.

The integrated development of land use, between cropped land, grazing land and forestry, also needs to be considered on a regional basis. Problems which this integration presents vary with the physical conditions. In the plantation areas of the Western Ghats,[1] the problems of land-use planning are concerned with the integrated exploitation of the land available for cultivation with existing land use which extends from the valley floor to the residual hillsides. Any effort to extend the spice gardens in the valley floor will have its impact on the adjoining forested slopes which are the main source of green leaf manure (Bhat, 1957). Likewise, the land-use plan for the foothill areas adjoining the coastal plains and the steep slopes of the Western Ghats must take into consideration relationships with the coastal plains which depend largely on the foothill areas for fuel and fodder crops.

Thus regional physical conditions, regional requirements and relationships with other regions are the criteria to be taken into account in preparing a regional land-use plan, and systematic regional studies should precede any plans for future patterns of land use. A regional framework for resource development should consider diversities in regional factors and planning problems in the context of national economic development, and should then be adapted to administrative boundaries as far as possible.

Distribution of resources: regional patterns and variations

In outlining a suitable regional framework for resource development it is necessary to understand in detail the patterns of distribution of resources and their causal relationships. It is difficult to draw clear regional boundaries and the patterns of regional structure that emerge are distinct in their cores rather than on

[1] Plantation crops include rubber, tea, coffee, cardamom, pepper, areca nut and a variety of fruit trees for which the humid forested slopes and perennial river valleys of the Western Ghats region are favourable.

their peripheries. This structure is better revealed by data compiled on the basis of administrative units which conform to regional boundaries (Tables I and II). In the following pages an attempt is made to show the distinctiveness of regions in their physical conditions, the distribution patterns of crops, industries, towns and natural resources and then to indicate how administrative units may be regrouped on the basis of the common patterns or problems of development, taking the District as a unit for study.

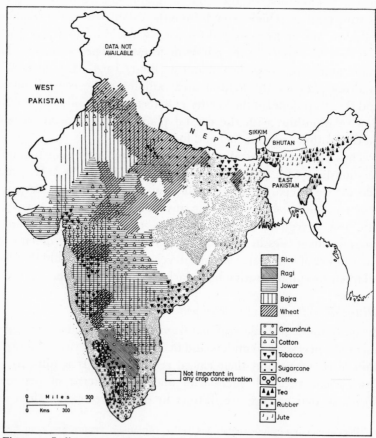

Figure 4. India: crop regions. (Based on District-level data and *Agricultural Atlas of India*)

Cropping patterns

The map of crop regions based on the District-level data for 1955 shows broad regional crop associations with distinct contrasts which reflect variations in regional physical conditions (Figure 4). The coastal region, the black and red soil plateau (with the exception of the unirrigable red soil and sand areas) and the Ganges plain are distinct crop regions and they contribute the greatest share in the total agricultural production of India. The North-eastern Plateau and the Western and the Eastern Ghats region are less important in agriculture, particularly for cereal farming. Intensive paddy cultivation is practised locally but their overall position in national crop production is low (e.g. the North-eastern Plateau as a whole has only about 10 per cent of the total cultivated area of India). A detailed analysis of regional variations in cropping patterns and yield against the background of physical conditions serves to distinguish the core areas of crop association which should be given priority in planning. The map based on the District-level data should be viewed with caution against over-generalization of the cropping patterns, particularly in the peripheries of the major crop-association regions (e.g. the West Coast and the Western Ghats). Studies in South India have revealed that at least *taluka*-level data should be used in the preparation of a map of crop regions (Indian Statistical Institute, 1962).[1]

Industrial and urban patterns (Figures 5 and 7)

There are two distinct regional industrial patterns; the agro-industries (e.g. rice and oil mills, ginneries, sugar factories) follow the regional agricultural patterns, while the basic and heavy industries (e.g. iron and steel, electrical and heavy engineering, chemicals, cement, fertilizers), and even the textile industries, are concentrated in large urban centres or are located near to their resource base. With the exception of the large industrial

[1] The scale and level of mapping necessary to draw generalized regional boundaries is itself a systematic study which is yet to be pursued in India.

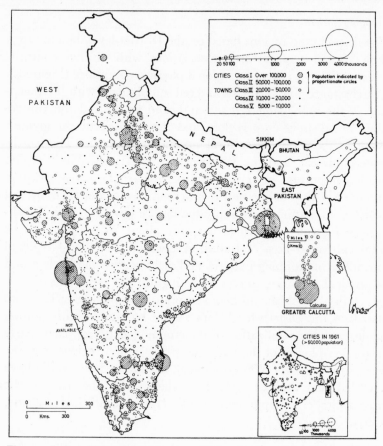

Figure 5. India: cities and towns in 1951 and (inset) 1961

complex of the Chota Nagpur Plateau, industries do not exhibit distinct regional patterns. Detailed study of industries in South India has shown, however, that distinct regional patterns of industrial development are in the making and has indicated lines for the possible development of these embryonic complexes.[1]

There are distinct regional contrasts in number, size, distribution and growth of towns. Some areas stand out because of the

[1] A regional industrial complex is one which exhibits generic relationship between industries and the region in which they are located.

concentration of large numbers of towns and high percentages of urban population: these include the Ganges plain (with the metropolitan cities of Delhi and Calcutta at its extremities), the Kerala coastal plain, the Bombay-Poona area, the Gujarat coast from Surat to Ahmedabad, the cluster of towns and cities (Miraj, Kolhapur and Sangli) along the Mysore-Maharashtra border, the Krishna-Godavari delta and the Salem-Coimbatore tract. They contrast with areas like the North-eastern Plateau, western Rajasthan (except for the junction of the Aravalli foothills and the sandy plains which has favoured the growth of towns and particularly cities like Jodhpur and Bikaner), Assam, the Western Ghats and the Eastern Ghats which have few towns or none at all. Urbanization is an important element in the processes of economic and social development, particularly in facilitating diversified occupational patterns with the growth of urban-based industries, and by providing services and amenities, not only for the urban dwellers but for the entire population dwelling in the urban spheres of influence. Towns have regional problems of various dimensions, particularly metropolitan and large industrial agglomerations which are functionally inter-related to distant areas (Alexander, 1954).

Urbanization is not always related to the location and growth of industries. While the North-eastern Plateau has an extensive industrial complex of iron and steel, engineering and fertilizer industries, by comparison with the nucleated patterns of industries in cities elsewhere, this area is the least urbanized in India. Only 9·6 per cent of the total population is classed as urban dwelling in 11 cities (with more than 50,000 population) and 149 towns (the majority with less than 20,000 population), while for the whole of India 18 per cent of the total population is urban – in 2,960 cities and towns. Nearly 56 per cent of the total urban population is concentrated in 248 cities which are distributed very irregularly. Even in 1901, 20 of the 35 cities in India were in the Ganges plain; the North-eastern Plateau, the Krishna–Godavari delta and the West Coast as a whole, with the exception of the area north of Bombay, had no cities. The distribution and

311

growth of cities during 1901-61 indicates that each region has different characteristics and problems in its pattern of urbanization, making it difficult to devise a common development policy for all.

Regional norms of urbanization and the inter-relations between the processes of urban growth and type of industries need to be worked out in regional urban studies. A general study of the distribution patterns suggests that there is a relationship between urban and industrial development and the regional character. The smaller urban centres (less than 50,000 population) mostly serve the regions in which they are located, while the larger cities develop functional inter-relations between regions. It is possible to recognize an urban hierarchy in which towns of the lowest order are market centres for regions with common patterns of land use and settlement; these towns in turn are related to larger centres which are of higher order in the hierarchy.

Natural resources

The resources of forests, minerals (including oil), and water (for irrigation and power development) are concentrated, as compared with the agricultural resources which are dispersed. The regional dimensions of the problems associated with their development would therefore appear to be narrower but the locational aspects of the related industries establish inter-regional relations through transport and power networks. Forest resources are mostly peripheral to the areas of cereal farming and are mainly concentrated in the humid and hilly areas of the Western and Eastern Ghats, the North-eastern Plateau, and the northern and north-eastern (Assam) hill ranges. Nearly 80 per cent of the total coal production is from the North-eastern Plateau, where the coalfields of the Gondwana series are distributed in a 'horseshoe' pattern. In addition, coal occurs in small quantities in the Godavari trough (Singareni coalfields), Assam, Jammu, Kashmir and Rajasthan. Hydro-electric power resources are concentrated in the perhumid Western Ghats region, and in the headwaters of the Ganges and its tributaries. Thermal power is associated with the highly localized distribution of coal, and the problems to be faced are those of more economical generation and distribution of power to all parts of India which must be approached on a regional basis rather than on the basis of administrative States.

Another problem associated with the development of natural resources is that of their occurrence either in clusters or in isolation which compels planners to lay emphasis on regional priorities in the development of these resources. For example, while the North-eastern Plateau has all the advantages for the development of single or multiple industrial complexes based on iron ore and coal, the Hospet-Sandur iron ore area (Mysore State) has to depend on the Damodar coalfields. Likewise the iron ores of the Shevaroy and Kalrayan hills of the Eastern Ghats are awaiting exploitation in association with the newly developing lignite fields at Neyveli near Madras. Regions which have the best opportunities of developing industrial complexes are few and far between and hence they need to be linked with parts of the country which have poorer opportunities or none at all.

Regional planning is concerned with two facets which are inter-linked and yet need to be distinguished. One relates to the natural environment, agricultural land use and agro-industrial development; the second is concerned with large-scale industrial development, mainly based on natural resources and on towns, which is necessary for faster national economic development and which will in turn stimulate development at other levels.

REGIONAL SYNTHESIS AND A SCHEME OF REGIONS FOR RESOURCE DEVELOPMENT

The analysis of various distribution patterns of resources permits a synthesis to be made of various related elements and the identification of distinct regions for development. To this end a map of boundary girdles was prepared from the individual maps of natural environment, cropping patterns and the distribution of urban centres, natural resources and major industries (Bhat and

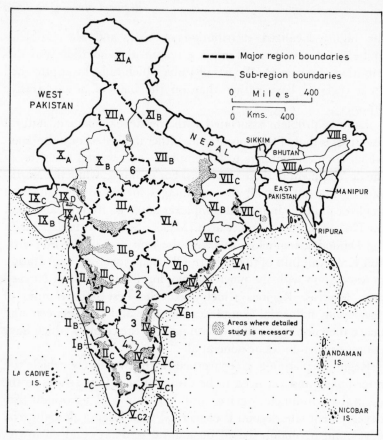

Figure 6. India: resource regions and sub-regions. *Boundaries are adapted to the nearest District boundary. For regional statistics, see Table II*

KEY

I. West Coast: A. North.
   B. Central.
   C. Southern.
II. Western Ghats: A. North.
   B. Central.
   C. Southern.
III. Central Plateau: A. Malwa Plateau.
   B. Khandesh.
   C. Balaghat.
   D. Karratak Plateau.
IV. Eastern Ghats: A. North.
   B. Central.
   C. Southern.
V. East Coast: A. North.
   A1. Mahanadi Delta.
   B. Central.
   B1. Krishna—Godavari Delta.
   C. Southern.
   C1. Cauvery Delta.
   C2. Ramnad Coast.
VI. North-eastern Plateau: A. Chhattisgarh.
   B. Chota Nagpur.
   C. Orissa Hills.
   D. Dandakaranya.

VII. Ganges Plain: A. Upper Ganges Plain.
   B. Middle Ganges Plain.
   C. Lower Ganges Plain.
   C1. Hooghly Delta.
VIII. Assam: A. Brahmaputra Valley.
   B. Assam Hills.
IX. Gujarat: A. Gujarat Plain.
   B. Saurashtra.
   C. Cutch.
   D. Gujarat Highlands.
X. Rajasthan: A. Western.
   B. Eastern (Aravallis).
XI. Kashmir and
Northern Hills: A. Jammu and Kashmir,
   North Punjab, Himachal,
   Pradesh.
   B. Montane U.P.
   Other sub-regions
   1. Godavari Trough.
   2. Telangana.
   3. Rayalaseema.
   4. Mysore Plateau.
   5. Coimbatore Plateau.
   6. Chambal Ravines.

Rao, 1962). The overlapping of the boundaries of these different elements suggest that regions exist in reality. Eleven major regions and fifty-one sub-regions have been identified and their characteristics and regional norms of development are qualitatively stated (Figure 6). The guiding principle is that major regions should have minimum disparities within their boundaries and maximum distinctiveness from their neighbours, in respect of their character and resources for development. While the regional development norm is common for the major region as a whole, sub-regions are identified according to the concentration of resources, problems of development and administrative convenience. For example, the present and probably also the future regional norm of development for the North-eastern Plateau is based on forestry, minerals and allied industries, while the norm for the adjoining black soil plateau consists of numerous and diverse local variations on cotton-groundnut-millet cultivation, with related commerce and industry. Areas around the metropolitan cities need to be treated separately since the problems of development in these are distinct.

It must, however, be stressed that these regions for resource planning are dynamic and their character changes during the phases of economic development, with technological developments and changing policies.

SALIENT FEATURES OF RESOURCE REGIONS

1. *The West Coast Region* consists of the perhumid coastal plains and hilly interior, with the economy oriented to agriculture and fishing, with paddy-coco-nut cultivation on the coastal plains and paddy and spices in the coastal hinterland and particularly in the central sector. There are plantations in the Kerala coastal hinterland. The economic development of this region is concerned with coastal fishing, the intensive development of agriculture in the coastal plains through tank irrigation, with allied industries, and the development of horticulture, and with grazing, livestock rearing and forestry in the interior.

II. *The Western Ghats* are humid forested hills and constitute a region of potential economic development, mainly based on forestry, minerals (bauxite, iron ore and manganese) and hydro-electric power. Agriculture is of secondary importance and is oriented particularly to cash crops like spices, and in the south to plantation crops like coffee, tea and rubber.

III. *The Central Plateau* is the semi-arid black soil region with a diversified crop economy (cotton, groundnut, wheat, jowar, bajra, sugar-cane and tobacco). Future developments in intensive agriculture are possible through small irrigation projects and agro-industries (textiles, oil extraction, sugar production and tobacco processing). Hilly areas may be developed for afforestation for conservation, grazing and livestock rearing, and quarrying.

IV. *The Eastern Ghats* are forested hills, a region of potential development based on forestry, minerals (iron ore, mica, manganese and graphite), and tourism (including pilgrim centres). Agriculture is of secondary importance and is based on small-scale tropical and temperate fruit culture.

V. *The East Coast* consists of the sub-humid coastal plains and a foothill zone. Agro-industries and fishing may be developed on the coastal plains with specialization in the foothills in pastures and rotational grazing, animal husbandry, and tree crops; woodlands are used for soil conservation and fuel. Intensive agriculture can be developed in the deltas. The agricultural economy is diversified with an emphasis on the cultivation of food and cash crops (rice, sugar-cane, oilseeds), with associated industries (e.g. tobacco on the inner plains).

VI. *The North-eastern Plateau* consists of hills and valleys covered with humid and dry deciduous forest; the Chhattisgarh plain is the only large agricultural tract, devoted to paddy. Economic development is based on forestry and minerals (iron ore, coal, manganese, graphite and associated by-products); it is perhaps the only region in India with such a large concentration of raw materials. Even at the present stage of development this region, particularly the Chota Nagpur plateau, stands out as the 'core' area of industrial development, unlike the scattered and isolated industries in other parts of India.[1]

VII. *The Ganges Plain* is one of the major and undisputed natural regions of India with a strong agricultural base. Diversified cropping and the development of agro-industries should form the basis for future development. This is the region where future agricultural policy should perhaps be consciously directed towards mixed farming with multiple-cropping throughout the year, where water resources and topography permit.

VIII. *Assam.* Physical and political considerations make this region unique. There is vast resource potential in forestry (with valuable timber and other forest products, and the biggest bamboo reserves in India which contribute nearly 42 per cent of the country's total output), minerals (coal, petroleum, limestone) and associated industries. Jute, tea and paddy are the important crops. Soil conservation requires priority in physical planning.

IX. *Gujarat.* The plains specialize in agriculture and allied industries (notably textiles). Further industrialization is possible with the discovery of oil (refining, petro-chemical and allied industries). Development problems of the Saurashtra and Cutch are concerned mainly with afforestation, pastures and livestock rearing, dairying and land reclamation. The northern highlands of the Gujarat are dry and are mainly agricultural, with cotton as the chief crop. Agricultural planning needs to take anti-famine measures into account.

X. *Rajasthan* covers the arid and semi-arid north-western parts of India. Western Rajasthan comprises arid sandy wastes with a sparse natural vegetation of stunted thorny and open scrub, while eastern Rajasthan is rocky, but with fertile lands in the valleys. The economy is heavily dependent on the development of pastures and afforestation, mainly for soil conservation. Livestock rearing and rural industries (blanket weaving, cloth printing, carpets and

---

[1] The unsuitability of the river-basin concept for resource development is well illustrated in this region which cuts across the drainage basins of the Godavari, the Mahanadi, the Narmada and the Son, and yet possesses unity and homogeneity in regional structure and norm of development.

317

stoneware) are important in the local economy. Industries based on minerals and agriculture (wheat and millet under irrigation) should form the main economic developments in eastern Rajasthan.

XI. *Kashmir and the northern hill areas* stand out in contrast to their neighbours in respect of physical conditions and agriculture. There is much diversity within the region and detailed studies are necessary to identify sub-regions with distinct problems and norms of development.

MACRO-ECONOMIC REGIONS (Figure 7)

The framework of regions suggested above indicates the regional characteristics and potentialities which are basic for planning development. Some major aspects of planning, like the development of basic and heavy industries, are vital to the national economy and also to the acceleration of regional development. But the natural resources like minerals, forests and power resources are highly localized and hence there is need for regional grouping of resources so as to include groups of States and even parts of different States for purposes of efficient production and utilization of these resources. Each major region will tend to develop production complexes for which it has the best advantages. Such an approach might have far-reaching effects on the competing tendency of each State to develop basic and heavy industries. From the studies that have been made seven macro-regions emerge, based on the distribution of resources (including power resources) and the possibilities of developing regional production complexes.

I. *South India* (Mysore, Kerala, Madras and Andhra, with parts of Maharashtra, Madhya Pradesh and Orissa). This region is based on the three industrial complexes which are likely to develop around Bhadravati (iron ore, manganese, power and forestry resources), Neyveli–Salem (iron ore and lignite) and Hospet–Sandur (iron ore with coal from the Singareni fields).

II. *Western India* (including major parts of Maharashtra and

Gujarat). The production complex is made up of textile and associated industries and the recently developing oilfields. Measures need to be considered to modify the growth of industries, population and urban centres in the relatively restricted Bombay–Poona and Bombay–Ahmedabad areas.

III. *East-central India* (including parts of Madhya Pradesh, Orissa, Maharashtra and Andhra). This region has potentialities for developing industrial complexes based on iron ore from

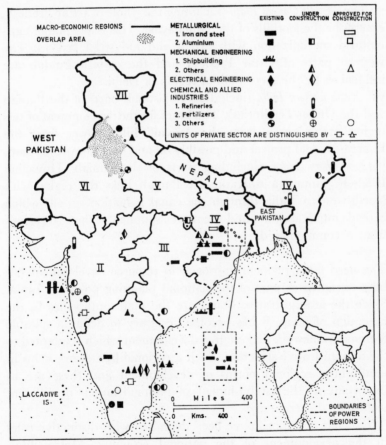

Figure 7. India: macro-economic regions. *Boundaries are adapted to the nearest District boundary*

Chanda–Bastar and coal from the Singareni and the Damodar fields.

IV. *North-eastern India* (including Bihar, West Bengal, Orissa and Assam). The industrial complex of Damodar and the city of Calcutta form the foci of the region. The multiple industrial complexes of the Chota Nagpur plateau, the urban-industrial complex of Calcutta, and the forestry, minerals and plantations of Assam are inter-related through common transport and power networks.

V. The *Middle Ganges Plain* (including the whole of Uttar Pradesh, except for the foothills of the Himalayas). This is a region of agricultural specialization with urban and industrial centres. The western parts of Uttar Pradesh and the eastern Punjab are influenced by the metropolitan region of Delhi.

VI. *North-western India* (including Rajasthan, parts of the Punjab and the Union Territories). The bases for the development of this region are minerals from the Aravalli hills, power from the Bhakra–Nangal project and possibly oil and coal from Rajasthan.

VII. *Northern India* (including parts of the Punjab, Himachal Pradesh, Jammu and Kashmir). Punjab links this region with North-western India through the canal irrigation system which extends into Rajasthan and the power supplied to the two regions from a common grid.

The need for a regional approach to resource development has been accepted as part of the national planning policy in India. Since the administrative States are the main authorities in the execution of plans, it has become necessary to define a suitable regional framework for resource development which is adapted to the administrative structure. Such a regional framework helps in establishing regional norms of development and these are as important as the establishment of national targets in different sectors of the economy.

Two sets of regions have been delimited with distinctive roles in the development of the national economy. Metropolitan regions, market regions and port hinterlands are other types of regions which exert their influence at different area levels. Further studies are required of the problems of evolving a regional hierarchy within which macro-economic regions are useful for overall national planning and sub-regions can be used for planning development at other levels.

ACKNOWLEDGEMENT

This essay is based on work undertaken by the Regional Survey Unit of the Indian Statistical Institute, New Delhi, in 1962 and was completed in its present form during 1962-3 when the writer was Leverhulme Research Fellow in the Department of Geography, University of Liverpool.

REFERENCES

ALEXANDER, J.W. (1954) 'The basic-nonbasic concept of urban economic functions', *Econ. Geog.*, *30*, 246-61.

BAKER, J.N.L. (1928) 'Natural regions of India', *Geography*, *14*, 447-56 and 502-06.

BHAT, L.S. (1957) 'Geography of the spice gardens', *Bombay Geog. Mag.*, *4*, 21-28.

— (1963) 'Regional contrasts in population density and growth in India (1951-61)', *Geography*, *48*, 313-17.

BHAT and RAO, V.L.S.P. (1960) *Planning regions in the Mysore State–the need for readjustment of District boundaries*. Indian Statistical Institute, Regional Survey Unit, Calcutta.

— (1962) *A regional framework for resource development in India*. Indian Statistical Institute, Regional Survey Unit, New Delhi. Mimeographed.

BOSE, N.K. (1961) *Peasant life in India*. Anthropological Survey of India.

CENSUS OF INDIA (1961) *Final population totals*. Paper I of 1962. Registrar-General of India.

COUPLAND, R. (1944) *The Indian problem: report on the constitutional problem in India*. New York.

DESHPANDE, C.D. (1948) *Western India: a regional geography*. Dharwar.

INDIAN STATISTICAL INSTITUTE, REGIONAL SURVEY UNIT (1962) *South-India: a macro-regional survey*. New Delhi. Mimeographed.

LAND USE PLANNING (1958) *Report of the working group on land use planning*, Ministry of Food and Agriculture, New Delhi. Mimeographed.

PLANNING COMMISSION, GOVERNMENT OF INDIA (1961) *Third Five-Year Plan.* New Delhi. Chaps. 2 and 9.

REORGANIZATION COMMISSION (1955) *Report of the States Reorganization Commission.* New Delhi, 22-25.

SPATE, O.H.K. (1954) *India and Pakistan,* 352-63.

STAMP, L.D. (1929) *Asia,* 274-78.

A. T. A. LEARMONTH

Retrospect on a project in applied geography in Mysore State, India

INDIAN NATIONALISM AND PLANNING

As the Indian nationalist movement gathered strength between the wars, largely through the Congress Party, some able thinkers, while participating in the struggle against the British *raj*, were able to see beyond and to think ahead constructively. One important strand in their thinking was that national planning would be necessary, after independence was attained, in order to raise the very low standards of material living – then, of course, ascribed almost solely to the colonial system. It is significant that the chairman of the committee which reported on this subject was Jawaharlal Nehru, who despite heavy burdens as Prime Minister has remained the chairman of the Planning Commission of independent India since it was formed in 1950.

Another important strand of thought concerned the reorganization of internal political boundaries. Nationalist critics were confronted on the one hand with the large units of the then British India, the Presidencies or Provinces, which were mechanically well administered, especially in terms of law and order. Their boundaries were, however, haphazard in that they had grown by historical accident, at first by conquest fanning out from the East India Company's coastal factories, and then by expansion piecemeal according to the lesser or greater bites by which the Company and then the Crown engulfed the inland parts of the sub-continent as complete domination became necessary to the colonial régime. On the other hand, interspersed with these large units in a patchwork pattern, were the 'native states' of rajahs who had allied, or come to terms, with the British power. These were most varied in size, from the Nizam's Dominion of Hydera-bad with an area of 82,313 square miles and a population of 18,652,964 in 1951 to small states of a few square miles and a few thousand people. Some of these units were particularly notorious for the splitting of cultural unities by a haphazardly drawn political boundary. Thus the Nizam's Dominion included speakers of Mahratti, Kanarese and Telugu, while the court and official language was Urdu. There were also very marked dis-crepancies in the standard of administration: that of the then princely State of Mysore, much smaller than the linguistic State of today, for instance, compared at least favourably with most of British India, but at the other end of the scale some states were by comparison very badly administered. Many were subject to op-pression and neglect by court officials to maintain absentee rajahs in a life of ease, sometimes of dissipation, in the great cities or resorts of India or of Europe – and too often to enrich the officials also.

The nationalist movement was also associated, and its member-ship overlapped, with the participants in a strong cultural renais-sance, as for instance in Bengal. This renaissance was based on not one language but on several of the dozen or more really impor-tant languages of the sub-continent. It is not suprising, therefore, that a reorganization of States based on linguistic units became a main plank in Congress policy for India once independence should be gained. It was hoped, no doubt, that the cultural unity engendered or reinforced among groups politically separated for a century or more under the British régime would more than compensate for any disturbance of economic and social lines of communication. After India, along with Pakistan, gained inde-pendence in 1947, implementation of this policy ran into con-siderable difficulties and took some time to develop. As a first step the 'native States' of the new India were integrated wholly into the new republic, using 'police action' if necessary as in the Nizam's Dominion; the whole vast operation of absorbing over 550 native States was carried through with remarkable speed under the direction of the 'strong man' of Congress, Villabhbhai

Patel, and a very distinguished civil servant, V. P. Menon, who has recorded these events (Menon, 1956). Somewhat *ad hoc* federal States were formed at first, based largely on the Presidencies and Provinces of the former British India. However, the undertaking to form linguistic States had to be honoured, and in 1956 much the greater part of India was re-divided into linguistically based States. The process continued, not without strife and political upheaval, with the formation of Gujarat and Maharashtra in 1960, mainly from Bombay State, and up to the present with occasional agitation for fresh linguistic States, e.g. by Punjabi speakers in the Hindi-language State of Punjab (India). A comparison of the old and new State boundaries shows how great were the changes, and the wonder is not that problems emerged, for instance in the allocation of development projects under the Second Five-Year Plan (1956-61), but that on the whole these problems were successfully surmounted.

Regional survey for planning

At the date of the reorganization of states in 1956, the writer was in Mysore State to carry out for the Indian Statistical Institute a pilot project in regional survey for planning purposes. This essay discusses, much more discursively than in other published work, the regions of the new linguistic state that was established, particularly with reference to resource development. It must be emphasized that the actual work on which the essay is based was carried out early in the Second Five-Year Plan, whereas the Third Plan (1961-6) is now in progress. To some extent it draws on work done by the Regional Survey Unit of the Indian Statistical Institute since the writer left in 1958.

SOME MYSORE LANDSCAPES DURING THE SUMMER MONSOON

In July the Indian summer monsoon is at its height. The south-westerly stream of equatorial maritime air blows strongly, and in the main steadily, across the Arabian Sea towards the coastline of western Mysore from just north of Karwar to just south of Mangalore. Wind-driven waves lash the shore, closing the ports and immobilizing the fishing fleets. On land, fiercely heavy rain soaks the countryside. It beats on the coco-nut groves of the coastal sandbars and the valley sides. It trickles in the age-old system of controlled flooding from higher to lower embanked paddy fields on the coastal strips of lagunar alluvium between sandbars, on the broader alluvial plain in the south behind Mangalore, and on the valley ribbons of riverine soils gouged into the 200-foot laterite plateau clad in savanna, scrub or forest, or yet more deeply and steeply cut into the wilder forests of the Ghats Edge or the dissected hills which meet the sea in magnificent cliffs and bays south of Karwar. Heavy rain is usual over the rain forests yielding hardwoods, over the spice gardens and the valley strips of paddy, over all the hill country called the Malnad, including the dissected hill country east of the Ghats Edge. Here until recently mosquitoes breeding in jungle streams were the vectors of very debilitating hyper-endemic malaria. The monsoon is less, and less pervasive into every aspect of life, in the mixed evergreen-deciduous and the deciduous forest country farther east, where forest or plantation teak is important. It is less again, though still the focus of the agricultural year, in the more gently accidented longitudinal zone of alternating belts of forest and of very varied farming sometimes referred to as the Semi-Malnad.

Eastward again, on the great open dry plateaus of the Deccan, there is a contrast between north and south. In the north, July with the main flow of monsoon air brings scanty and fickle rainfall to the very level, endless-seeming plateaus of black cotton soils mainly over Deccan lavas; here the main rains are later, coming with the retreating monsoon. In the slightly wetter and more broken country of the extreme north-east of Mysore, round Bidar and Gulbarga, July rainfall is both higher and more reliable. Throughout this large tract there are wide expanses of open fields with tightly nucleated flat-roofed settlements constantly beset by shortages of drinking water which is traditionally taken from guinea-worm infested, excavated and embanked tanks that store surface flow from the fields. Wells are used wherever possible, and are dominant in the wetter area in the north-east, mainly over sedimentary rocks which are better aquifers than the lavas. In July, shallow multiple ploughing, or more often harrowing, is going on, to conserve moisture even in retentive black soils for crops of *jowar*, cotton and groundnuts. In the tank irrigation country of the south, the height of the monsoon often brings grey skies and a strong, steady, cool wind, with only occasional showers or drizzle to replenish the triangular reservoirs ponded behind a simple dam at intervals down a valley or around a hill-mass. The tanks are found wherever the topography permits in this more undulating plateau on Peninsular gneiss diversified by steep-sided ridges of Dharwar schists or of granite. In July, around the nucleated tiled villages and thatched outcaste hamlets, there may be farming activity in the irrigated fields below the tank if the early rains have been good. Over the main expanse of gently sloping dry fields destined for eleusine millet, pulses and oil crops including ground-nuts, the farmer is awaiting the main rains of September and October. In the south-west, however, near Mysore City, the thin green flush of brairded *jowar* is coming up from seed planted with the moderate, reliable early rains of April and May.

AGRICULTURAL BASES OF SETTLEMENT

This sketch of Mysore at a season of climatic activity and contrast is almost literally a vignette. The firmly delineated strokes fade out on the margins; some information, however, is available else-where to complement this essay, and to make the descriptive material more quantitative (Learmonth and Bhat, 1960; Lear-month, 1962*a*). Figures 1 and 2 are some guide to the agricultural bases underlying what may be called the settlement matrix – in the geological rather than the mathematical sense – of agricultur-ally based homesteads and hamlets, villages and market towns.

Village types

Throughout the wetter western quarter of Mysore, the basic settlement type is one of linear dispersion of homesteads isolated

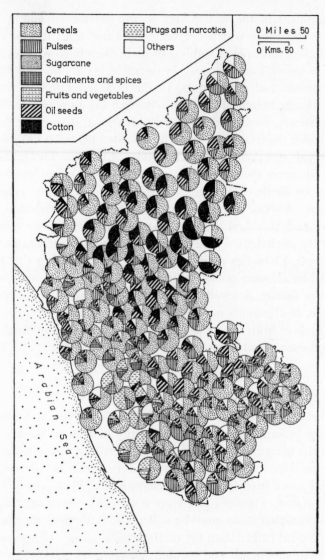

Figure 1. Mysore State: main crops

in an orchard-and-garden patch, aligned along a sandbar, on the junction between alluvia and laterite, or along a valley side. In the Malnad the houses are often concealed within the fringe of the forests; the trees are preserved as shade for spices or coffee. So dispersed are the homesteads that there is something approaching the privacy, almost the isolation of the individual farm pattern. Associated with this settlement pattern there may be rather greater individual independence and initiative, though to be sure the village unit does function as a whole for taxation purposes, in caste or minor land disputes, and increasingly for welfare and development purposes if the Government is successful in encouraging *panchayat raj*, i.e. local government by village councils.

On the open plateaus of the east, on the other hand, village settlements are markedly nucleated. In the north there are the very tightly packed villages of flat-topped mud or masonry houses, adapted for heat, dust and drought, often arranged in streets, and sometimes still within defensive walls. They give an impression of unity but there is often a quite marked cellular structure of caste and occupational groups within the village (Spate and Deshpande, 1952). In the tank country of the south, the separation of the mainly thatched outcaste hamlet of the *Harijans*, or untouchables, from the mainly tiled caste Hindu village makes apparent the most glaring social cleavage. But there are other caste and faction groups, fluctuating and reforming in almost amoeba-like fashion, absorbing parts of other groups in some circumstances, undergoing fission in others (Epstein, 1962; Tinker, 1959). The caste system is changing, but change is less rapid in economically static areas or in areas where economic development reinforces traditional lines of employment especially in agriculture. In contrast the system is being rapidly eroded in areas of marked economic activity linked with personal participation by village people in economic activities outside the village; though even here some traditional forms of seeking prestige and status may be increased by prosperity. In many, even most, villages the legal abolition of untouchability and the right to participate in the *panchayat* is very far from being accompanied by

x

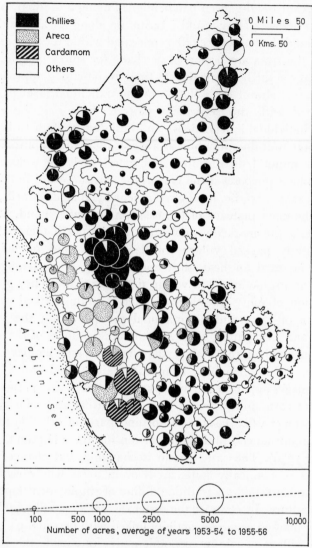

Figure 2. Mysore State: spices and condiments

full and genuine acceptance and engagement of the *Harijans* in village democracy (Epstein, 1962).

Community development

The community development scheme in Mysore in the late 1950s was having some success particularly in projects that were oriented more towards amenity than to production. Even where it is successful, say in raising agricultural productivity, it is liable to make the rich richer and the poor only a little less poor through increased demand for their labour for wages in kind or cash. Land division and reallocation, which might promise to redress the balance, are at best patchy in effecting significant benefit for the landless. Village co-operatives of broad enough scope to deal with poverty within the village are very rare indeed in Mysore (Learmonth, 1962b). In consequence, the scheme may well fail to be truly communal in impact. Some additional vitality may have been gained recently from the subsequent emphasis on *panchayat raj* linked to local command of land revenue on an unprecedented scale. But too much should not be expected, at least in the short term, from measures like *Harijan* participation in *panchayat raj*, or from the ability of the *panchayat* to adopt measures leading to all-round development and raising of living standards, if the necessary action conflicts with the real or fancied interests of influential caste-groups or factions.

The village populations are naturally oriented chiefly to agriculture, whether as landlords, landlord-moneylenders, owner-occupiers, tenants for cash or kind, farm labourers, or by mixing these activities in varying proportions. Some of the people also gain their living in other ways. Frequently there is an association with caste-occupation groups, as with the smiths in copper and tin, gold and silver, or the potters and brickmakers, carpenters and wheelwrights, or the leather and oil workers. Occupation and caste are constantly tending to be less closely associated, particularly in villages more accessible to modern transport and drawn more fully into the cash and trading economy. At least some members of a caste-group, however, tend to adhere to its traditional occupation, particularly if it has ritual significance, accompanied by some advantage to both the provider and the user of the ritual service; hereditary priest and medium, barber and washerman, and sweeper and drummer, are still important in many villages. A large village may have a shop, and if it has been influenced by urban ways a coffee-stall, with some, though looser, caste-associations connected with tabus on taking food from lower castes (Epstein, 1962).

Completely subsistence villages or even tribal economies have been quite exceptional for several centuries. Even the remotest village has had some exports, and these are increasing if only to pay taxes and to buy a few commodities in cash. Cloth and kerosene at present are such staple purchases over much of the State, though in cotton-growing areas there may still be some very local self-sufficiency in cloth. Some commodities like areca nuts are so valuable that they find their way to market by special delivery to the merchant in a centre or to an itinerant agent. But main staple foods are often marketed in villages, at intervals of five miles or so and with some nodality, which have a weekly, monthly or seasonal market. Such market villages grade into small- to medium-sized market towns at intervals of fifteen or twenty miles, some of which have mushroomed under the stimulus of modern trade and industry. These are mentioned later.

TRADITIONAL SETTLEMENTS AND THEIR DYNAMIC ELEMENTS

The traditional settlement matrix may be said to comprise agricultural villages, with at least residual craft and service groups, market villages, and market towns, some of which have also an administrative role as headquarters of districts, or *talukas* (larger and smaller administrative divisions), or of community development blocks which are expected to be of increasing importance in the future. Agriculture persists surprisingly in quite large towns and even cities, while it is so dominant in some towns, particularly in the tobacco-growing towns of the north-west round Nipani and

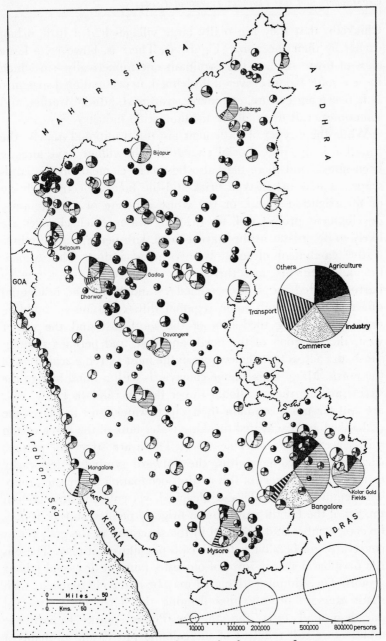

Figure 3. Mysore State: the size and occupational structure of towns

Chikkodi, that they are really large villages lent a little urban cachet by their sheer size (Figure 3). There is, however, a large class of town – in fact the dominant one numerically – in which there is some balance, even if ill-defined, in occupational structure as between agriculture, commerce, transport, administration, and sometimes craft or small- or medium-scale industry.

While these types of settlement are the traditional matrix, the situation is dynamic. Social changes in the village have already been noted, and there may also be recent elements in the land-scape – a new urban-type brick-and-tile house, electric lighting or lift-irrigation pump, or the white concrete of a community development project well for drinking water. Such changes are likely to be greater in the market town with perhaps an administrative catchment of some twenty miles' radius. The autochthonous elements are there. The crowded bazaar street of narrow-fronted shops has screened verandahs on the residential quarters above, with some regional differentiation in building type – the sloping tiled roof of the south-east and the wetter west, the flat roofs of the north and east, and perhaps summer sunshades across the whole street in the most extreme arid areas of the north. Many houses have courtyards with a blind face to the street save for the occasional upper floor verandah. Draw wells are still far more common than piped water, and in places the embanked and excavated drinking water tank of the black cotton soils serves even a sizeable town. There are streets of potters, carpenters, or coppersmiths, the outward symbol of less easily seen cellular quarters of this or that occupation and caste group. The temple may be old and bleached, yet enlivened by modern images of the Hindu pantheon in brightly painted stucco; it may be cool, sombre and dignified in the sanctuary of the god, yet its courtyard will be alive with the calls of children at play. There is the peripheral shanty-town of outcaste, migrant or casual labour groups. The administrative area may be relatively spacious, with shade trees in orderly lines fringing the harsh open space of parade-ground type, the angular Public Works Department architecture still redolent of the colonial phase, and probably a rather stark, graceless and over-severely functional school, lacking in shade-trees and landscaping.

Compared with the village, the newer elements are more significant, and more obtrusive though not necessarily to be deprecated. There may be a shop with a modern concrete frontage and glass-fronted display of cloths or men's ready-made clothes; a modern oil firm's petrol and service station, perhaps continuing the maroon-and-white colour scheme of the outer wall of the adjacent temple; a bus-stand, sometimes spacious and well-planned, with a fruit, spice and sweet stall and often a little café (*hotelu* in Kanarese), ornamented with brightly coloured pictures of Hindu gods, gay with a string of coloured electric lights and fragrant from an offering of jasmine; and facing these there are often portraits of the political pantheon – Gandhiji, Jawaharlal Nehru, Villabhbhai Patel, and less frequently Netaji Subhas Chandra Bose. There may be a cinema, in concrete or merely under the tattered, weathered canvas of a large marquee, displaying posters of a film in Kanarese, glamorous, heroic, or more seldom homely; perhaps a little park, garden and playground in memory of Ghandhiji.

URBAN AND INDUSTRIAL FOCI

Alongside this picture of a traditional though changing settlement matrix, there must be depicted something of the complex, dynamic and catalytic patterns of modern transport-oriented, power-oriented urban centres, with industry, commerce and services on a much larger scale, commanding spheres of influence varying from fifty miles' radius to the whole State and even beyond it. The State capital and growing metropolis, Bangalore, has a countrywide market for some products, such as electronic equipment, as also does a very different, highly specialized town like Kolar Gold Fields. The iron-and-steel town of Bhadravati, equally dependent on industry, at present commands rather a local market, owing to its very modest scale of operation, though this may change if it specializes in alloys and special steels. These last

335

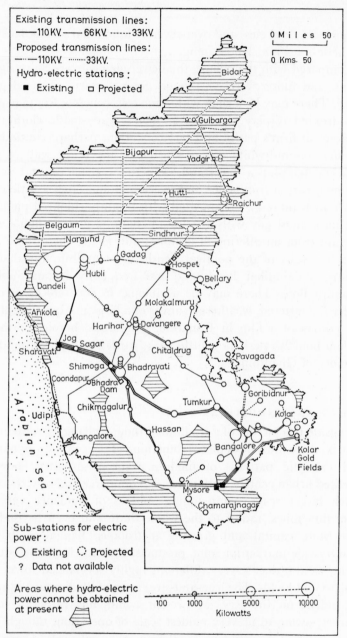

Figure 4. Mysore State: the distribution of electric power

two towns are distinctive (Figure 3), though some other small towns have similarly high proportions of their population dependent on industry, mainly centres of small-scale textiles commanding a local market. The large towns and cities, however, generally show a reasonable balance in occupational structure as between industry and commerce, administration and retail services; once a growth element is introduced, the urban complex seems to form around it in reasonable balance, in a manner comparable to towns and cities in Europe or the U.S.A. There are differences in detail such as the persistence as yet of cheap personal servants as a considerable proportion of the urban population in India, as against other forms of service. The complex of growth factors in these larger towns has much in common within the group, as with other cities in India and indeed elsewhere; administration, for example, notably during the colonial phase but also in the period since independence; and the railways and railway-based industry, mainly of Mumford's palaeotechnic type. In contrast neotechnic industry based on the availability of electric power, precocious in the old princely State, is now expanding there and as rapidly as possible into backward areas such as the border area between old Bombay and old Hyderabad territory. During the last fifteen years there has been the growth of a considerable movement of passengers and goods by road, and so lighter industry is less tied to the railway than formerly. State-owned industry, again precocious in the old State and now large nationalized industries of the Central Government, as well as private industry, have been encouraged in certain sites under the Five-Year Plans, e.g. sugar factories in new irrigation areas. Data concerning these variables are presented in Figures 4, 5, 6 and 7.

Industry and its location factors

Most of the older large-scale industry – indeed most of it of whatever age – is closely tied to the railways. Textile manufacture was generally among the earlier large-scale industries in India, and in Mysore it displays changing relationships to railways rather well. The largest units are commonly on broad-gauge lines, avoiding

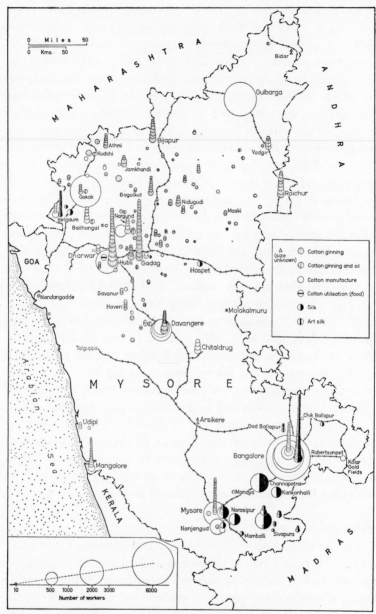

Figure 5. Mysore State: the distribution of large-scale textile industries

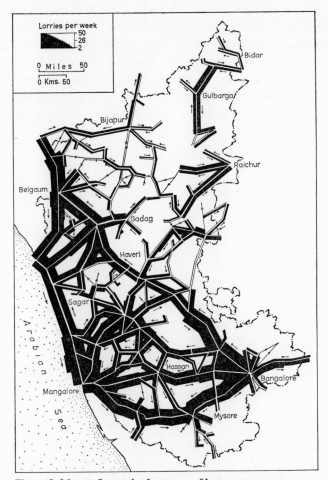

Figure 6. Mysore State: the frequency of lorry movements

break of bulk in trade to and from the main ports and centres of industry and population. Gulbarga, for instance, is an island of factory industry in the generally little developed areas formerly in Hyderabad. Bangalore is a special case, at the end of the broad-gauge line but also able to draw on the metre-gauge line of the former Mysore State Railway. Hubli is a considerable centre of

339

metre-gauge railway traffic, including much from the cotton-growing tracts, with engineering industries introduced through a large railway workshop; at the time of mapping it had a large, rather old-fashioned cotton mill, but this has now been closed down. Very substantial industry, however, remains on metre-gauge lines, lending diversity to the gracious princely capital of Mysore City with its palaces, temples, parks and gardens, and

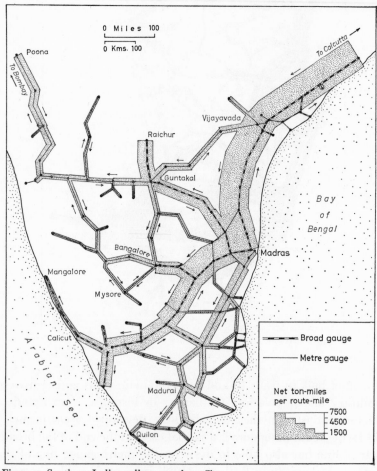

Figure 7. Southern India: railway goods traffic

the rather trim electrified towns nearby; to Channapatna, a main centre of the silk industry, Chitaldrug, a small railhead cotton-ginning centre, and Davangere, a rapidly expanding centre of cotton manufacture in units mainly of medium size with modern electric-powered plant.

These larger centres of production include clusters of smaller and ancillary units, some probably antecedent, but some like textile engineering arising around the large units of production. One large cotton factory at Gokak was specifically sited in order to use hydro-electric power from a fall on the Ghataprabha River, a few miles from the metre-gauge railway between Hubli and Poona. Several small textile factories are powered by electricity from the grid, particularly in the old princely State; they include rayon mills at Dod Ballapur (using imported yarn) and a high quality silk mill at Melur, none of which is on the railway. These small units are in clean and light modern buildings, and with housing and nutrition standards for their workers which compare favourably with those for all but the most privileged workers in large city factories run by enlightened employers. They are important for this reason, and also because in this area they represent the larger among many small-scale producers of silk, a traditional industry. They may point the way towards really desirable and efficient dispersed industry, of catalytic benefit to both small town and village populations.

There are other small centres of production, often in small units. Belgaum, for instance, has traditional production of cotton and woollens, now with the aid of effective weavers' co-operatives. Jamkhandi, hardly significant for large-scale production, is a centre of handloom production of *saris* and *dhoties* commanding a considerable local market. The widespread rural ginneries in the cotton-growing area, mainly diesel-powered units at present, are an essential part of the industry and a useful source of seasonal employment in an area where wage labour is important to a considerable landless class with small prospect of becoming farmers. Similar tendencies may be seen in relation to the larger factories among the innumerable small units processing agricultural products largely for a local market; there are some special cases such as the processing of cashew nuts, partly locally grown, in and around Mangalore – an extension of the industry of Kerala – or again the clear relation between State-planned major irrigation projects, sugar-cane production, and State-planned and partly State-owned factories producing refined sugar, as at Mandya and near Hospet.

EARLY STATE PLANNING

Mysore State planning which dates back some sixty years is also responsible for some other interesting State-owned factories, including the iron and steel works at Bhadravati, already mentioned, an agricultural implements factory at Hassan, and a group of factories in Bangalore producing electric bulbs, sandal soap, and ceramics in a factory recently expanded with Central Government and Japanese aid to include a large production of electric insulators. Not least among these achievements is the State's remarkable lead in hydro-electric power production dating from the partial harnessing of the 300-foot fall of the Cauvery River at Sivasamudram in 1902, primarily to supply the Kolar Gold Fields at the then formidable transmission distance of over ninety miles. There were later developments nearby and at the 800-foot Jog falls in the Western Ghats. This early progress in the development of electric generation and transmission, though overtaken in recent years by adjacent areas of Madras, has profound significance in several ways. It has shown the potentialities of rural electrification for lift irrigation, street-lighting and small food-processing plants; potentially also for house-lighting with implications for the spread of literacy. It has shown, even if only on a relatively small scale of numbers and size of plants, the possibility of dispersed electrified industry such as the small textile factories mentioned earlier. Not least, it has played its part in the growth of neotechnic industries in Bangalore, a city with more than a million inhabitants, with all the implications of the metropolis for the towns and countryside alike in the surrounding region.

CENTRAL GOVERNMENT FACTORIES: THE FIVE-YEAR PLANS

The Central Government factories in Bangalore manufacture aircraft (an industry based on a war-time repair and assembly plant), machine tools (and recently watches), electronic equipment, telephones and telephone exchanges. Locational factors doubtless included the pleasant lay-out and climate of the former cantonment town, the presence of earlier industries attracted by these factors and the progressive Mysore government, the foundation of experience in recruiting management and labour for nationalized industries in the Mysore government factories, and not least a desire to put some substantial investment under the First Five-Year Plan into South India, stimulated by political pressure groups within the Congress Party. The direct impact of a group of factories employing workers is considerable, and to this must be added their demand for goods and services and people to provide these. It must be stressed that even a relatively humble factory worker by reason of his regular employment at good wages ranks as middle class in terms of status and spending power. It is also believed that a tendency has begun to be evident towards the growth of ancillary industries. There is certainly a general buoyancy in industrial and commercial entrepreneurship. There may have been some evidence of this trend, even at the time of mapping, in the group of small engineering works in Bangalore. At the time of independence Bangalore was no mean city, in character, in culture, in layout, at least in the cantonment area, and in population (778,977 in 1951); by 1961 it had increased in population to 1,206,961. There is a fever of building activity, and a water shortage only likely to be finally overcome with the tapping of the Cauvery, 85 miles away and 600 feet lower. New townscapes of factory and associated townships with houses for different grades of employees have been added to the old dichotomy of fort and old city on the one hand and cantonment on the other. Well-to-do houses, often clean and functional in design, sometimes rather ornate and garish, spread along the gneissic ridges, while the ill-drained hollows are filled with more modest dwellings or at

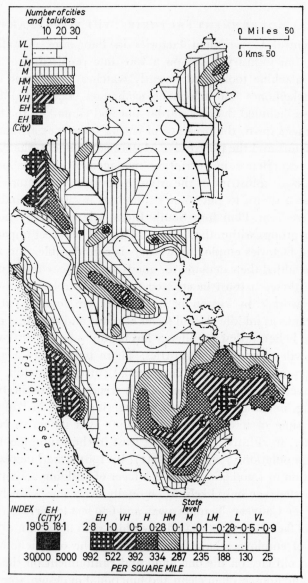

Figure 8. Mysore State: population density

worst with rather mobile and transient yet persistently recurring slums of mud, flattened kerosene tins and palm thatch. These slums, in small patches but considerable in total, contain immigrant Tamil and Telugu casual labourers from *Harijan* hamlets in Madras and Andhra.

This dynamism, this ferment of good and bad, this mixture of language and caste groups in immigrant communities, could be matched from the graceful and vivid former princely capital, Mysore City; from the crowded wharfside markets or the more spacious upper town and sprawling orchard-girt suburbs of Mangalore; from the clean white factories and bustling streets of Davangere or nearby Harihar, from the steel town of Bhadravati or its seeming twin-town Shimoga, older, less regimented, more traditional; or from the railway town of Hubli and its administration-oriented sister town Dharwar a few miles off; and in lesser degree from other rising towns.

It is this picture which underlies the final maps illustrating this essay. The maps of road and rail transport of goods (Figures 6 and 7) give some indication of the sphere of influence of towns and cities, and the extent of actual penetration of the countryside by urban-based commerce, and potentially of possible new sites, e.g. for dispersed electrified industry. These are only two of a series of maps of an important and relatively easily mapped aspect of the communications pattern. The flow of information, of innovation, is equally worthy of study, though certainly more difficult, in this only partly literate society aiming at planned development to raise standards of living. The map of population density (Figure 8) reflects the overall man/land relationships implied in the traditional settlement matrix as modified by these recent, dynamic urban-industrial elements. But it presents too static a picture and has been complemented by a map of population growth and variability of rate of growth of population, reflecting both the upsurge of urban population and the change in demographic trends effected by the abolition of malaria (Figure 9). Migration, unfortunately, could not be mapped in this project, nor could regional standards of living, though some experimental attempts were made.

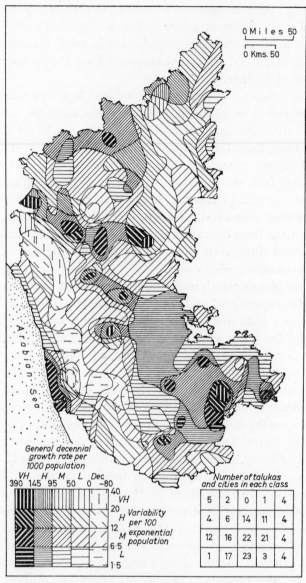

Figure 9. Mysore State: population growth and variability

FROM REGIONAL GEOGRAPHY TO REGIONAL PLANNING

At the end of two years' work by a handful of trained workers and up to a score of lay assistants at times, it was possible subjectively to attain an ecological – in many ways a visionary – view of a more stable and well-doing rural society adapted to the widely differing physical environments even of one State, with prosperity more widely and equitably spread through the whole community. Modern urban facilities and services might be much more widely diffused in town and country alike by applying appropriate regional planning techniques, not only to metropolitan regions but throughout the length and breadth of a State such as Mysore, as the basic planning unit in a federal country. The needs of the metropolitan regions are so clamant that they are already receiving a great deal of attention in India. The techniques of studying town and country interactions, and of planning to produce desirable interactions in future, might, however, be carried over a whole State, and down to the reactivation of small market towns and their small spheres of influence by a moderate diffusion of electrified industry, on the example of towns in the old princely State, one or two of which have been mentioned. This much could be attained, mainly at an academic level, but with insufficient force, with insufficient quantitative and especially technical backing, wholly to convince the politicians, officials and planners either in Bangalore or in New Delhi. Implementation of a regional planning programme seems quite distant, in this region at least. However, since the writer left India in 1958 the work of the Calcutta Metropolitan Planning Organization has begun, and promises to carry ideas, such as those suggested here, right through to the phase of implementation. In South India the writer's friends and former colleagues have made progress in two directions: the Mysore studies have been fitted into a wider context, and some valuable experiments in technique have been made which will be of further use as data concerning a few more vital variables become available. There may be in prospect some kind of wedding of the techniques of regional geography with those of

347

regional econometrics or even with Walter Isard's regional science. It may be that in this way regional studies of the kind discussed can become comprehensible and useful to the macro-regional analyst – and the economic determinist – so powerful in Indian planning today. This will be all to the good so long as the results and projects can be constantly reviewed in the light of current, and we may hope much improved, knowledge of the physical and human geography. Plans based on *gestalt* models must be reviewed in the light of geographical factors even if we cannot as yet fit all into a mathematical model – the rains and their vagaries, the slope of the land and its vegetal cover, its soils and their varying exposure to accelerated erosion; and on the other hand the web of social and economic relationships, the flow of goods and of information, and not least the trends over time in towns and townsmen, in real live earthy countrysides and country-men.

REFERENCES

EPSTEIN, T.S. (1962) *Economic development and social change in South India.*

LEARMONTH, A.T.A. and BHAT, L.S. (ed.) (1960) *Mysore State, Vol. 1: an Atlas of Resources.* Calcutta and Bombay.

LEARMONTH, A.T.A. (1962a) *Mysore State, Vol. 2: a regional synthesis.* Calcutta and Bombay.

— (1962b) *Sample villages in Mysore.* University of Liverpool, Department of Geography Research Papers No. 1.

MENON, V.P. (1956) *The story of the integration of the Indian States.*

SPATE, O.H.K. and DESHPANDE, C.D. (1952) 'The Indian village', *Geography*, 37, 142-52.

TINKER, H. (1959) 'Authority and community in village India', *Pacific Affairs*, 32, 354-75.

Liverpool and the Tropics

'MERSEYSIDE is built and founded on commerce' (Smith, 1953) echoes the view expressed a century ago that 'Liverpool owes its position . . . entirely to its commerce and shipping' (Baines, 1859). In this commerce the tropical lands have played, and still play, a vital role. The stranger in Liverpool will find much to remind him of this: the varied tropical cargoes; the house flags of ships as familiar along the Guinea, Malabar and Caribbean coasts as on Merseyside; the street names – Goree Piazzas, Jamaica Street, Carnatic Road, Oil Street and the like – redolent of tropical lands and their products; the great oil mills and sugar refineries fed by raw materials from the tropics; the cosmopolitan population of richly varied colour and culture. In all these the importance of tropical trade to Liverpool is manifest.

In seeking to delineate the distinctive claims of Liverpool as a vital link between Britain and the tropics, this essay discusses briefly the origins and growth of Liverpool's commerce with the tropics and then the ways in which these are reflected in the trade, shipping, industry and people of the city today.

THE EARLY NINETEENTH CENTURY

The borough of Liverpool, granted its first charter in 1207, was of little importance in medieval times. As a port it was over-shadowed by Chester and, as late as the sixteenth century, mainly traded with Ireland, ranking low even among the ports of north-western England (Routledge, 1953). However, the beginnings of British trade with the tropics in the late sixteenth and early seventeenth centuries received early expression in Liverpool, which began to compete with London, Bristol and Glasgow for a share in trade with the West Indies and West Africa (Baines, 1852). The

349

first record of Liverpool's trade with Barbados occurs in the Moore rentals in 1641. In 1667 a cargo of Barbados sugar was brought direct to the port and in the same year the town's first sugar refinery was built, 'which will bring a trade of at least forty thousand pounds a year from the Barbadoes, which formerly the town never knew' (Heywood, 1847). By the 1670's there are frequent references in the Port Books to shipments of sugar, molasses and tobacco. Richard Blome reported in his *Britannia* (1673) 'divers eminent merchants and tradesmen whose trade and traffic, especially with the West Indies, made it [i.e. Liverpool] famous', and drew attention to the export, 'proper for the West Indies', of cottons from 'adjacent parts'.

After 1697, trade with the west coast of Africa between Sallee and the Cape of Good Hope, hitherto the monopoly of the Royal Africa Company, was freed. Liverpool merchants were not slow to take advantage and by 1700 had ships trading with the Guinea coast. Already the prime objective of this trade was slaves; in 1700 the *Liverpool Merchant* sold 220 negroes in Barbados, while the *Blessington*, having taken cargo to the Gold Coast, shipped slaves to Barbados and returned to Liverpool with sugar, cotton and ginger on board (Parkinson, 1952). Thus, by the early eighteenth century, the salient features of Liverpool's initial trade with the tropics were established, though the port was still inferior to both London and Bristol in tonnage and value of trade. Nevertheless the shrewd Defoe noted in 1715 that ''tis already the next town to Bristol, and in a little time may probably exceed it, both in commerce, and in numbers of people'. Only a quarter of Liverpool's trade was now with Ireland and the Isle of Man, and the next major area served was America and the West Indies, accounting for one-eighth of the tonnage using the port between 1715 and 1717 (Customs House Accounts, quoted by Parkinson, 1952).

During the eighteenth century Liverpool grew rapidly, the total tonnage clearing the port increasing from 36,742 in 1716 to 65,406 by 1751, and to 708,314 by 1805 (Troughton, 1810). Its dominance in trade with West Africa and, to a lesser degree, with the West Indies became pronounced. Benefiting from the reduced role of chartered companies in British overseas trade from the 1720's, Liverpool merchants increasingly controlled the slave trade to both British and Spanish colonies in the Americas, a trade in which London had passed its peak after 1701. According to Williamson's *Liverpool Memorandum Book* of 1753, Liverpool had become 'of late the most flourishing seaport (London excepted) in Great Britain', and in the new Company of Merchants trading to Africa Liverpool had 101 members as compared with Bristol's 107 and London's 135. But in 1754 only thirty-two vessels cleared Bristol for Africa as compared with seventy-four from Liverpool, and '. . . in the second half of the century Liverpool was beyond all doubt the principal slaving port, not only in England, but in Europe' (Muir, 1907). At the height of the slave trade Liverpool ships were carrying over 50,000 slaves a year, together with an estimated five-eighths of British trade with Africa and three-sevenths of that between Europe and Africa (Troughton, 1810).

The triangular trade between Liverpool, West Africa and the West Indies was a persistent feature until the abolition of the slave trade in 1807. Manchester cottons, cheap Birmingham toys and metalware, and cheap spirits were sent to the Guinea coast. There they were bartered for gold, ivory and dyewoods, but chiefly for slaves who were transported to the West Indies and the southern Atlantic coast of North America. The return cargoes to Liverpool were mainly of sugar, rum and molasses, cotton, tobacco and spices. The relationship between these trades was not, however, invariable and vessels not infrequently came from the West Indies in ballast (Hyde, 1953). Profits were, in aggregate, high, averaging 30 per cent, and amounting to £300,000 per annum in the decade 1783–93, although the returns to individual owners, many of whom were in business on a relatively small scale, fluctuated (Hyde, Parkinson and Marriner, 1953).

The import of tropical produce gave a firm basis to the commerce of the port. In 1770 Liverpool imported from the tropics, in addition to the commodities already mentioned, coco-nuts, ebony and other hardwoods, ginger, Guinea grain, palm oil, rice and sago (Enfield, 1774). The basic trades grew rapidly: between

1770 and 1810 sugar imports increased five-fold, rum imports three-fold, tobacco three-fold and cotton (for which Liverpool became the chief port) fifty-fold (Hyde, 1953). By the early nineteenth century the commodity trades of Liverpool also included coffee, cocoa and indigo as the range of trade with the Caribbean widened.

In 1807, the year of the abolition of slaving, the setting up of the West India Association in Liverpool pointed the way to a new phase of development. Despite the loss of this valuable traffic (a loss to which many Liverpool men such as William Roscoe, who campaigned long against the slave trade, willingly subscribed), Liverpool's trade continued to grow in bulk and variety. Trade with the U.S.A., especially in cotton, boomed after the war of 1812. New tropical connections were also forged. Liverpool merchants pressed the claims to independence of the rebel republics of the former Spanish and Portuguese territories of Latin America and, in 1825, George Canning, a former Liverpool M.P., was the Foreign Minister who recognized these new states. In 1813, after a lengthy campaign in which Liverpool merchants played an important part, the East India Company's monopoly of trade with India and the East Indies was broken: in March 1814 John Gladstone sailed in the *Kingsmill* via the Cape, the first Liverpool vessel to trade with India (Smithers, 1825). The China trade was opened to Liverpool merchants in 1833, further stimulating contact with the East Indies as well as the Far East. Between 1805 and 1824 the shipping using the port more than doubled and the dock duties paid on cargo increased nearly four-fold; moreover by the 1820s, there was a Liverpool Ship-owners' Association and commercial associations in the following trades: East Indian; West Indian; Portugal, Brazil, South American and Mexican; American; Irish (Smithers, 1825).

THE MID-NINETEENTH CENTURY

By 1857, when the Mersey Docks and Harbour Board was formed to administer the port, Liverpool handled about one-third of the commerce of the United Kingdom and an even greater share of its foreign trade (Baines, 1859): tonnage of shipping registered (936,022 tons) was the greatest of any port in the United Kingdom. It was the main port of entry and principal commodity market for an increasing range of both tropical and temperate foodstuffs and raw materials. The overall trade had grown enormously since the early nineteenth century, the shipping moving through the port in 1857 reaching almost nine million tons, as compared with less than three-quarters of a million in 1805. Much of the increase in foreign trade was with North America, but trade with the tropics, especially Latin America and southern and south-eastern Asia, had also grown rapidly. The total East Indian trade of Britain increased from 57,591 tons in 1814 to 339,934 tons in 1850, when Liverpool, excluded from it in the earlier year, handled 135,597 tons (40 per cent). By the 1850's this trade was second (to the North American) in value in the port. Though smaller in volume, both the West Indian and

TABLE I

Overseas trade of the Port of Liverpool, 1857-8[1]

| | 1857 | | | | 1858 | |
| | *Vessels arriving* | | *Vessels clearing* | | *Value of dock dues Total* | |
Area	Number	%	Number	%	(£s)	%
U.S.A.	934	20·8	842	17·3	137,156	40·9
British N. America	493	11·0	454	9·3	34,353	10·3
Mediterranean	933	20·7	968	19·9	35,634	10·6
Baltic	240	5·3	422	8·7	6,329	1·9
Rest of Europe	665	14·8	587	12·0	17,629	5·3
India, East Indies, China & Australia	362	8·1	603	12·4	54,794	16·3
West Africa	114	2·5	65	1·3	7,258	2·2
West Indies and Gulf of Mexico	246	5·5	332	6·8	17,124	5·1
West Coast of South America	505	11·2	597	12·3	11,128	3·3
Brazil and R. Plate					13,855	4·1
Total	4,492	100·0	4,870	100·0	335,260	100·0

(Based on Baines, 1859)

[1] The Port of Liverpool includes the Liverpool and Birkenhead Docks of the Mersey Docks and Harbour Board.

West African trades continued to be of importance, and Liverpool handled the greater part of West Africa's trade with the United Kingdom.

As an export port, Liverpool shipped products valued at over £55 million in 1857; this represented 45 per cent of all British exports and twice the value of those despatched from London, its nearest rival. These were mainly manufactures, including cottons (42·4 per cent), other textiles (19·9 per cent), metals (13·6 per cent), machinery, hardware and cutlery (6·5 per cent)

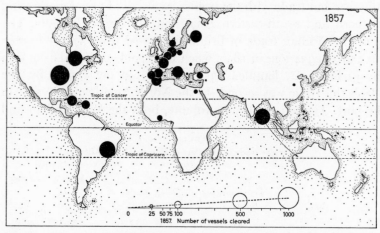

Figure 1. Vessels clearing the Port of Liverpool for overseas, 1857. (Based on Baines, 1859.) *A single symbol includes all vessels for Central and South America, and also for India, South-east Asia and Australia*

and clothing (4·7 per cent), coming largely from Lancashire, the West Riding of Yorkshire and the West Midlands. There was also a growing re-export trade in tropical raw materials and in foreign goods for tropical markets. Sailings from the port of Liverpool in 1857 (Figure 1) give an indication of the extent of trade. Although North America, with Europe and the Mediterranean, dominated the picture, substantial numbers of vessels sailed for the West Indies and South America and were engaged in the relatively recently-established trade to India, South-east Asia, the Far East and Australia (Table I). Rather surprisingly, tropical Africa had only 1·3 per cent of overseas sailings.

The tropics were almost equally important in the import trade (Figure 2). Latin America, the West Indies and Caribbean, India, South-east Asia and the Far East, and Africa accounted for over 27 per cent of arrivals as compared with 31·8 per cent from North America and 41·1 per cent from Europe (Table 1). The commodities imported in 1857 consisted overwhelmingly of raw materials and foodstuffs; in order of bulk the chief raw materials were cotton, wool, tobacco, hides, vegetable oils and oilseeds, jute, dyestuffs and timber; the most important foodstuffs were temperate grains, rice, sugar, tea, lard and coffee.

Unquestionably, Liverpool had a dominant share of the country's imports of many tropical and sub-tropical commodities. In 1857 over 90 per cent by value of the United Kingdom's imports of cotton came through Liverpool, of which the tropics contributed a substantial part, though the United States' crop clearly dominated (Table II).

TABLE II

Cotton imports into Liverpool (1791 and 1962) and the United Kingdom (1828, 1857)

	1791		*1828*		*1857*		*1962*	
	Packages	*%*	*Bales*	*%*	*Cwt.*	*%*	*Bales*	*%*
U.S.A.	64	0·9	444,390	59·3	5,879,034	68·1	294,011	28·9
British East Indies	–	–	84,855	11·3	1,602,213	18·5	20,037	2·0
South America	34,500	50·5	167,362	22·3	267,061	3·1	223,294	21·9
Egypt and the Levant	2,242	3·3	32,889	4·4	219,038	2·5	184,937	18·2
West Indies	27,827	40·7	20,056	2·7	11,887	0·1	–	–
Tropical Africa	–	–	–	–	–	–	190,549	18·7
Other	3,771	4·6	–	–	635,400	7·4	104,635	10·3
Totals	68,404	100·0	749,552	100·0	8,654,633	100·0	1,017,463	100·0

Figures for imports into Liverpool in 1791 from Smithers (1825), and in 1962 from information supplied by the Liverpool Cotton Association Ltd. Figures for imports into United Kingdom in 1828 and 1857 from Baines (1859).

Liverpool's import of cotton was destined mainly for the Lancashire cotton-manufacturing area, for the town never developed its own industry, despite the abortive appearance of two or three cotton mills in the late eighteenth century.

Already long-established by the nineteenth century, the Liverpool sugar industry continued to grow, the sugar houses extending from their early eighteenth century location by the Old Dock into the Vauxhall Road area of the North Docks in particular. Trade

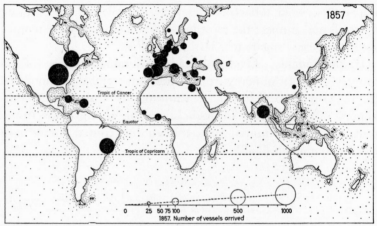

Figure 2. Vessels from overseas arriving in the Port of Liverpool, 1857. (Based on Baines 1859.) *Symbols are on the same basis and scale as in Figure 1*

in sugar was shared with London and Greenock, two of the most important of its refiners being Macfie's and Fairrie's, who transferred their headquarters from Greenock to Liverpool in 1788 and 1797 respectively. In the 1820s Liverpool handled about one-sixth of British sugar imports, the amount rising by some 44 per cent between 1810 and 1850.

Oilseeds provided the basis of an increasingly important Liverpool industry from the late eighteenth century when mills near the site of the present Anglican cathedral and a water-powered mill at Otterspool were the forerunners of the nineteenth-century dockside industry. In 1810 Earle and Carter's mill (later to be merged with Lever Brothers) gave Oil Street its name (Chandler, 1960).

The varied sources of supply included, by mid-century, not only West Africa for palm oil, but new areas of trade in India and in the East Indies. Commercial development in the first half of the nineteenth century both demanded and gave the opportunity for the extension of Merseyside's shipping interests. Shipbuilding declined in Liverpool itself with the rapid growth of the dock system and was transferred to the Cheshire shore. Special ships for pioneering new areas were often designed on Merseyside; thus Lairds built troop transports for use on the Indus and Sutlej, and also the *Quorra* and *Alburca* which were used in the exploration of the lower Niger by MacGregor Laird in 1832 (Baines, 1852).

More important was the lead taken by Liverpool merchants in establishing regular shipping services 'which, by the end of the nineteenth century, brought the whole world within the sphere of activity of the Liverpool merchant' (Hyde, 1953). These developments were most pronounced in the specialist trades with North and South America and with various parts of the tropics. Liverpool ship-owners played a leading part in the development of steam navigation which gave regularity and frequency of service. In 1857 about one-third of the 4·5 million tons of shipping which paid dock dues was steam and there were over 200 steamships registered at Liverpool.

From 1852, the Africa Steamship Company ran a regular monthly service to Madeira and the Guinea coast and other companies developed later in the century. The Africa trade was growing rapidly, especially for the supply of palm oil to the growing Merseyside soap industry which was linked closely to chemical manufacture, initially in Liverpool, then, from 1828, at St Helens and, from 1847, at Widnes. Liverpool had a near-monopoly of palm oil imports and a considerable re-export trade in this as in other West African produce. Indeed, in no other area of world trade did Liverpool commerce and shipping become so dominant as in West Africa.

Brocklebanks were the first of a number of Liverpool shipping firms serving India, having transferred their headquarters to Liverpool from Whitehaven in 1820, shortly after entering the

Calcutta trade in 1816 (Chandler, 1960). In the 1820s hides, cotton, sugar, indigo, pepper and ginger were all important East Indian commodities handled by Liverpool (Smithers, 1825) and the port's interests were extended to the tea trade and to the Far East from the 1830s. By 1857 the East Indies trade, as a whole, was the second trade of the port and was increasing rapidly. Further stimulus was given by the growth of emigrant traffic to Australia in the 1850s and the Harrison Line, which originated in 1853, served both the Indian Ocean and Australia.

The growth of Liverpool's trade with Latin America and continued interest in the Caribbean are reflected in imports not only of sugar and cotton but also of hides and coffee. By the 1850s the Pacific Steam Navigation Company (founded in 1835) was operating regular services to the Pacific coast of South America via the Magellan Straits, and Lamport and Holt were trading with South America (and other parts of the tropics). Josias Booker, a Liverpool merchant resident since 1815 in Georgetown, established a shipping company for trade with British Guiana in 1835.

Liverpool shipping increased in importance to reach its zenith by the First World War, but even in the mid-nineteenth century shipping and commercial interests played an enormously important part in the economy both of Merseyside and of the United Kingdom. The dependence of Merseyside on the port at this time is strikingly illustrated by the high proportion of its population employed in shipping, trade and commerce, particularly as compared with those in manufacturing industry. A detailed analysis of the occupational structure of some 14,000 persons in Liverpool, based on the enumerators' books of the 1851 census (when the population of the town numbered 375,000), showed that industry, including craft industry, employed only 19·7 per cent of the occupied population; transport employed 9·9 per cent, commerce and trade 14·2 per cent and services 38·9 per cent (Lawton, 1955). The connections of Liverpool merchants can well be illustrated from Abercromby Square, then one of the city's premier residential areas; amongst its households were included a Jamaica-born timber merchant, two East India merchants, a general merchant, whose wife and two elder children were born in Barbados, and two Brazil merchants. Tropical links were beginning to colour Liverpool's population in another sense at this time, though the number of immigrants from tropical dependencies was still small.

The distinctive trades of Liverpool led to the formation of a number of commercial associations, especially in the early nineteenth century. By mid-century, the Liverpool Chamber of Commerce (established in 1849 'to promote measures calculated to benefit the mercantile and trading interests of its members, and of the town and neighbourhood . . .') had under its aegis twelve trade associations each providing a deputy to the Chamber. Included were the Africa Association, the East India and China Association, the West India Association (the oldest in the port) and the Cotton Brokers' Association, while a Brazilian Association was being organized. These associations played an important role in formulating British policy in trades in which Liverpool's interests were often pre-eminent.

MODERN LIVERPOOL AND THE TROPICS

Trade

Stimulated by the expansion of overseas markets, notably in America and the tropics, the commercial and shipping interests of Liverpool proliferated in the later nineteenth century. The total volume of shipping using the port increased four-fold from 4,441,943 tons in 1858 to 18,433,269 tons in 1913, when 80 per cent of Liverpool's trade was overseas trade. In 1913 Liverpool handled 41 per cent of the export trade and 30 per cent of the import trade of the United Kingdom and was estimated to have one-seventh of the registered shipping in the world. Today, the port handles a total foreign trade of 12,965,304 tons (1962), excluding petroleum of which there is an import of 7,549,563 tons. This comprises some 23 per cent by value of the United Kingdom's foreign trade (1958–60) as compared with 22 per cent in pre-war years (1936–38).

As an import port Liverpool declined relatively to London between the wars but it still handles about 20 per cent of the United Kingdom's imports. Since the mid-nineteenth century the overwhelming dominance of North America has been offset by the increase in imports of tropical raw materials, especially from Asia and Africa from which 10·3 per cent and 14·4 per cent respectively of the tonnage entering Liverpool in 1962 originated (Figure 3). In addition, 8·5 per cent of the tonnage entering the port came from the West Indies and Caribbean and 3·2 per cent from elsewhere in tropical Latin America. Thus while Liverpool's imports are world-wide, two major trades are pre-eminent, North America with 30·1 per cent of tonnage entering and the tropics with 36·4 per cent (see also Table III).

TABLE III

Foreign trade of Liverpool, 1962[1]

	Imports		Exports	
	000s tons	%	*000s tons*	%
North America	2,660	31·3	414	9·4
Western and Mediterranean Europe	938	11·0	615	14·0
U.S.S.R. and E. Europe	235	2·8	90	2·0
N. Africa and Levant	168	2·0	167	3·8
Arabia and Persian Gulf	40	0·5	141	3·2
India, Pakistan and Ceylon	318	3·7	488	11·1
S.E. Asia	383	4·5	354	8·0
Far East	182	2·1	201	4·6
Australasia	678	8·0	488	11·1
West Africa	772	9·1	449	10·2
East Africa	450	5·3	218	5·0
South Africa	224	2·6	154	3·5
West Indies and Caribbean	718	8·5	334	7·6
Latin America	728	8·6	289	6·6
Total	8,586	100·0	4,380	100·0

(Based on Mersey Docks and Harbour Board, *Port Statistics*, 1958-62; imports of petroleum are excluded)

[1] Liverpool includes the docks of the Mersey Docks and Harbour Board shown on Figure 5.

Petroleum, with ores and scrap metal, are the bulkiest imports, followed, in relative order of tonnage, by flour and grain, sugar and molasses, fruit and vegetables, animal feeding stuffs, wood, cotton, oils, fats and resins, oilseeds and kernels, and rubber. Other important imports are hemp, jute, sisal, tea and cocoa. In many tropical commodities Liverpool dominates, or shares United Kingdom imports with London and, in certain cases, Bristol and Glasgow. Liverpool, with its important local market, takes half

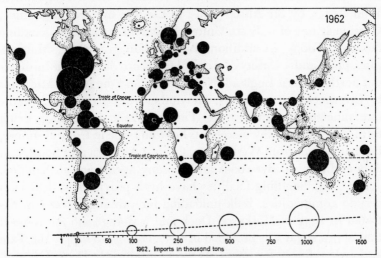

Figure 3. Imports into the Port of Liverpool from overseas countries, 1962. (Based on Mersey Docks and Harbour Board, *Port Statistics*, 1958-62)

of the United Kingdom import of groundnuts, one-quarter of the cotton-seed, two-thirds of the palm kernels and four-fifths of the palm oil. Although cotton imports declined in the inter-war years, 70 per cent still comes to Liverpool where it forms about 6 per cent of the total value of imports. The dominance of the United States is less pronounced than in the mid-nineteenth century and tropical lands now supply some 40 per cent of Liverpool's cotton imports (Table II).

In addition to cotton, for which Liverpool is solely an importing and marketing centre, a number of other tropical products give rise

z

to important commodity markets but do not contribute to the manufacturing industry of the area. Cocoa has some place in local confectionery industries, but most of it is sent to major chocolate manufacturing centres elsewhere. Similarly tea (1·3 per cent by value of imports) and coffee are packed and despatched to a wide hinterland, while rum imports are distributed to bottlers throughout the United Kingdom. Fruit imports developed from the trade in Mediterranean citrus fruit in the 1880s and extended into the tropics through this and the banana trade. The latter was developed with West Africa by Sir Alfred Jones in the late nineteenth century; Garston is one of only six United Kingdom docks with handling facilities. Today, in addition, West Indian grapefruit, Malayan pineapples and a variety of tropical fruits are distributed throughout north-western England, North Wales and the North Midlands by Liverpool fruit importers. The timber trade grew rapidly in the late nineteenth century, the Timber Trade Association being formed in 1877. Many merchants have no trade in tropical timber, but hardwoods from West Africa, Central America and South-east Asia and tropical dyewoods and tanning agents are all handled.

Specialist handling facilities have been provided to deal with certain commodities. Bulk unloading for raw sugar was concentrated in 1952 at Huskisson Dock and a storage silo for 100,000 tons of raw sugar was provided in 1957, enough to supply the Tate and Lyle refinery for about six weeks. Stalbridge Dock, Garston, is equipped with four banana elevators which transfer cargo from the specialist Elder and Fyffe vessels (trading with Jamaica and Cameroun) into steam-heated trains. Bromborough Docks, built specifically for the vegetable oil and oilseed trade, provide unloading and storage for the Unilever industries of Port Sunlight, while tank storage for vegetable oils is provided at Victoria Dock, Liverpool. Such special facilities naturally concentrate the trades involved in particular parts of the docks.

As an exporter Liverpool led the ports of the United Kingdom between the wars, though there have been considerable changes since the mid-nineteenth century in the character and direction of the trade. The export of cottons has declined while that of metals, engineering products and vehicles and chemicals has greatly increased. Today the proportion of tonnage sailing to the tropics is even greater than that arriving (Figure 4); altogether about half the departures in 1962 were for tropical areas, principally in tropical Asia (23 per cent), tropical Africa (15·2 per cent), and the West Indies and tropical Latin America (11·3 per cent). (See also Table III.)

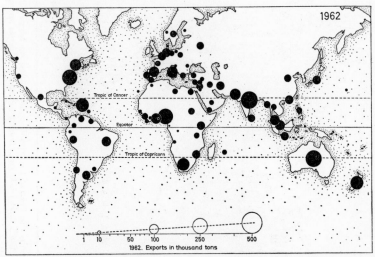

Figure 4. Exports from the Port of Liverpool to overseas countries, 1962. (Based on Mersey Docks and Harbour Board, *Port Statistics*, 1958-1962.) *The circles are on the same basis and scale as in Figure 3*

Within the port, specialization of trade is reflected in appropriated berths which act as the Liverpool base of the companies which regularly occupy them (Bird, 1963, and Figure 5). The West African trade is mainly concentrated in the southern docks (Queen's, Brunswick, Toxteth and Harrington) where most of the trade in groundnuts, palm oil and kernels (apart from that going to Port Sunlight), cocoa and hardwoods is handled. Birkenhead Docks specialize in shipping for South and East Africa, India, Pakistan, South-east Asia and the Far East. Canada and Alexandra Docks handle most of the South American trade, together with some African and Asiatic trade.

363

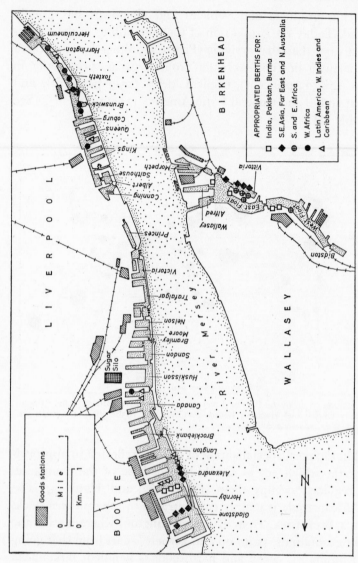

Figure 5. Appropriated berths within the Port of Liverpool, 1960. (Based on Mersey Docks and Harbour Board plan of the Port of Liverpool, and Bird, 1963.) *The symbols show the number of berths appropriated by shipping companies trading with various parts of the tropics*

Shipping

Much of the shipping engaged in the major trades of the port is owned by Liverpool lines. From the mid-nineteenth century Liverpool merchants increasingly entered the shipping industry to provide regular transport for the main areas of trade, and today there are 4·6 million tons of shipping registered in Liverpool, about one-quarter of British tonnage. One of the chief characteristics of the Liverpool merchant fleet is the provision by cargo liner of regular sailings to regular ports of call, giving specialized services in trades which have been followed for many years. The pattern of sailings to tropical ports is remarkably comprehensive (Figure 6). Each vessel sailing from Liverpool has a number of ports of call: for example, Elder Dempster vessels call regularly at all West African ports; the Booth Line have regular monthly sailings for Lisbon, the West Indies, Belém and then up the Amazon as far as Leticia; Blue Funnel vessels have itineraries which include the ports of Malaya, Singapore, Indonesia and the East Indies, Bangkok, Manila and the Far East. Altogether some fourteen Liverpool lines, together with other British and some Commonwealth and foreign lines, operate regular services throughout the tropics with the Port of Liverpool.

One of the oldest established routes is that to West Africa. The Africa Steam Ship Company of Liverpool combined, in 1870, with Elder Dempster (originally a Glasgow firm) to provide regular sailings. By the end of the century practically the whole of the carrying trade to West Africa was from Liverpool. The Guinea Gulf Line joined the trade in 1910 and in 1912 Levers entered shipping to carry vegetable oil and oilseeds, a trade which expanded rapidly after their commercial expedition of 1907 to West Africa. In 1962, Elder Dempster and Palm Line (the modern successor of the Lever fleet) provided seventy-one and twenty-three sailings respectively to all ports between Port Etienne and the Congo. General cargo out is replaced largely by bulk vegetable oils (for which vessels have special facilities), cocoa and refrigerated cargo on the home voyage.

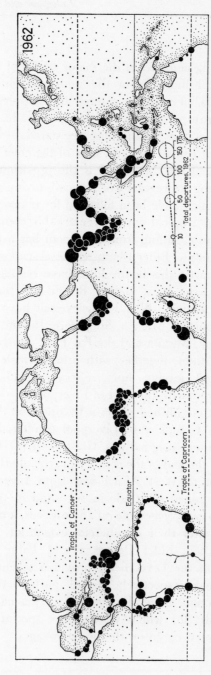

Figure 6. Destination of vessels sailing from the Port of Liverpool, 1962. (Based on the Port of Liverpool, *Official Monthly Sailing List and Shipping Guide*, January – December, 1962.) *The circles are proportionate to the total number of sailings to all ports within the tropics and include all ports of call for individual vessels*

John Holt of Liverpool established regular trade with the Calabar coast in his twelve years there between 1862 and 1874, and this Company still has extensive interests in Nigeria, West Cameroun, Dahomey and Togo, together with a large share in trade in groundnuts, coffee, ginger and rubber from these countries. In 1884 the African section of the Liverpool Chamber of Commerce was formed. Its members were destined to play an important part in the commercial development of West Africa, none more than Sir Alfred L. Jones. From 1879, as a partner in Elder Dempster, he did much to foster West African trade in cotton; he also founded the Bank of West Africa, started the banana trade (shipped, from 1889, in refrigerated ships) and was a great benefactor of the University of Liverpool and of the Liverpool School of Tropical Medicine. The tradition of his gift of the Jones bequest, in 1913, to promote technical education in West Africa, continues in the Elder Dempster Educational Trust established in 1957 to mark the independence of Ghana.

Even more long-standing are the connections between Liverpool and the Caribbean. Many shipping companies combine Caribbean operations with South American trade which was pioneered by Liverpool in the early nineteenth century. Today there are regular services to the north Brazil coast and the Amazon (Booth Line), to the Pacific coast, where the Pacific Steam Navigation Company has dominated British traffic since 1840, and to the West Indies. Though some companies (e.g. Lamport and Holt) are not exclusively concerned with the tropical trade, combining this trade with that to southern Brazil and the River Plate, others (e.g. Booth Line and Bookers) deal solely with tropical Latin America. The import trade consists mainly of cotton and cottonseed, coffee, hides, nuts, timber, sisal, non-ferrous metals, and West Indian sugar and fruits.

Liverpool's interests in Asia go back to the Calcutta trade of the Brocklebanks started in 1820. Bibby's, another old-established firm, traded with the East Indies in 1821, their concentration on the trade with Ceylon and Burma coming with the formation of the Bibby Steamship Company in 1891, with an associated

367

company concerned with produce brokerage in Liverpool for sugar, hemp, rice, oilseeds and other tropical commodities. With the opening of trade to the Far East and to Australia the whole of the Indian Ocean and western Pacific was progressively entered by Liverpool shipping, especially after the opening of the Suez Canal in 1869. The Blue Funnel Line (Alfred Holt and Company) developed its interests in this area from 1865 (Hyde, 1956). The growth of the Malayan rubber industry from the end of the nineteenth century led to a great increase in traffic, and today the Blue Funnel fleet of fifty-four ships is mainly concerned with trade to South-east Asia and the Far East (seven sailings per month as against one to Australia). Rubber, oilseeds, tobacco, hemp, tea, coffee, fruit and spices, timber and tin dominate inward trade, together with manufactures from Hong Kong.

The Indian Ocean trade focused on Birkenhead is one of the most active in the United Kingdom. Clan Line began sailings to Bombay and Colombo in 1878, later extending operations to Madras and the Malabar coast, and then to East and South Africa. Sailings now come to about 100 per year. The City Line originated in Liverpool in 1839 for the tea trade and, with the development of the cotton trade with India during the cotton famine of the American Civil War, it extended its services to Bombay and Calcutta. Now it is associated with the Hall Line (formed in Liverpool in 1868 to trade with India but later extending activities to East Africa), running regular services to Karachi, Bombay, the Malabar coast and East Africa.

Much of the labour force of these shipping companies is drawn from the tropics: Bibby's crews include 750 Indians; all Clan Line crews, other than officers, are Indian or Pakistani; Ben Lines, who sail into Liverpool from South-east Asia and the Far East, employ some 570 Malayan and Hong Kong Chinese; Blue Funnel have 2,200 Chinese and Malays on their pay-roll. Elder Dempster and Palm Line have large numbers of West African employees, both in shipping and in agencies throughout West Africa.

Manufacturing industry

The bulk import of raw materials has given rise to a variety of primary processing industries on Merseyside, located close to the docks. Those based on tropical products lie mainly in the Vauxhall Road – Great Howard Street area of the North Docks and at Bromborough Port. Sugar refining is the oldest, but the majority date from the 1880s when economies in large-scale processing made possible by new techniques led to a great concentration of sugar refining, oilseed crushing, tanning, and associated industries, at the great importing ports. Liverpool took a large part in the processing of tropical products and the importance of such industry on Merseyside before the Second World War has been demonstrated (Smith, 1942). Industries which are particularly important include vegetable oils, soap, margarine, cattle and poultry foods, sugar, rubber, tanning, cocoa and confectionery, together with secondary industries based on these, such as biscuit-making.

It is not possible to analyse comprehensively the role of tropical commodities in Liverpool's industry, for many firms use only small amounts of such raw materials. Only the major industries using tropical raw material imports will be discussed, information having been obtained from questionnaires sent to sixty-two firms of which thirty-two replied in full.

Sugar-refining employed less than 1 per cent of the work-force of Merseyside in 1950 (Smith, 1953) but it had a high location quotient of 5·8.[1] The industry is dominated by Tate and Lyle Ltd., who in turn dominate the refining of cane sugar at Liverpool, London and, through their associate John Walker and Co., at Greenock. The Liverpool refinery (built in 1872) absorbed older-established firms and now has a production of over 14,000 tons per week and a labour force of 3,000 (about one-third of the total employed by the firm). The industry is tied to a dock location,

[1] The location quotient is the ratio between the percentage of British workers in a specific industry employed on Merseyside, and the percentage of all British workers employed on Merseyside (Florence, 1948). A location quotient of more than unity indicates a concentration of the industry concerned on Merseyside.

but it is not accessible for direct discharge from the ships (as in the Thames refineries) and the sugar is transferred by a constantly-operating fleet of trucks. Since 1952 bulk handling at Huskisson Dock has added to facilities and the Huskisson Transit Company's sugar silo now stores seasonal surpluses of raw sugar. In 1962 three-quarters of a million tons of raw sugar reached Liverpool mainly from the Caribbean, East and South Africa, Fiji and Australia. Some of this is carried in Tate and Lyle's own vessels (Silvertown Services Ltd.), the rest by the Harrison Line and tramp steamer. Most of this is refined for home consumption but Tate and Lyle have a wide export trade, especially to West Africa, where 90 per cent of the sugar imported comes from Liverpool.

Confectionery and jam-making (with location quotients of 3·1 and 2·1 in 1950) are secondary industries linked with sugar refining but not tied to a dockside site. Although they also use a variety of tropical nuts and oils, they are attracted more by open sites near to good rail and road communications as at the Edge Hill and Aintree industrial areas.

The second major group of primary industries using tropical raw materials are those crushing and processing oilseeds and vegetable oils; oilseed crushers, cattle cake, soap and margarine manufacturers had in 1950 location quotients of 12·1, 4·9, 4·7 and 3·9 respectively. Groundnuts (from West Africa and India), palm oil and kernels (West Africa), copra (the Pacific and South-east Asia) and cotton-seed (especially from Nigeria, East Africa, Indo-Pakistan and South America) are the chief raw materials. Cattle cake manufacturers use rice bran, chiefly from Burma and India, and other tropical meal. Unilever concerns are supplied from their own plantations or by regular contracts and a good deal of oil is shipped in their own Palm Line tankers. Specialist importers such as John Holt and Company handle much of the rest of the trade for sale to manufacturers in Britain and for re-export. Though it was established at the end of the eighteenth century, the main concentration of the industry in Liverpool dates from the 1880s when the invention of the hydraulic press enabled large-scale manufacture to develop at the ports. Large loss of weight in manufacture ties the industry to dock sites mainly in the Vauxhall Road area (Silcock's, Bibby's, Crosfield and Calthrop, Peerless Refining Co.) and at Bromborough (the Unilever British Extracting Company), with smaller works elsewhere (e.g. the C.W.S. African Oil Mills, behind the South Docks).

In practice the various branches of this industry are inseparable; they may be carried out in different departments of a single large plant (e.g. Bibby's which employs 3,750) or in separate factories as in the Unilever complex, employing 11,000 workers, where the British Extracting Company extracts oil and makes cattle cake, Price's (Bromborough) produces textile oil, fatty acids and alcohols, Lever Brothers, soap, detergents and glycerine, and Stork, margarine. Smaller firms have a more restricted range, specializing variously in stock concentrates (Silcock's with 968 workers, Crosfield's with 600) or in edible oils and cooking fats (Peerless Refining Company with 340 workers). Among secondary industries partly dependent on vegetable oils, paint manufacture is important on Merseyside. But the special oils required (e.g. copal gum, tung oil) are not always imported through Liverpool. A more potent locating factor in one case (British Paints Ltd.) is the marine trade within the area.

Of smaller scale industries importing raw materials from the tropics, the milling of grains (notably rice) and spices are of some significance. Liverpool is no longer the centre of the spice trade as it was in the nineteenth century, this having passed to London, but small old-established firms processing spices, seeds and pulses for animal and bird food remain, though some of their raw materials now come through London. Rice milling goes back to the eighteenth century, and is tied to a dock location in which bulk handling facilities are valuable; 1962 sources of supply included Thailand, Burma and Vietnam.

Tanning (location quotient 2) remains on Merseyside as a dockside industry, although there was migration to the mid-Mersey area in the nineteenth century. Hides are imported from all parts of the world, but the tropics have been important suppliers for the last hundred years, and tanning agents include a variety of tropical products (mimosa from East Africa, mangrove from the East Indies, myrabolam from India) which are a further raw material factor in location.

The British rubber industry which developed rapidly after 1840 imported most of its raw material through Liverpool up to the First World War. Supplies then came mainly from the Amazon and from tropical Africa, areas with which Liverpool's trade pattern was already established (Woodruff, 1958). In 1900 Liverpool handled 76 per cent of rubber imported into the United Kingdom. But with the dominance of plantation rubber from Malaya from the First World War London became the leading world market and today Liverpool's share of imports is 30 per cent, of which perhaps one-fifth is re-exported (Bird, 1963). Rubber was processed in Liverpool at the end of the nineteenth century, though it was not a major manufacture. Dunlop's first Liverpool factory was opened at Walton in 1925; others were subsequently added at Speke (1938) and Bidston. The industry now employs over 10,000 on Merseyside, about one-quarter of Dunlop's British workers (Chandler, 1957).

The closeness of the tropical world to Liverpool is manifest along its waterfront and in its dockside industries. Liverpool accents are heard in ports throughout the tropics and, increasingly, natives of the tropics are becoming Liverpudlians by adoption. In the last forty years the numbers of such immigrants have grown rapidly (three-fold as compared with 52 per cent for England and Wales) (Table IV). The major elements were formerly Asian (a high proportion being seamen) but West Indian and West African elements are now increasing more rapidly. However, the numbers are still relatively small, and long-standing contact with the tropics, reflected in the old-established Chinese quarter around Pitt Street and Great George Square and the Negro area around Parliament Street and west of Princes Road, has eased the problem of adoption.

There has been little of the friction associated with the more sudden influx of coloured people into parts of London and the Midlands. The coloured population of Liverpool is, indeed, larger than census birth-place statistics indicate, for many of them are Liverpudlians of the first and even second generation.

TABLE IV

Birthplaces of natives of tropical areas enumerated in Liverpool, 1911 and 1951

| | *1911* | | *1951* | |
| | *Resident in Liverpool* | *Liverpool as % of England and Wales* | *Resident in Liverpool* | *Liverpool as % of England and Wales* |
Birthplace				
I. ALL COLONIES AND DEPENDENCIES	3,015	1·9	19,346	7·9
India, Pakistan and Ceylon	916	1·4	1,020	0·8
As a % of I.	30·4		5·3	
Rest of tropical Asia	268	6·5	278	2·2
As a % of I.	8·9		1·4	
Tropical Africa	140	5·7	631	6·2
As a % of I.	4·6		3·2	
West Indies and Caribbean	198	1·8	458	2·8
As a % of I.	6·6		2·4	
II. ALL FOREIGN	12,580	3·4	15,760	2·4
Tropical Asia	52	2·8	149	1·1
As a % of II.	0·4		0·9	
Tropical Africa	126	3·9	232	1·5
As a % of II.	1·0		1·5	
Tropical Latin America	233	2·5	207	1·8
As a % of II.	1·9		1·3	

(Based on the Censuses of England and Wales, 1911 and 1951.)

Founded in commerce, the contacts of Liverpool with the tropics have undoubtedly brought great gain to the city. But Liverpool and Liverpool men have also contributed much to the tropics. Their role in the commercial development and the modern economy of the West Indies and of West African countries in particular has already been indicated. But there have also been notable contributions to the advancement of education and scientific research in the tropics. Contact with the dangers of life in the tropics, which made West Africa in the nineteenth century 'the white man's grave', the cholera epidemics which ravaged Liverpool in 1832, in 1834 and again in 1866 (Hope, 1931), and the constant threat of smallpox, did much to focus the attention of philanthropists and scientists on the control of disease and on health in the tropics. Sir Alfred Jones led in the establishing of a School of Tropical Medicine in Liverpool in 1898, the first of its kind in the world (Mountford, 1953). It has seen the dramatic investigations into yellow fever by Sir Ronald Ross and continuing research on malaria; it long maintained a laboratory in Sierra Leone and has sent many expeditions to the tropics. The School is still governed by representatives of Liverpool shipowners and merchants, and of the University of Liverpool, a symbol of the close and reciprocal ties of Liverpool and the tropics in many fields of human endeavour.

REFERENCES

BAINES, T. (1852) *History of the commerce and town of Liverpool.*
— (1859) *Liverpool in 1859*
BIRD, J. (1963) *The major seaports of the United Kingdom.*
CHANDLER, G. (1957) *Liverpool.*
— (1960) *Liverpool Shipping.*
ENFIELD, W. (1774) *An essay towards the history of Liverpool.*
FLORENCE, P.S. (1948) *Investment, location and size of plant.*
HEYWOOD, J. (ed.) (1847) 'The Moore rental', *The Chetham Society*, First Series, *12.*
HOPE, E.W. (1931) *Health at the Gateway.*
HYDE, F.E. (1953) 'The growth of Liverpool's trade, 1700-1950', in SMITH, W. (ed.) *Merseyside.*
— (1956) *Blue Funnel.*
HYDE, F.E., PARKINSON, B.B. and MARRINER, S. (1953) 'The nature and profitability of the Liverpool slave trade', *Econ. Hist. Rev.*, 2nd. series, *5*, 368-77.
LAWTON, R. (1955) 'The population of Liverpool in the mid-nineteenth century', *Trans. Hist. Soc. of Lancs. & Ches.*, *107*, 89-120.
MOUNTFORD, J.F. (1953) 'The University', in SMITH, W. (ed.) *Merseyside.*
MUIR, J.R. (1907) *History of Liverpool.*
PARKINSON, C.N. (1952) *The rise of the port of Liverpool.*

ROUTLEDGE, F.J. (1953) 'History of Liverpool to 1700', in SMITH, W. (ed.) *Merseyside.*

SMITH, W. (1942) *The distribution of population and the location of industry on Merseyside.*

— (ed.) (1953) *Merseyside: a scientific survey.*

SMITHERS, H. (1825) *Liverpool, its commerce, statistics and institutions.*

TROUGHTON, T. (1810) *History of Liverpool.*

WOODRUFF, W. (1958) *The rise of the British rubber industry during the nineteenth century.*